GREEN
MEDICINE

The Search for Plants that Heal . . .

GREEN MEDICINE

The Search for Plants that Heal ...

Margaret B. Kreig

RAND McNALLY & COMPANY
Chicago · *New York* · *San Francisco*

This book is dedicated to the
American Society of Pharmacognosy*
a nonprofit scientific organization
with
an international membership of
pharmacognosists
botanists
chemists
pharmacologists
and related specialists
who
discover, identify, analyze, and test
natural products

*Pharmacognosy: the science encompassing those phases of knowledge relating to natural products which are generally of medicinal value and primarily of plant origin.

Foreword

THIS BOOK, SO FAR AS I HAVE BEEN ABLE TO DETERmine, is the first to deal with the modern, world-wide resurgence of *scientific* interest in medicinal plants. It focuses upon the exciting investigation of the vegetable kingdom for new sources of botanical drugs—a matter of jungle search and laboratory research, as scientists of many disciplines combine their special talents in an all-out quest for cures.

In the early 1900's, before the Synthetic Era, fully 80 per cent of all medicines were obtained from roots and barks and leaves. The fluid extract was in vogue; one pound of a crude botanical was percolated with a pint of alcohol, much as we make coffee. "Take a teaspoonful of this before meals," the family doctor would say, perhaps adding that a mustard plaster or vegetable poultice would do no harm. Every household had its favorite teas and tonics. Trusting humanity placed its faith in the belief that for every ill, there existed a cure in the plants of field and forest. As Kipling wrote, "Anything green that grew out of the mold/ Was an excellent herb to our fathers of old."

Ask a dozen physicians today: "Do you use many preparations obtained from plants?" They will probably answer that they do not, except for old standbys like Digitalis and opium-derived narcotics. "Everything, nowadays, comes out of the test-tube," was one man's sweeping statement. It's easy to get this impression because substances extracted from natural products often have misleading, synthetic-sounding names. For instance, the alkaloid reserpine from ancient Indian snakeroot is known chemically as 3,4,5-trimetho-xybenzoyl reserpate.

The fact is, of the 300 million *new* prescriptions written last year, over 47 per cent contained a drug of natural origin as the sole active ingredient or as one of two or more main ingredients, according to an analysis by the prescription auditing firm, R. A. Gosselin & Co. Put another way, the average doctor in the United States writes at least eight prescriptions for natural drugs every day. According to industry figures, sales of drugs from botanical sources alone increased at least five-fold from 1950 to 1960 and the trend is sharply upward. The market for medicinal plants is rapidly approaching the $300,000,000 mark.

As long ago as 1946, the late Dr. Ivor Griffith of the Philadelphia College of Pharmacy and Science, predicted what he called, "A great botanical renaissance, heralding a new day in preventive and curative medicine." Botanical suppliers trace the upswing in scientific interest in drug plants back to World War II when the door was slammed on many vital imports. Explorers began a frantic search for substitutes in their own backyards and in nearby accessible countries. A replacement for quinine from Java's Cinchona plantations was obtained from South American barks, for example. The Australians discovered that Duboisia trees were rich in important alkaloids formerly found only in European belladonna. Thus, research gathered momentum.

Mr. Ellis Meer, president of Meer Corporation, a leading botanical drug house, told me: "Before 1950, our industry was in the doldrums. Few, if any, of us were engaged in basic scientific research on the active constituents in medicinal plants. There were virtually no requests from pharmaceutical manufacturers for samples to be used in controlled laboratory screening programs. But in the past year, out of thousands of requests that came along, we shipped at least 200 different ten kilo working samples destined for specific chemical and pharmacological investigation. This does not include routine shipments of old line drug plants such as Cascara, Ipecac, and so forth. In addition to at least 80 new botanicals currently being tested, scientists in leading laboratories are using modern techniques to examine many home remedies and patent medicines compounded from vegetable ingredients. Quite a number of time-honored nostrums, including some American Indian cures, have been vindicated by putting folklore under the microscope, so to speak."

One botanical success story had especially far-reaching consequences: In the early 1950's, Western scientists began to examine the claims made for the ancient Hindu snakeroot, *Rauwolfia serpentina,* in the treatment of insanity. After the first modern tranquilizer, reserpine, was extracted from these roots, it was found particularly effective in easing high blood pressure. Currently, sales of finished reserpine products in this country amount to $30,000,000. Commenting on this "botanical boom," Dr. Max Tishler, president of Merck Sharp & Dohme Research Laboratories, a noted scientist in his own right through his work on vitamins, antibiotics, and corticosteroids, wrote me: "The discovery of reserpine and the concomitant developments in isolation techniques and in methods of determining chemical structures of complicated molecules have given new dimensions to the scope of scientists. Without doubt, plants will continue to play an important role, either as factories of nature or as stimuli to basic research."

At a National Institute of Mental Health conference it was stated that very few useful drugs have been developed strictly on an empirical basis in the laboratory of the organic chemist. In most cases, they are improvements over what nature has already provided. Pharmacognosy Professor C. C.

Albers of the University of Texas explained: "Plants provide blueprints for thousands of medical substances a chemist can synthesize. Plant explorers search for promising plants, then a valuable extract is produced and the chemists take over. They juggle and shuffle the molecules and come up with a variety of derivatives of natural products." That the variety is infinite is evident in the observation of Dr. Albert Raymond, G. D. Searle & Company's Research Director: "We can make as many as 10 million chemicals out of diosgenin, the steroid derived from Mexican yam starting materials."

Competition among the many hundreds of pharmaceutical manufacturers in the world is intense. Drug officials note, for example, that more than two-thirds of the estimated 4,000 drugs being used in this country today have been developed only during the past ten years. "You can't stay in business," one executive pointed out, "unless your research division comes up with better new drugs to make yesterday's products obsolete." In answer to the question, "Why all the emphasis on botanicals?" the answer was given, "Simple—we hope to find something new!"

For each new drug reaching patients, about 6,000 compounds examined had to be discarded along the way. Industry spokesmen, of course, underscore this costly aspect of their overhead, but even those with no vested interest in profits from pharmaceutical manufacturing have a certain empathy for those who take the risks. Dr. David P. Carew, a pharmacognosy professor at the University of Iowa, emphasized that, "Tremendous sums are spent by the pharmaceutical industry on research. In many cases these investments are a complete loss, therefore, this research money has to be recouped from successful products."

In establishing the fact that there is "a botanical boom" and in outlining some of the reasons behind it, I may seem to be echoing the publicity handouts of pharmaceutical trade associations. The reader has a right to know, it seems to me, how and why a book was written. I have been asked many times, "Have 'they' commissioned you to write about natural products as a sort of an antidote?"

The answer to that question is, "No, GREEN MEDICINE is not a subsidized book." Here is how it came about:

While I was medical editor and staff science writer on a national magazine in 1960, Rand McNally's New York editor, Miss Cynthia Smith, asked me to see if there was a book idea in news items about "The Drug Boom Sparked by Exotic Plants," "New Miracles in Jungle Medicine," and "Witch Doctors and Your Health." I had, for some time, been collecting fascinating reports from research centers on old folk remedies that were making good, by modern standards. For instance, the University of Pennsylvania Radiology Department had found the juice of *Aloe vera,* a succulent used by Cleopatra, more effective in treating radiation burns in patients than any other available preparation. There was a lot to ponder in that. Two more examples from my bulging file folders: The American Chemical Society's Biochemistry Award Winner, Dr. William Shive, was using a common amino acid found in cabbage juice with good results in the treatment of alcoholism. This report was filed under "Cabbage," with a quotation from the Roman, Cato: "If you wish to drink much at a banquet, before dinner dip cabbage in vinegar and eat as much as you will. When you have dined, eat five leaves. The cabbage will make you as fit as if you had had nothing and you can drink as much as you will." I added the notation from another source that the early Egyptians ate cabbage seed to prevent intoxication, and the fact that sauerkraut juice is a popular morning-after pickup.

Remember the penny candy counter with its array of red and black licorice whips? A clipping from *Oil, Paint, and Drug Reporter* stated that investigators at the Food and Drug

Research Laboratories in Long Island had found active materials in licorice root with a molecular structure similar to that of hormones from the adrenal cortex. Besides being useful in treating chronic skin conditions, derivatives from licorice were synthesized and given to patients with gastric ulcers, with the result that the ulcers disappeared in 37 per cent of the cases, and were greatly reduced in the remainder, according to the researchers.

I have not highlighted these reports because I believe that A.A. chapters are about to lose their alcoholic members to the A&P's vegetable counter, or that gastroenterologists will soon be bypassed by ulcer victims in favor of the corner candy store. These were random selections from hundreds of similar brief accounts of research studies involving common fruits, vegetables, garden flowers, and exotic jungle vegetation employed by medicine men. Some of this work is still going forward, some has been dropped along the way; but all of it is interesting, if not downright fascinating. To a science editor, duty-bound to cover medical meetings and translate papers with such titles as "Antineoplastic Effects of Fluoropyrimidines (f-fluorouracil)" into layman's terms, learning about the possible health benefits from apple of Sodom, badman's oatmeal, old-maid's nightcap, and other quaint botanicals seemed to promise more fun than work!

After about six months of spending all of my free time on this project, I realized that I would have to resign from the magazine in order to obtain the firsthand up-to-date information required to round out the book. (What I had produced, so far, was an odd combination based upon histories of pharmacy, old herb remedy manuals, abstracts from highly technical pharmaceutical journals, and trade paper tidbits that often proved impossible to follow-up.) My husband, Albert Kreig, even then believed so strongly in the importance of this subject that he was willing to underwrite the not inconsiderable research expenses, and also to help me with much of the research itself. My parents, Walter and Gladys Baltzell, took over the care of our three young sons, while I traveled more than 35,000 miles in this country and abroad. During the next four years, I interviewed hundreds of people involved with the discovery and development of new drugs, in industry, in government, in universities, and in private practice as physicians or business consultants.

It was not my purpose to set out to build a strong case for botanicals or to take sides in the developing controversy over the use of synthetics. Botanical drug research was to me, a journalist, simply an exciting subject for investigation and all the more challenging because it was an untold story. In writing the book, I knew that I would have to be selective in the material I included—I couldn't describe, for instance, all of the useful drugs available for each condition I mentioned, otherwise I would have ended up with an encyclopedia. I did hope to remain objective—in fact, this was a professional obligation. As I went along, I tried to obtain "the other side of the story" from scientists and pharmaceutical producers generally associated with man-made chemicals. Even these people pointed out that certain extracts from plants have never been duplicated, much less improved upon in the laboratory. I asked a top-ranking organic chemist, Professor Robert B. Woodward of Harvard—best known for his role in synthesizing quinine, reserpine, strychnine, cortisone, and lysergic acid, some of nature's most complex substances—whether he thought that interest in botanicals would continue. I rather expected him to say that, in his opinion, time spent on crude drugs might better be employed in manipulating molecules. Instead, he told me, "The investigation of medicinal plants has formed a very small part of the modern research effort up until now, but it is increasing, and I expect this to be a very active field for many years to come."

Mr. S. Barksdale Penick, Jr., chairman of the board of S. B. Penick & Co., generally described as the world's largest botanical drug house, reported that a questionnaire submitted to the membership of the Pharmaceutical Manufacturers Association (Mr. Penick is board chairman of the PMA) showed that "more than two million dollars was spent in 1961 by about twenty-five members in seeking new drugs from plant sources. Single companies were budgeting as much as $400,000 in one year for this purpose. It is believed that these budgets have been increased since the questionnaire was circulated."

Botanical research takes many forms, but often it consists of the sponsorship of expeditions in various parts of the world. Different methods are used to solve the problem of plant selection: one company may concentrate only on poisonous plants; another will work only with those known to contain alkaloids. Or, all available plants in one family, such as the Solanaceae, or nightshades, may be gathered exclusively. All botanicals growing in a circumscribed area may be systematically screened. Once a promising lead on a new drug is found, as much as 10 million dollars may be spent on perfecting the end product as happened in the development of steroids from plant sources.

Some idea of the magnitude of this task is gained when we consider that there are about 350,000 botanical species, with around 2,000 new plants identified and added to the total in an average year. Only an estimated 4 per cent of these have been analyzed, so far. Almost all of the research reported in this book pertains to the 175,000 higher plants that bear flowers; while lower plants—molds and fungi—produce lifesaving antibiotics, I felt that they had been rather extensively covered in other books and articles. No claim is being made that every important or potentially useful medicinal plant is given its due. Rather, botanicals and specific research efforts were chosen because their histories contained certain elements needed to complete the over-all picture of natural products investigation. In compiling the table of contents, I felt as if I were turning my back on old friends after all my reading and interviewing, and so I informally polled a number of experts in this field and used the plants most frequently nominated as a guide. Dr. Maurice L. Tainter, who created the Sterling-Winthrop Research Institute, was one of the valued consultants who placed a strong vote for the opium poppy, about which he has written most interestingly himself. But of all botanicals, it seems that narcotic drug plants have been the favorites with writers in search of fascinating material. Since I could not hope to improve on some of these articles and books, I have instead listed a few of them in the Bibliographical Notes on further reading at the end of the book.

The scattered membership of the American Society of Pharmacognosy was an unfailing source of specific information. Many of these men and women, and a number of other authorities, as well, kindly reviewed the manuscript for technical accuracy, but they are not, of course, responsible for the viewpoints expressed, or for any mistakes or omissions.

I am particularly grateful to the drug plant explorers who permitted me to select material from their unpublished field journals and personal correspondence. The book would not have come alive without the opportunity to observe such field collections firsthand as those of the Pfizer expedition to Peru, led by Dr. Bruce Halstead, and the Syntex botanical program directed by Dr. Don Cox, in Mexico. All of the scientists were not only co-operative, but very good sports about having their life's work "popularized," usually, for the first time. Most drug companies eventually provided the basic information I needed, without regard to the brand names or special corporate image that they happened to be interested in publicizing at the time.

However, no book is written in a vacuum. Unfortunately,

the first two years when I was most anxious to collect information on pharmaceutical research programs (never too easy to obtain), industry spokesmen were the least inclined to speak freely. As one later remarked to me, "You chose the worst possible time to write this book!" In some cases, I had to obtain the information from many other sources, write the chapter, and then submit it to the individuals or company involved. This pump-priming technique added several years to my own research period, but it eventually paid off as details here and there were filled in by the insiders.

Lest this sound like unrelieved drudgery, I hasten to say it wasn't, by any means. For instance, on one of my first interviews, I had been asking Chairman Dermot Brownrigg Taylor of the Pharmacology Department, University of California at Los Angeles, about curare, the arrow poison he collected in Peru. As he described the action of neuromuscular blocking agents, I scribbled words like "anticholinesterase" at a great rate. Seeking a moment's respite, I asked, "What is that?" pointing to a knobby dried stick about a yard long that was leaning against a sack of twisted curare vines labelled *"Chondodendron tomentosum."*

"That is blackthorn," Dr. Taylor replied.

"And what is it used for?" I pursued.

"It's an ancient Hibernian tranquilizer," he said.

"And the scientific name?" I queried, pencil poised.

Dr. Taylor picked up the blackthorn and gave the sack of *C. tomentosum* a good whack to punctuate his answer: "In Gaelic they call it a Shillelagh!"

I must confess that some parts of this book are written for Irish professors and kindred souls.

Margaret Kreig
New York City, 1964

Contents

Part 3
Frontiers of Research

Photographs

Joseph Rock in chaulmoogra tree plantation, Hawaii, 1924
The Aztec *Badianus Manuscript,* (16th century)
William Hodge examines "elephant foot" tropical yams
H. Scott Gentry with flowering top of an Agave
Norman Applezweig who helped on Mexican Yams
Don Cox and Agronomist Luis confer on yam cultivation
A Mexican yam and its derivatives
Facsimile of Linneaus' herbarium sheet

PART 3
Between pages 352–353; 368–369

Gordon Svoboda adjusts flow rate of thin-layer chromatograph process
separating *Vinca*
William Meer studying *Vinca Rosea*
R. L. Noble and C. T. Beer of the Cancer Research Centre,
U. of British Columbia
Jonathan Hartwell with botanical extracts
Norman Farnsworth planting *Vinca*
T. F. D. Haines, A. Ammann, and Father Callens
receive African Rauwolfia from local chief
Aldous Huxley, a drawing by Bachardy
Albert Hoffman talking with R. Gordon Wasson in Basle
R. G. Wasson, first known white man
to participate in sacred mushroom rite
Curandera Maria Sabina passing mushrooms
through aromatic plant smoke
Mexican herb dealer selling vegetables for use in mushroom rite
Roger Heim (Paris Natural History Museum) trying to paint
exact colors of mushrooms
Mary Belle Allan aboard the *Stella Polaris*
"The Table Cloth is Impatient," a painting in oils by Marvin Malone,
while under the influence of mescaline
Heber W. Youngken, Jr., examines ergot cells
E. Yale Dawson collecting marine specimens on the sea floor
John Sieburth making tests with ringed penguin
Ross Nigrelli with a sea cucumber, Bimini, Bahamas
Sir Henry Wellcome on the Nile aboard his floating
tropical disease laboratory
Edson Woodward greets Russell Polden, who had motorcycled
around the world collecting soil samples
An African drug market
Richard Schultes feeding manioc flour to young Amazonian
Finn Sandberg with small African friend
Bruce Halstead checks a feverish little Campa

After Mrs. Kreig's article on periwinkle, "Vinca: Green Hope Against Cancer," appeared in *This Week* magazine, August 11, 1963, many hundreds of letters were received requesting specific information on new cancer therapies. It seems important, therefore, to remind readers that only a patient's own doctor is in a position to prescribe for his particular condition. If a drug described in this book seems to promise help "where all else has failed," the attending physician is best qualified to determine whether its use is indicated.

Drug companies usually maintain Medical Departments to assist physicians in working out special dosage schedules, etc., when such help is requested—by the doctor, not the patient. When a new prescription item becomes generally available, drug producers make every effort to inform the entire medical profession first, before any news is released to the general public.

It should be kept in mind that many portions of this book deal with basic research. While there may not be finished drugs today, as a result of all the work reported here, there most certainly is hope for tomorrow.

The Editors

1

Medicine Scouts and Their Methods

INTRODUCTION

WHAT SORT OF PERSON IS A PLANT HUNTER? A few lines abstracted from a field journal sometimes constitute a self-portrait. The following were written by the foremost authority in his field while going up an Amazon tributary in 1947. Aboard the decrepit *batelao,* a 30 by 12 foot barge, were fourteen people, including a pitiful little girl suffering from an advanced case of leprosy, a dozen dogs, pigs and other animals, plus baggage and a cargo of reeking dried fish.

The barge leaks alarmingly; an Indian boy bails continuously, the sloshing and scraping keeps us all awake every night. One side of the broken cabin is missing, exposing us to the rain. Going through the first rapids today was very difficult and dangerous— I feared we wouldn't make it because we were balanced on a sharp rock. I am discouraged because the formaldehyde I bought is very inferior and nearly all of my collections for the past month and a half are rotten. . . . This afternoon I came down with a very high fever. Have rheumatic pains in every limb and back, continuous nausea, some vomiting. . . . Vomiting continuously, very weak, probably mostly from malnutrition—we have had no warm food, only a tin of sardines for supper last night. . . . [Entries are brief for next week or so because the explorer, although he didn't know it at the time, was suffering from malaria and polyneuritis as a result of beriberi.] A strange accident happened this morning. About 5 AM there was a jolt and a loud crashing and splitting of wood. The barge had run into a leaning tree along the river's edge and the already badly damaged cabin was smashed. With my flashlight, I saw that the tree was in young fruit, with a recently fertilized ovary, that is, so I broke off a few branches to put in the press later. When dawn came, I examined the plant—it was *Micrandra* minor, which I am especially anxious to collect! Naturally, all on board were highly amused at my joy in collecting branches from a tree that had caused them so much fright. Late in the afternoon we came upon a most wonderful sight: three distinct peaks rising above the forest canopy, the Tapir Mountains. I also have noticed beautiful coconut trees here, disproving the notion that the palm cannot thrive far from the sea. While the boat is being patched up, I am anxious to do some collecting along the bank. . . . [Next day] Overdoing brought on violent vomiting with blood, am very weak. Will have to leave the intensive work until we come back downstream, when I hope to feel better.

This scientist, Dr. Richard Evans Schultes of Harvard whose experiences will be more fully described later, had been in the Amazon for six years and after a period of hospitalization and home leave, returned for another seven years. When interviewed, he did not mention any of the hardships and dangers encountered, and he denied that he had had any "adventures" worth recounting. But a forgotten field journal turned over to me with a lot of technical papers told the tale.

Professional plant hunters are usually botanists or pharmacognosists, but they may also be chemists, microbiologists, pharmacologists, physicians, or, even, psychiatrists, to mention just some of the specialists involved. Only a few women have collected medicinal plants in the rain forest, but, as we shall see, many men and women are making vital contributions in other areas. All are explorers in a sense. This book, focusing largely upon the more-fascinating-than-fiction jungle searches, begins with the greatest all-out quest for a drug plant in history. In Part I, other highly individualized plant hunting approaches are described in detail, along with profiles of the plant hunters themselves. Here you will meet strong, positive personalities whose opinions differ markedly, as do their methods. There is no One Right Way to accomplish a task so vast and complex; if we are to make the most of the plant kingdom's medicinal potential, we need a crash program incorporating every possible approach.

Some plant hunters travel light and alone; others work with teams of experts, utilizing helicopters, mobile laboratories, and Scuba for underwater collecting. One young man went around the world on a motorcycle gathering soil samples for antibiotic testing. While adventure story writers dramatize attempts to extract tribal secrets from medicine men, professionals play down sensational aspects and concentrate on obtaining classifiable botanical specimens suitable for laboratory analysis, even when these may be derived from exotic witch doctors' brews and quaint old wives' potions. In many cases, the results have withstood clinical evaluation and are now providing pills for patients. It's worth noting that some "failures" can be more interesting than successes; expeditions that seemed fruitless, at the time, proved to have important, far-reaching consequences in later years.

Whether hacking through rain forests with a machete, speeding over desert miles in a Land-Rover, or toiling around the clock in a laboratory or herbarium, the medicine scouts' chief aim is the same—*to find a plant that heals.*

The Quest for the Lost Strophanthus

"Arthritis remedy in quantity promised by African Seed. . . . Discovery of Cortisone-Yielding Plant Adds to the Great Advances Against Arthritis." The stories following these August, 1949, headlines in the *New York Times* went on to explain: "The seeds of an African arrow poison plant called Strophanthus hold the answer to the prayers of millions for Compound E, or cortisone, the adrenal gland hormone that pours new life into bodies tortured by arthritis, and by rheumatic fever—the number one killer of children. It promises new hope for victims of other chronic ills as well as the mentally afflicted."

The world-wide plant hunt touched off by this page one exclusive actually began four months earlier in the Detroit hotel room of William L. Laurence, science editor of the *Times*. He was about to turn into a botanical Sherlock Holmes, although he would have protested then that he knew less about botany than almost any subject you could name. After covering a meeting with the usual arid stretches, he was looking forward to a relaxing evening with Alton Blakeslee of the Associated Press.

Halfway down the hall, he heard his telephone ring. Well, let it. But at the elevator something made him turn back.

The call was from Dr. Howard A. Rusk in New York. He had a tip: The Mayo Clinic doctors who had been testing Compound E were going to report their findings. But Laurence would have to leave at once, without stopping to pack, or even getting in touch with his dinner partner. Otherwise, he would never reach Rochester, Minnesota, in time.

After a sleepless night, the haggard reporter arrived at the Mayo Clinic only to be greeted with the news that the press was barred from the scientific session. Further, there were no copies of the reports available. What to do? Somewhere en route, he had managed to place a quick call to his paper, asking them to save space on the front page of the next edition for a story that would be a medical milestone.

Now Dr. Philip S. Hench, co-author of the report, was telling him, "We don't want a lot of hysterical claims for a cure to appear in the lay press. We have been working with only fourteen people and this is *not a cure*. It is symptomatic relief for a chronic disease."

"As a science writer, I long ago dropped the word 'cure' from my vocabulary," was Laurence's exasperated reply. The rheumatologist, who was later to become his friend, was not convinced.

Fortunately, just then Dr. Edward C. Kendall, the Mayo chemist who had isolated Compound E from ox bile in 1935, arrived to present his later findings at this meeting; recognizing Laurence as the winner of a Pulitzer Prize for his series on the atomic bomb, he invited him into the closed session. The first paper consisted of complicated diagrams projected on a screen, and as the reporter struggled to note down such terms as 17-hydroxy-11-dehydrocorticosterone in the dark, he was convinced that he would end up with a lot of chicken scratches and no scoop.

But when Dr. Hench began to show his colored motion pictures of patients, Laurence recalls that he was literally lifted out of his chair with excitement: First, he saw pain-wracked cripples, bedridden, scarcely able to move. Then, just thirty-six hours after medication with Compound E, these same people were dancing jigs and running up and down stairs. Laurence says that he visualized all of the 11,000,000 arthritis sufferers in the United States dancing the conga with gusto. This wasn't just a milestone—it was a miracle!

At 11:30 P.M. the discussions were over. By now, the first two editions of the April 20 *Times* on the East Coast had gone out, but Laurence called in a world beat that was to earn him his second Pulitzer Prize as well as the Lasker Award for the best medical writing of the year. When the newspaperman finished dictating, he learned that Alton Blakeslee, after a fruitless manhunt, was calling in the Detroit police, convinced that his friend had met with foul play—how else to explain his sudden disappearance, his toothbrush and clothes remaining in his hotel room, and two editions going to press without the promised front page story?

William Laurence was immediately off on another trail. Sadly, there was a catch in the wonderful news about Compound E. A single day's treatment for a patient required bile from forty head of slaughtered cattle. Billions of head of cattle, perhaps a dozen times the entire cattle herd in the United States, would be needed to treat the arthritics in this country alone. Merck & Co. Inc., which supplied the drug, spent $18,000 to produce a three weeks' supply for just one patient. If only there were another way——

A week later, at the National Academy of Science meeting in Washington, D.C., Laurence asked Dr. Louis F. Fieser of Harvard, a leading authority on hormones: "Isn't there any cheap, convenient substitute for ox bile?" Fieser recalled that he had mentioned a plant seed with a similar structure in his newly revised chemistry textbook, but the name escaped him for the moment and, besides, nobody knew exactly which species of the plant produced the substance.

Laurence was overwhelmed by the possibilities in this off-hand tidbit, and as soon as he returned to New York he began to devote every spare minute to tracking down this lead. Library research revealed that the plant in question was Strophanthus. His best source of information was six blocks from his East Side apartment, at the Rockefeller Institute. Here, Dr. Walter A. Jacobs told him a fantastic story: Back in 1915, a twenty-pound bag of seeds, labeled *Strophanthus hispidus,* had been tossed into a hopper and the pulverized material analyzed. A glycoside called strophanthin, similar to Digitalis, the heart drug, was extracted. (Glycosides are compounds containing sugars.) Then they discovered a strange substance known today as sarmentogenin.

The odd thing was, the Rockefeller scientists had worked in the same way with *S. hispidus* many times, but never before had they obtained this new glycoside. They realized too late that the bag of seeds must have been mislabeled. Now there was no way to trace their botanical origin. For ten years, they continued to test batches of Strophanthus seed without getting the elusive material; then, one day in the eleventh year, two packets of *Strophanthus sarmentosus* seeds produced surprising results: sarmentogenin was obtained from one batch, but not from the other.

What was so great about sarmentogenin?

It was the only plant material described in scientific literature as having the proper chemical configuration for starting the cortisone process: oxygen on a double bond at the number 11 position. By building on this structure, as one would with an erector set having a handy projection, the number of steps required to synthesize cortisone could, theoretically, be reduced from thirty-five to about eighteen, thus greatly reducing the cost to manufacturers and to patients.

Writer William L. Laurence seems to have been the only person in America at that time to associate the possibilities

in the Strophanthus plant with the pressing need for cortisone. Later, he was to learn that Dr. Tadeusz Reichstein, who
had isolated Compound E in 1935, and who was to share the
1950 Nobel Prize in medicine with Kendall and Hench, was
working along these lines in his Swiss laboratory. At this
point, however, as Laurence tried vainly to interest investigators in his own country, he had to conclude that science
was suffering from "hardening of the categories." His biologist friends didn't know what the physicists were up to, and
the botanists could hardly have cared less about chemistry.
As in everything else, there are fads in research, and he
found that the study of medicinal plants from Africa was
decidedly out of fashion.

The big emphasis in cortisone and related research, ironically, had been based upon a rumor which later proved to be
false. Namely, our World War II espionage system had picked
up the information that the Germans were buying adrenal
glands from Argentina and injecting the extracts into their
Luftwaffe pilots. Compound E, obtainable from this source
as well as ox bile, was supposed to help them to fly at high
altitudes by diminishing the amount of oxygen needed during stress. Our air force began to demand the material and
the National Defense Research Council coordinated a vast
research program with the objective of chemically construct-
ing a laboratory substitute for the natural product. Still working feverishly toward this goal in the post-war era, Laurence's
friends in pharmaceutical laboratories thought his preoccu-
pation with his "Cinderella plant" just a little more than
quaint. He actually had Strophanthus growing from seed
in his apartment!

Without mentioning his project to any one except his
wife, he devoted all of his weekends and evenings to the
genus Strophanthus. He did not feel that he was slaving
beyond the call of duty. This was his duty. Being a respon-

sible science writer meant more than just serving as a mirror or a sieve, he felt; one should also be a synthesizer.

Very little had been written about the plant since 1861, when Dr. David Livingstone, the missionary-explorer, had noted in his journal: "We observed natives hunting with poisoned arrows. The poison is called 'Kombé' and it is obtained from a species of Strophanthus. It is very virulent, but Kombé may turn out to be a valuable remedy."

Dr. Livingstone's companion, Sir John Kirk, wrote: "The source of the poison, namely *S. Kombé,* was first identified by me. I had long sought it, but the natives invariably gave me some false plant until one day on the River Shire, I saw the Kombé . . . climbing on a tall tree. It was in pod and I could get no one to go up and pick specimens. In mounting the tree myself to reach the pods, the natives, afraid that I might poison myself if I handled the plant roughly or got the juice in a cut or in my mouth, warned me to be careful and admitted that this was the Kombé. . . . I brought specimens home to Kew Gardens, where they were described."

By accident Dr. Kirk found that the poison had the effect of lowering the pulse. In using his toothbrush, which had been in a pocket containing traces of the poison, he noticed a bitter taste. Soon afterward he observed that his pulse, which had been raised by illness, was back to normal. Kirk's discoveries stimulated experimentation by many scientists, with the result that the cardiac glycoside strophanthin was isolated at the University of Edinburgh in 1885, and *S. Kombé* became the commercial source of an official drug in many of the pharmacopoeias of the world. The firm of Burroughs Wellcome & Co. in London was largely responsible for the introduction of Strophanthus products in medicine.

Might not sarmentogenin, the hormone-like substance, also prove as useful?

By the middle of June, 1949, William Laurence was convinced that Strophanthus was slated to become one of the most important plants ever known, and he sat down to write a Sunday feature article about it. Then the thought struck him: the plant grew in areas of Africa that were under foreign control! What if these nations decided to slap an embargo on export, as had been done in the cases of rubber and quinine? Now he was torn between his desire to see his story in print after so much painstaking research—and the nagging suspicion that it ought not to be published at all. At least, not yet.

Mrs. Laurence had the answer: "Why don't you call the President of the United States and tell him about it?" When her husband hesitated, she picked up the phone and called the White House herself. Charles Ross, the press secretary, was doubly intrigued by what he heard. As a former newspaperman, he figured there must be something to this, if Laurence was willing to sacrifice such a good story; and because of firsthand experience with arthritis, he hoped it would prove true. He requested a detailed memo for President Harry S Truman, and a day or so later he called Laurence to say that the President would see him in person.

The next Tuesday, Laurence asked for the day off, volunteering to make the time up over the weekend. He told no one at the office where he was going. The President saw him promptly at the appointed hour and agreed that the United States ought to consider sending an expedition to Africa. Various officials, such as the head of the Federal Security Administration, consulted with the newspaperman, whose only request was that when the story was finally released, he be given first crack at it. Meanwhile he emphasized the need for secrecy because it seemed that the plant was quite rare, and it was conceivable that whoever got there first might corner the world's entire supply.

Learning that Dr. Leonard A. Scheele, the Surgeon General of the United States Public Health Service, was on his way to a World Health Assembly, Laurence called him at the airport to say that Swiss scientists were working with Strophanthus seeds and might even now be exploring Africa. Scheele stopped off in Basel, where he found that they had been in Africa and had arranged for someone in an unnamed African colony (French was Scheele's guess) to gather and send in seeds. Reichstein was said to be then so interested in this research that whenever investigators sought problems for study, he took them into a room filled from floor to ceiling with bags of seeds and said, "Take your pick."

After talking with these investigators, Scheele returned to Washington and asked the director of the National Institute of Health to do whatever was necessary to obtain Strophanthus seeds. As a result, Dr. John T. Baldwin, Jr., a biology professor at the College of William and Mary, who had just returned from two years in Nigeria, was given the title of principal botanist for the United States Department of Agriculture and sent back to West Africa in July, 1949.

One day in August, as Laurence was sitting at his typewriter, he received a call from his friend Scheele. It seemed that a high-ranking official was planning to capture the headlines by announcing at a press conference that "Strophanthus will be to medicine what the atom bomb is to physics." The promise to give the hardworking reporter a head start, in appreciation for all that he had done, was being kept by Scheele. Thanking him for this tip, Laurence told the whole story to Turner Catledge, his managing editor and then left for Washington. There he learned that Strophanthus had been found growing in Liberia, where there were large investments of American money for the development of the country's resources. Relations were amicable and an embargo was unlikely, so there was no longer any need for secrecy. On Tuesday morning, August 16, the news was broken on page one of the *New York Times,* and a day or so later, the government made a more detailed announcement.

In his story, Laurence explained: "Strophanthus seed has several advantages over the animal product: It can be grown in unlimited quantities; it is seventeen chemical steps closer to cortisone than the animal product; and one ton of seed would yield as much cortisone as 12,500 tons of beef animals. Because of this, it is expected to become one of the most important plants in the world, serving as a veritable 'Elixir of Life' for millions. . . . As an added boon, it will aid Africa and other underdeveloped countries. Plantations may be started in Venezuela, the Philippines, East Indies and Pacific Islands, enabling natives to become self-supporting and, at the same time, making a real contribution to the United States economy. Here is an entirely new product for which the demand will greatly exceed the supply for many years to come; just what 'the doctor ordered' for a sick world, both from the medical and economic point of view."

This done, he made one more telephone call regarding Strophanthus—to the technical director of S. B. Penick & Co. in New York City, the world's leading supplier of botanical drugs. He felt that they should be involved in the search for sarmentogenin. Penick had been buying and selling *S. Kombé* and *S. hispidus* seeds for some time because of the cardiac glycoside strophanthin, which was preferred by many European physicians to Digitalis in the treatment of heart disease. Penick had shared their information about the plant with Dr. Baldwin before he left for Africa, but they were not anxious to outfit a costly safari for a quest of their own.

Their botanical experts had been trying for some time to obtain seed samples of various species through their contacts overseas, but the results had been disappointing for many reasons, not the least being that Strophanthus was outlawed in many colonial territories because witch doctors favored it as a means of dispatching troublesome persons; just a little of the poison under the fingernail was said to be sufficient.

There was also the problem of botanical identification. Some forty-five or more species were known to exist, thirty-six of them in Africa alone, the rest in Southern Asia, Malaya, and the Philippines. How many (besides *S. sarmentosus*) actually contained the potent sarmentogenin; once found and tested, would the plants be available in sufficient quantity for harvesting? If not, could they be cultivated?

The response to Laurence was on the order of "Thank you, but no."

At this point, The Upjohn Company of Kalamazoo entered the picture with an offer to put up a good share of the necessary money if Penick would attend to the details of an expedition. Upjohn had half of their staff of 300 researchers attacking the cortisone problem from six different directions, and they were now determined to get to the bottom of the Strophanthus matter, regardless of the gamble. They would be a logical manufacturer of the finished pharmaceutical.

When Penick's management pointed out the slim chances of success, an Upjohn official replied, "We don't care how small the chances are—knowing just this much about the possibilities in Strophanthus, we have got to go ahead."

As it turned out, the Upjohn-Penick Expedition for Botanical Exploration lasted nine months, covered 13,000 miles in the heart of Equatorial Africa, and was probably the most exhaustive, all-out effort of its kind on record. The goal: to bring the availability and cost of cortisone within reach of all who needed it. The method: to leave no pathway unexplored. The cost: whatever it might be, in energy and money. The outcome: the answer is never known in the beginning, else why pursue it to the end? And even now we may not know the end of The Great Strophanthus Search.

But here is the story to date, and for the first time, from the recollections, field notes, and correspondence of the young pharmacognosist who put the expedition together.

In that autumn of 1949, Edson F. Woodward, an energetic six-footer with red hair, was working in the import department at Penick, an interesting spot, but all the same a desk job. As a registered pharmacist just graduated from the Massachusetts College of Pharmacy, he had gone first into the control laboratory, then into purchasing—most of the time on the technical side—and finally into foreign commerce. Whenever anything odd or peculiar needed to be obtained, be it ant eggs in quantity or frankincense and myrrh, Woodward was asked to look into it. His educational background was particularly applicable to the needs of this company: he had studied economic botany, chemistry, French, some German, Spanish, and Latin. His graduate work in pharmacognosy was done under two outstanding men, the late Dr. Heber W. Youngken and Dr. Maynard W. Quimby. He had earned a fellowship in materia medica, had designed and dug the first medicinal plant garden at the College, and had partly worked his way through school as a professional photographer. His proficiency with a camera would prove to be a valuable asset in the field, as would his endurance training in long-distance swimming and running.

One September morning, after the president of the company told him, "We want to look around in Africa for Strophanthus," Woodward got busy. He was now officially the business manager of the Upjohn-Penick Expedition, as well as its pharmacognosist. Although he had never been on an expedition before or traveled outside the United States, in a few weeks he would be arranging for the collection of seed in commercial quantities, or for cultivation, if and when any of his finds showed the presence of the elusive sarmentogenin. In charge of the expedition at New York headquarters would be Dr. W. G. Bywater, Penick's present director of research.

Woodward's immediate concern was to locate at least

one, preferably two, specialists in plant collecting, men with the same ability as a stamp collector, who can go through a pile of stamps and pick out one of each, plus variations, without duplication. It was the object of the expedition to collect, for chemical study, positively identified samples of as many species of Strophanthus as possible, together with allied plants used as arrow poisons.

Perhaps the secret of obtaining sarmentogenin lay in collecting just the proper species, or a certain strain of one of the species. Perhaps everything depended upon the time of year, the geographical location, the soil characteristics of the area . . . or factors unknown. The source of the glycoside was clouded in mystery because there had been no definitive botanical work on those original samples of seed at the Rockefeller Institute. Were they really *S. sarmentosus?* It would take a specialist to find out.

Not just any botanist would do. He had to be familiar with the flora of Africa, preferably from firsthand experience, and he would have to be able to leave the country on a few weeks' notice. Although Penick was told that it usually takes about six months to get an expedition organized, equipped, and underway, there wasn't that much time. The season for the ripening of the fruit north of the equator was fast approaching. After it ripened, the seeds would be wind-dispersed and all would be lost until the next year. By working constantly, including evenings and weekends, Woodward expected to have things lined up in about three weeks.

But it is the nature of botanists to be roving far afield, and while the National Geographic Society, the Explorers Club, botanic gardens, universities, and missionary organizations were all called, not a single well-trained man could be found who was free to travel on such short notice.

Pressure was building for another reason: competition. Merck's economic botanist, B. A. Krukoff, an authority on plants used in arrow poisons who usually worked in Central and South America, had reviewed Strophanthus material at a botanic garden and had departed shortly thereafter on a secret mission. Already in the field were the USDA man and the Swiss group; rumored soon to be leaving were scientists from England and from France. To be the first to bring back the lost Strophanthus was the desire of individual men, companies, and governments. Despite the widespread publicity about the need for plant precursors for cortisone, everyone connected with the search—in this country and abroad—was trying to be as discreet as possible.

The Upjohn-Penick enterprise made its first inquiries indirectly through academic contacts, who contributed appraisals such as: "X is well qualified but is noted for being a lone worker, brusque. Y is getting along in years; this might be too rugged for him. Z has just returned from a year abroad." In one case, a devoted secretary volunteered the information that her employer "may be over fifty but looks much younger and is very vigorous, strong, and robust." This was all to the good, but, unfortunately, he knew nothing about the flora of Central Africa.

Some of the best prospects, such as Professor of Botany Robert E. Woodson, Jr., the noted authority on the family that includes Strophanthus, the Apocynaceae, did not wish to leave their students in mid-term. Other good men had books nearing deadlines or research projects in a critical stage. The last hope lay in some names being checked out by the Smithsonian Institution. When they reported that they could find no one available in the United States with the required background, it looked as if Woodward might have to solo first time out, one inexperienced man on an expedition built for three.

The search was widened on September 30, when the heads of departments of botany overseas were cabled: APPRECI-

ATE YOUR ADVISING US AS TO BOTANIST BEST
QUALIFIED AND AVAILABLE TO DO FIELD WORK
IN EQUATORIAL AFRICA ON STROPHANTHUS
STOP WOULD LIKE YOU TO CHECK AVAILABIL-
ITY ANY NAMES GIVEN YOU STOP SCREEN AND
CABLE US YOUR OPINION OUR EXPENSE STOP AN-
TICIPATE TRIP STARTING WITHIN THREE WEEKS.

There were both advantages and disadvantages in this.
If a non-American joined the expedition, there would be
access to another country's "inside" information and resources;
there would be entree into its colonies in Africa; with two
vehicles, more ground could be covered and in case of trouble
it would be safer; there was less chance of an embargo if the
drug plant were found in its territory; and the expedition
could travel under either the American or X country's flag,
whichever seemed more advantageous at the time.

As to drawbacks, there was a greater possibility of personal conflict. Also, the other country would know right
away about any successful finds and there would be the
bother and expense of making duplicate collections of specimens. There was a chance of increased resistance in Africa
from rival European nations with interests there. And there
would be the additional item in the budget of at least five
or six thousand dollars. Nevertheless, a questionnaire was
prepared for any prospects who might turn up. Besides the
usual queries about education, health, and travel experience,
there was the blunt request to state fully what might be
expected if "your country sponsors a similar expedition to
the same area and for the same purpose."

Unexpectedly, word came that the American Museum
of Natural History's Archbold Expeditions, based in Florida,
might have just the man, recently back from Australia. On
October 6, a letter, followed by a call, went to Richard Archbold, research associate of the Museum: "This is a matter

considered to be of the utmost national importance, the problem of obtaining in Africa the necessary source material for the manufacture of cortisone. It is now most urgent and imperative that we send an expedition. From our knowledge and information, the best botanical collector to join with us is Mr. Leonard J. Brass, in your employ. . . . It would be appreciated if you would consider releasing him almost immediately for about six months' duration. . . ."

What a stroke of luck if Leonard Brass were able to go. Born in Australia, he had received his training at the Queensland Herbarium. Now an American citizen, he was considered by his colleagues to be the leading modern authority on the flora of New Guinea. Unquestionably, he was experienced in the field: he had begun his explorations for Harvard's Arnold Arboretum in 1925. During a 1938–39 trip to New Guinea's Snow Mountains with Mr. Archbold, Brass took part in the discovery and exploration of the "Shangri-la Valley" of the Balim River. The 1948 trip that he led to the Cape York peninsula of Australia was the first major American expedition to this remote area. What was especially important, now, was the fact that he also had explored in Africa. But he was incommunicado in the Smokies on a vacation, and was not due to return for some days. The question was, if Archbold released him, would he be interested?

Pending these answers, Woodward was absorbed with a thousand details. His museum and missionary consultants were busy answering questions: What is the best ratio of helpers to botanists? Two to three natives to each. . . . Should they be hired on the West Coast and kept for the whole trip? Get motor boy, personal boy and cook on Coast, pick up guides in each territory as you enter. . . . What about sleeping sickness? No serum available, but look into the spinal meningitis cure. . . . Food? Go light and live off the land. (This turned out to be poor advice, as food isn't that easily picked up in the rain forest.) . . . Hunting? Take buckshot for wild hogs; use number seven for guinea fowl, and be sure to hang these for a day and a half; don't give your boy more than four shells at a time. . . . Clothing? Low-cut sneakers, ten inch boots, shorts, and long wool socks for the bush; dark glasses, felt hat for the sun; don't bother with rainwear, just plan to get wet. . . . Be sure to take extra springs and rear axle for truck. A flour sieve is handy for sifting out the bugs.

Despite the uncertainties, a seventeen-page, single-spaced list of equipment and supplies was ordered shipped to Douala on the coast of French Cameroun (now the independent state of Cameroon), to be picked up on October 25. Among the many items were a one-ton stake body truck; a three-quarter-ton pickup truck; three sleeping bags; a movie camera, film, telephoto lens, developing tank; a Coleman cookstove, four lanterns; three cases of food, ten cartons of cigarettes; a portable radio and a typewriter; five plant presses, two bags of rags, four, forty-pound bales of newspapers, and five hundred tags for trees; six machetes; lineman's tools and safety belt. The firearms: a 12-gauge double-barreled shotgun, a 30-06 rifle, a .22 caliber rifle, plus forty-five boxes of shells. Reading matter: *Flowering Plants and Ferns, How to Make Movies,* an index to a map of Africa with a set of maps, a pocket dictionary, an almanac, and a tropical medicine textbook. For doing business along the trail: the Penick catalogue and manual, a list of African exporters, and a box of business cards. Letterhead stationery for the expedition was ordered, but didn't catch up until the trip was partly over. Medical supplies ranged from artery forceps to Q-tips, from adrenalin to vitamins, eighty-eight items in all. Insect repellent? A dozen bottles and six bombs.

By October 19, Edson Woodward's last day at the office, word had been received that Brass would join him in Africa as the field director of the Expedition, after studying the herbarium sheets on Strophanthus at the New York Botanical Garden. Brass had by now mapped the itinerary and made many valuable suggestions. There was a very good chance that Mr. X, a foreign botanist, would be coming along, too. As the goodbyes were said, Penick executives agreed that "Woody" had done a good job. But he was by no means through with his desk work, for they expected to receive daily written reports of botanical findings and a monthly itemized expense account. This last was to prove a jolly pastime as equivalents for half a dozen currencies were calculated; what they really needed in a third man was a combination stenographer and certified public accountant. Woodward would not have been so cheerful if he had known that many a weary midnight would find him still pushing papers after a rugged stretch of Congo collecting.

At home in the suburbs, it was not so easy to leave his wife, Ruth, and their four-year-old daughter, Elizabeth. How to explain to such a little girl that he was "going to work," but that he would not be able to come home to see her until "sometime next summer"? He could hardly believe it himself. There were promises to write often, and they were kept. But there turned out to be only six stops for mail pickup in the next nine months.

The first destination for Woodward was not Africa, but England's Royal Botanic Gardens at Kew, where he could study the outstanding collection of plants from British African colonies. Just as a library is measured by the number of volumes on its shelves, a botanic garden is gauged by the number of its books, plus the number of herbarium sheets, and the selection of growing plants in its gardens and greenhouses. The herbarium is a collection of pressed, dried, and preserved specimens of plants useful to botanists in studying the relationships of one plant to another—and in learning the flora of an area, or what plants are found in what region.

Kew officials had a co-operative attitude: they tended to pick the brains of plant hunters passing through, but they gave valuable help in return, such as lists of the flowering and fruiting seasons in all areas. (Botanists must have flowers and fruits in order to make accurate identifications.) At Kew, it was learned that Baldwin was already sending back plants for study, but no Strophanthus had been included.

Next came Brussels, where there was supposed to be a fair collection of the Belgian Congo species of the plant in question. From the director of the garden there, information was obtained that the Belgians, having followed up Reichstein's early work, had an eighteen-month head start on collecting Strophanthus in Africa. Six or seven expeditions from various countries were now intent upon beating the bush.

In Paris, at the Jardin des Plantes, there was a surprise meeting with Professor Chevalier of the Laboratoire Agronomie Colonial. The Professor, an expert on the flora from Dakar down into the Gabon, was leaving December 2 for Senegal and the Ivory Coast. Strophanthus, of course, what else? Despite his seventy-eight years, he was competition to be reckoned with; he was just as eager as the next man to be first home with the prize. Nevertheless, he shared his private collection of seventy-five herbarium sheets with the American, gave him some sample seeds, and told him where they had been gathered.

At last, Africa! As soon as his plane landed at Accra on the Gold Coast (now the independent state of Ghana), Penick's plant hunter sought out the local botanist, who told him that both Krukoff of Merck and Baldwin had passed through. Krukoff had collected no flowering material, but he had sent back a parcel of about thirty pounds of *S. sarmentosus* fruits which were immature by two months, plus leaves, stems, and roots. Two days after that, in the northern section of the Gold Coast, a botanist in Tamale remarked, "You are by no means the first Strophanthus seeker in these parts. I'll tell you just what I told the others: *S. sarmentosus* is the only species between here and Timbuctu (now Tombouctou). The natives cultivate it to a slight extent. In fact, three weeks ago a native used it in a Saturday-night killing."

Woodward wondered if he was ever going to hit some virgin territory or ask a question and not hear in reply, "You are the third man to ask me that—isn't it funny?" At Lomé, in Togo, he thought he had something. First he asked if anyone had inquired about Strophanthus. No one had. Well then, did they know of any specimens? The government botanist declared that actually there were no specimens around Lomé, which explained everything. Away from home a month now with little to show for it, the pharmacognosist flew down to Lagos in Nigeria for his rendezvous with Leonard Brass and, hopefully, with Mr. X. It was high time the Upjohn-Penick Expedition for Botanical Exploration started rolling.

Field Notes from Africa

FIELD DIRECTOR LEONARD J. BRASS HAD AN INTER-
esting Australian accent, was forty-nine and married. Physically, he looked built for a long race, trim and plenty tough.
His most outstanding characteristic—or so it seemed to the
younger member of the Expedition—was his piercing glance.

No doubt both men were wondering: How will it all
work out? Cause for concern wasn't so much the age
difference, but the vast gulf in experience. Edson Woodward, a New Hampshire boy, had botanized around New
England, but this was on a par with Scouting when compared
with Brass's intimate knowledge of the rain forests of the
world. Yet circumstances had forced the less experienced
man to anticipate many of their needs when purchasing their
supplies and equipment. Woodward could only hope that any
mistakes or omissions would not cripple their efforts to find
Strophanthus and that the theme song of the African trek
would not be: Where is the . . . Why didn't. you . . . You
should have . . . I always . . . and so on. Nothing to do
now but shake hands, smile, and wonder what the third man
would be like.

When Mr. X was last heard from, his immediate superiors
had approved his release; he had completed his inoculations,

purchased his gear, and was ticketed for Africa. He had said it was "the chance of a lifetime," not only because of the adventure, but also because he was a specialist in the type of plants they were seeking. He needed more field experience and they needed him. It was a good deal. All that remained was routine approval from some government official higher up.

At the very last minute, and without the slightest warning that such a thing might happen, the approval was denied. Later, a conflict of interests was cited. Between individuals? Rival companies? Nations? One could only speculate; nothing could be done. The file on Mr. X was closed and the two plant explorers had to shoulder his load and make the best of it. They caught the next plane to Douala, in French Cameroun, where the S.S. *Fernland* was scheduled to arrive with their trucks and equipment.

Here are some journal entries: "November 29, 1949. At this point you don't really need a map. The continent of Africa bulges into the Atlantic and just where it cuts back in and the coastline starts to run due south, right there in the corner is Douala, a port city up an estuary about fourteen miles. Hot, sticky, and no wonder—your map may say, 'Rainfall, eighty inches per year,' but don't you believe it. On the side of Cameroon Mountain, about fifty miles from here, it averages 374 inches a year, and in 1919 they measured 577 inches. We are staying at the Presbyterian Mission while waiting for the S.S. *Fernland,* delayed by strikes. Meanwhile, we have hired our help: The boy is Valentin Ekni, in his early twenties, with experience only as a houseboy. We settled on old Thomas Bikek as cook; he has a wide, infectious grin and assures us that he can cook very well over a campfire. Henrí Mondo will be our driver, having passed the test in a rented Citroen—during this trial run we spotted our first Strophanthus vine, *S. gracilis.* One year's flowers and leaves accompany the preceding year's fruit on the same plant. It had one ripe fruit yielding a few seeds!"

Gleaned from various expedition field notes, this composite picture of Strophanthus and its native uses emerges: Strophanthus, in the open by itself, takes the form of a bush, but it more often occurs as a beautiful, woody climber inhabiting the forest between the coast and the center of the continent. It coils on the ground and reaches to the tops of the highest trees, where it hangs in festoons of shining foliage. Usually, the stem is several inches in diameter, but it may be up to a foot thick. Many species are spectacular in full bloom and would serve very well as ornamentals. The funnel-shaped flowers, sweet-scented in the evening, are white, pale cream, or pinkish with deep purple throats and petals that terminate in long streamers. The fruits are shaped like thin cucumbers and they come paired, from ten to seventeen inches long. They are slow to mature, but when ripe the pods burst open milkweed-fashion, freeing handfuls of fluff surrounding a few seeds. The pale tan seeds, somewhat larger than those of cucumbers, are covered with silky hairs with a long tuft.

The natives call Strophanthus simply "the poison arrow plant." They make the poison in various ways, sometimes pounding the seeds into a red, oily mass and immediately putting this on their spears and arrows. At other times, or in other places, a fluid extract of the seeds is boiled down to a syrupy consistency and different plants are added, such as the cactiform Euphorbias. Some tribes use Strophanthus roots as well. The Fantis of the Ivory Coast believe that by fermenting the powdered seeds and leaves with banana flowers, they insure toxicity. Small mammals die quickly after being shot with Strophanthus-tipped arrows, seldom being able to travel more than 100 yards. For bigger game, such as elephants for meat and ivory, the natives use poisoned spears; hiding beside a jungle trail, they sneak up on a passing tusker and jab the spear into the elephant's stomach. In some areas, before the flesh of such an animal is eaten, sap from the Baobab tree bark is put into the wound to neutralize any remaining poison. (Barks contain tannin, known to have some precipitant action on the glycoside.)

Excessively large oral doses cause pronounced cardiac slowing, heart arrest, and death due to failure of respiration. Artificial respiration is ineffectual since ventricular fibrillation (wildly irregular heartbeat) results in failure of circulation. The substance is twenty to thirty times more toxic when injected into muscles, than when taken by mouth, and doubly so when injected intravenously.

In native medicine, Strophanthus is employed as a specific for venereal disease. The pulverized stem also is put on Guinea-worm sores, and a decoction of stems is drunk to cure weakness after severe illnesses, but this is administered with considerable care. Strophanthus is considered a cure-all by the Mano tribe of Liberia; when a Mano is sick, he is sent to a "sick bush" for isolation. His family may bring him food, but they must give it to an attendant to take to him so that the disease will not spread.

Some species of Strophanthus, such as *S. gratus,* contain a glycoside called ouabain or G-strophanthin, which is used by the natives in their trials by ordeal. This practice is a form of Russian roulette, jungle style: The person suspected of a crime is fed the poison. If he survives, he is innocent; if he dies, he is guilty. Since these glycosides are absorbed somewhat irregularly by the digestive tract, there is no way of predicting the outcome. A dose which is not fatal on a first offense might very well cause death the next time that person comes to trial. With this form of justice there are probably few habitual criminals.

On December 20, 1949, after the S.S. *Fernland* finally arrived at Douala with the Upjohn-Penick equipment, the transfer into barges, the unloading at the dock, and the passage through customs were all done in slow motion with an abundance of ritual and paperwork—a forecast of tedious days to come when the expedition crossed and recrossed the borders of countries in its 13,000-mile trek. The plant explorers were annoyed to find that the new vehicles required extensive adjustments. The high tops needed to be cut down, the flimsy sides had to be reinforced, and the auxiliary gas tanks, riding too low, reinstalled inside. What they didn't know at that time was that the gas pump on one truck and the steering mechanism on the other had basic defects that were to plague them halfway across the continent.

The men discovered that they could not replace the bottles of sulfuric acid that were missing. This meant that a simple chemical color test useful in distinguishing between seeds of certain species could not be made in the field. Actually, it was the little things that ate up their time and caused the most exasperation, like not being able to find the carton of pencils, or the burlap bags, or materials of a certain size or shape to build up the sides of the trucks. But eventually, all the kinks were ironed out sufficiently for the expedition to start up the road for Yaoundé.*

On December 22 at Bertoua, Woodward noted in his journal: "Today was a bit strenuous. Had to stop three times because there seemed to be water and sludge in the pickup truck's gas tank—probably New Jersey sludge at that. Gas, by the way, cost thirty cents a gallon at Douala, one dollar here. Len has run into an unfriendly bacterium and is not up to par, by any means. We hope the medical kit and a day of rest will fix all that. The cook is something of a slowpoke,

---

* Because the expedition doubled back and forth so many times and because African place names have changed, no attempt has been made here to trace the exact route. What follows is a condensation of many journal entries, rather than a day-by-day account.

but food is real cheap; coconuts and papayas are one and a quarter cents each, bananas five cents a dozen. The boys are working out O.K., but Valentin is always looking for a tip. 'You dash me, Mister?' is the way he puts it."

On Christmas Day, this entry was made: "We worked this morning putting the collected Strophanthus specimens in the sun to dry; then at noon we went to the mission for a visit and a nice canned chicken dinner. By the way, a good buy out here is a wife, around $20.00 each. They plant, cultivate and harvest the garden; they brick up the house, once the frame is erected; if you are moving, they are the ones who carry all the baggage; and, of course, they bear children. The males help farm until they are old enough to dislike work, and the female children can be sold for around $20.00 each, thus completing the cycle. Back in Douala, European dress was in style, but here it is just a bunch of leaves, fore and aft. The leaves always look fresh. Perhaps they change their greenery two or three times a day."

Woodward was a little surprised by the climate. They were now up on a 2,000-foot plateau most of the time and, while it was hot in the sun, they were glad to have their warm sleeping bags at night. They wore sun helmets to avoid getting the giant-sized headaches called "sun heads," which could last for several days.

As they scoured the countryside for Strophanthus, they usually made their headquarters in native villages because of the availability of food, laborers, and guides. They stayed in huts called *case de passage,* which were set aside for government officials, missionaries, and commercial people traveling through. One thing that was forever holding up their progress was the answer "Il est sorti" ("He has left") whenever they needed an official. No one ever knew where "he" had gone, or for how long.

Almost every night the plant drier was in operation. It

was a simple contraption, a collapsible wooden box on legs, no top, but with a bottom of perforated sheet metal. Under this frame went a couple of Coleman lamps for heat and on top went the day's collection of plants. The collection was meticulously arranged. First it was built up as a pile—blotter, specimen in its folder, blotter and corrugated drier, repeated until the stack was as high as the drier was long. The stack was then finished off at both ends with firm wooden plates and bound tightly with long canvas straps. When turned on their sides, with the corrugations of the cardboards acting as ventilating chimneys, the herbarium specimens were usually nicely dried before midnight. If there was too much heat, the specimens became brittle and scorched; if too little heat, they lost color or deteriorated. But a properly dried specimen should last for well over a hundred years as a positive record of who collected what, where, and when.

On December 31, Woodward described a trip out of Momjepom: "Going into the bush is old stuff to Len Brass, but yesterday's collection was very interesting to me—if only for the trip, let alone the Strophanthus. At 7:30 A.M. we started for a 'nearby' Pigmy clan. We were a party of five, guided by Kompi, the native 'botanist' of the village. His loincloth was not at all in evidence because he wore a blue chinchilla wool overcoat, sort of a Man of Distinction. He carried a very fine spear and a rattan handbag for his pipe and tobacco. With him was his boy, a well-built, slightly muscle-bound fellow, who carried the canteen, a spear, and a machete. Following the guide, came Len and myself, then the interpreter, David Kokola. David carried the collecting press and the kit bag. Len and I carried our cameras and binoculars and took turns carrying the 30–06 rifle—protection against gorillas, which are rather common hereabouts.

"It was a two-and-a-half-hour march, up and down little hills through mostly primary rain forest. There was a maze of trails in several places, but Kompi didn't hesitate at any junctions. (Perhaps due to the fact that he took Krukoff over the same trail a couple of weeks ago!) Not an animal did we see. There was a boar's nest, however, and we heard birds and monkeys at some distance. Plus the regular supply of insects. Kompi is rather tall but graceful and had no trouble setting a fast pace, but I am considerably taller at six feet two and judging from the looks of my helmet and the frequent taps it received, I am glad it was on my head.

"When we reached the village, my first impression of the Pigmies was: they aren't so small! Perhaps they had intermingled with taller tribes. There was a group of six thatched huts about the size and shape of Eskimo igloos, furnished with mats of palm leaves and an iron cooking pot. Eight men and women, four babies, and some dogs and chickens were gathered around the fire. One man was separating out Strophanthus seed onto a mat; two of the women were nursing babies—one was weaving a basket at the same time. The rest were just sitting around. Len and I took seats on a wooden drum and we all had a big palaver about Strophanthus. They collected a good bit of it because we saw a pile of pod husks about six inches deep and eight feet across.

"We bought one lot of seed and started back, soon to be followed by two of the Pigmies, who came in handy at the first *S. sarmentosus* vine we selected for a collection. Kompi's boy climbed up village fashion, using a long stick cut with a hook on the end to pull himself up whenever there was no hand hold. But the Pigmy went up the vine, sixty feet or more, as easily as the average person walks along the ground, making the perpendicular seem horizontal . . . an artisan to be admired in his own way. Down came the fruits, leaves and flowers, followed by the boy. Next we found a vine of *S. hispidus*. In contrast to the first vine, which had been about a foot thick, this one measured only nine inches. It seemed to reach upward a considerable distance before making contact with the tree and it finished its climb at about the 100-foot mark, where it was in fruit. By now, the Pigmies were too tired to climb, so Kompi's boy went up, more slowly and a bit clumsily, but very much on the up and up. After we obtained these fruits, we started home and were very glad to rest when we got there, a five-hour march being something we hadn't done for awhile. As with our pickup truck, which now has 1,000 miles on it, this hike 'broke us in.' No blisters, sprains, or twisted crankshafts, but we were happy to see that Thomas had a big 'chop-chop' on the fire. We hadn't eaten since breakfast.

"Along the trail we had tried to get an estimate from Kompi on the relative abundance of the local species and the possible optimum collection per year. About all we learned was that *S. sarmentosus* was the most common type and that you could collect 'a lot' if you tried. Kompi could savvy a kilo [2.2 pounds], but not a given number of kilos. Same thing when we tried to discuss a large number of baskets-full or the capacity of a truck body. He understood 'small-small,' but any quantity more than a few was simply 'much-much.' The unfortunate thing is that if he only understood numbers, he could have given us a very useful estimate because he knows the forest and the various species of plants. However, we did swap information about how to take out the seeds, how to operate a 30-06, and we had a few laughs —a bit of pantomime makes humor universal."

New Year's Day, 1950, at Momjepom, Brass and Woodward received a live chicken as a gift and reciprocated with presents and best wishes for a *Bonne Année*. They had found that fountain pens, cigarette lighters, and subscriptions to the *National Geographic Magazine* were very much appreciated by missionaries and government people who helped them. And they learned that they were right in not bringing the traditional trade goods for the natives, who much preferred money or cigarettes to colored beads and trinkets.

After Sunday School was out, they hired twenty-two boys to remove Strophanthus seeds. The younger boys got 5 francs each and the older ones 15 francs, the wage scale being set by the native preacher. Assorted, reasonably dry Strophanthus seed was bringing from 100 to 120 francs per kilo. The local natives were the middlemen; the Pigmies were the collectors. After the fruits split, the big fluffy balls holding the seeds had a tendency to lodge in the treetops. Once they were brought down, it required the most tedious hand carding to separate the lightweight seeds from the fluff. About fifty *S. sarmentosus* fruits produced one kilo of seeds. At that time, it was not known exactly how many seeds would be needed, but the Upjohn-Penick explorers were hoping to find a source which might supply 100 tons. The people back in Washington who spoke glibly of "picking cortisone off trees" would have been somewhat sobered by a day in the field with Brass and Woodward. Nevertheless, one ton of Strophanthus seed was said to equal 12,500 tons of slaughtered animals.

About this time, Penick's executives were advised: "Any crude drug industry in these parts would take a good bit of close supervision and development. The Africans are not a lively bunch of workers, but considering their wretched state of health and nutrition, one certainly can't blame them. We hear that the USDA man has finished in the Cameroons and has gone back to Lagos. He may have had instructions to return to Nigeria in order to make further collections of some species which the chemists back home have found promising. It is rumored that he is rather fed up with the Strophanthus search. Out here, one is collecting 'blind' so to speak. You don't know whether any sarmentogenin has been found in the species you have collected and sent back until long after you have left the area, if you ever find out. The constantly changing demands of the research efforts in the States produce seemingly erratic objectives—to one in the field, that is. We are so anxious for reports on what you are finding that when they told me there wasn't any mail waiting for us the other day, I insisted upon making a letter-by-letter, package-by-package, search of the whole post office. They were a maddeningly smug lot when I found out that they were right: no mail for us."

The expedition sent a cable from Batouri, "SOUTH-WESTWARD TODAY," to give the people at home some idea of their whereabouts, although their actual destination was unknown. Maps were often almost useless; a heavy blue line had a way of turning out to be a barely perceptible path. They spent entire days stuck in the mud or stranded because of tire or motor trouble, and while they were in motion their speed in many places averaged only six or seven miles per hour. This is a description of crossing on a ferry made of six or eight hollowed-out mahogany canoes fastened together with planks on top: "With our gear, we estimate our weight at close to four tons and we almost had heart failure the other morning. The boarding planks to the ferry were long and springy, but the ferry 'Captain' was pig-headed and insisted that they would do. He refused to use two stronger planks. Henrí 'put fire for the motor,' took aim and bounced up the slack boards. He carries his Bible in the glove compartment. Good thing."

As for the bridges: "Occasionally we must cross a wooden bridge of two parallel planks, all the rest having rotted off. In one case, we drove onto a bridge completely overgrown with tall grass, not knowing we were on a bridge at all until halfway across we were confronted with a chasm. Fortunately, we didn't take the plunge to the dried-out riverbed below. Len and I have done a great deal of the driving; Henrí Mondo has been sick with his incipient malaria and pleurisy, and the boys have had severe colds."

On January 14, they reached the Zenker Plantation near Bipindi, where they learned some discouraging things about the possibility of cultivating Strophanthus. The Zenker family had been experimenting with this since the early 1900's. The plants grew beautifully in open fields, but the trouble lay in flowering and pollination, possibly because the type of insect needed did not venture away from the natural forest canopy. There was also the problem of supporting the vines. Ideally, a second plant with commercial possibilities would be chosen—but what plant grew to the necessary height of around 100 feet in less than thirty years? It would be expensive and impractical to erect artificial supports. The Zenkers had also planted Strophanthus at the foot of mature trees in the rain forest, but for collection on a commercial scale, it would be difficult to find enough laborers to harvest the fruits. What was needed was a dependable corps of "trained Pigmies," but these terms were mutually exclusive. No one in the area collected forest produce on a commercial level; lumbering and cacao gathering were sporadic.

About this time Woodward wrote: "Len Brass did some nice botanical work in the bush, a collection that may be *S. ogovensis*. The fruits are smaller than we've seen before and they are joined at a slightly different angle from those of *S. sarmentosus*. Another undescribed species was found, very rare or perhaps new to science. Some of the known recorded areas for Strophanthus are not revealing what they should. Perhaps this is due to the generalities of the records consulted, but it is also caused by the changing vegetation. Even out here, there has been widespread destruction of the forest by natives and Europeans. We have to do our own prospecting, most places, and the vines are scattered around; ten *S. sarmentosus* vines per square mile might be the average. You never see them in quantity, like a grove of birch or a thicket filled with grape vines. Because of our time limit (Africa looks bigger every day!), we can't thoroughly comb a given piece of ground. A general botanical survey for the genus alone, never mind the species, in an area, say, the size of Rhode Island, would take thirty to sixty days."

The month of February seems to have been something of an all-time low. The plant hunters found themselves viewed with hostility and suspicion and had difficulty hiring guides. Because the use of arrow poison was forbidden in the area they were in, the natives probably thought that they were government spies trying to trap them into revealing the source of contraband. It was beginning to rain very hard and this coincided with the worst stretch of "road" they had yet seen. Their native boys, now out of the region where they had lots of "cousin-brothers," were homesick and quarrelsome. Brass and Woodward intervened in fights, talked them out of threatened desertion, and gave them an extra 1,000 francs a month for "chop" or food money.

The food, admittedly, was poor. There was no time for hunting or fishing; eggs and fruit were difficult to find. Whenever they stopped long enough, Thomas would bake bread, using palm wine or corn beer for yeast. When they had time, they roasted and ground their own coffee. Because their standard lunch consisted of a vitamin pill, sardines, and a swig of water from the canteen, it is no wonder that descriptions of "the tastiness of roasted tenderloin of wild bush pig," bought from a local hunter, and the few hot meals were the most lyrical entries in the journals. Here, for instance, is Woodward's recipe for palm oil chop:

" 'Chop' is pidgin English for food, which doesn't reveal much about the dish, actually it is a kind of chicken curry. Granted that some ingredients are not available at home, but here is an adapted set of directions: Saute lightly two tomatoes and two yellow onions in peanut oil—fresh palm oil being out of hand. Add half a cup of peanut butter and the milk of two young coconuts. Season with salt and pepper (both red and black) and a bit of curry powder. Now add one chicken, cut up into parts, and stew very slowly for three hours. Add a bit of water if necessary. Serve over rice with—and these make it interesting—chopped peanuts, grated fresh coconut, grated hard boiled eggs, fried bananas, raw onion rings, french fried onions, coarse ground chili pepper, chutney, chopped green pepper and most anything else you can think of. Wash down with beer. Delicious!"

It was almost his last meal. The next day he reached into some glistening leaves for a specimen and came close to 'shaking hands' with a little green Mamba snake. "These fellows finish you off so fast, you don't have time to add a codicil to your will," was his comment. Being thoroughly stung by wasps seems to have been an occupational hazard, also. But his most shocking experience, brief though it was, came one day when he was alone on a narrow trail deep in the forest. He glanced up and found himself confronted by a wild-looking native holding a spear. Not thinking what his gesture might convey, he quickly reached for a handkerchief to wipe off his clouded sunglasses and—back went the spear! The two men eyed each other for a long moment; then suddenly the African vanished. Taking the country as a whole, though, the explorers found the natives friendly.

A typical entry for February reads: "The extra gas tanks are a good thing. For example, we were told to get gas at La Lara, a relatively big place on some maps. Well, it is a couple of huts and three empty gas drums. We have just enough gas to make Libreville and right now we are using gas at the rate of seven miles per gallon. We spent 'small-small' time in top gear today and there are spears of twelve-foot grass in the radiators, in through the windows, and grass roots dragging behind. There is no such thing as a gas pump in these parts: it takes an hour to empty a fifty-gallon drum and plenty of hard labor. We siphon out of the drum into a five-gallon jerry can and out of the can into the trucks, using an old felt hat for a strainer. Henrí scoops and scrapes and blows on each gas filter several times before replacing it, because we have only one set of spares left. But we have our amusing moments, along with the dreary stretches. When we had our first flat, Henrí called, 'Foot he go broke!' "

In Libreville there was some interesting information from a pharmacist, A. H. Boquet, who was about to publish two books in French containing the results of using decoctions and plasters of the root barks of *S. sarmentosus* and *S. hispidus* in the treatment of arthritis and rheumatism. His studies were made among the Ashanti, Abron, and Agni tribes, and he had photographs to prove that obviously deformed people had been improved after treatment with the barks. After observing these beneficial results, Woodward wrote: "We shall now put more effort into getting samples of root barks and the roots of various species. Up until this time, we have collected roots, stems, leaves, flowers, vines, fruit parts—the whole works—only the first time we saw a species. After that, we just collected fruits or seeds. But, since no one ever has made a scientific study of the other parts of the plant to see if active principles are present, we will routinely gather roots, as well as seeds, from now on."

When the Upjohn-Penick explorers visited Dr. Albert Schweitzer's hospital at Lambaréné, they learned that he was much interested in the type of research they were doing. He and his capable nurses urged them to stay at the hospital in order to study the medicinal plants of the area. But they only had time to collect one herbarium specimen of a plant called "Eh-Beh," of the Leguminosae, and to find out that the natives made a decoction from a piece of this bark that increased the flow of milk in nursing mothers—a matter of life and death in that part of the world.

Deeply moved by what he saw at Lambaréné, Woodward

wrote: "Almost ten per cent of the population in this area is infected with leprosy, but only about ten per cent of these are hospitalized. You find the rest of the pitiful victims everywhere, little children, old people. . . . Sleeping sickness and syphilis are common diseases also, and filariasis, which in its advanced stage causes elephantiasis. We have seen natives with legs so swollen that the feet look like warts. I just can't describe what a shocking thing it is to see the misery of these people for the first time. There is seldom an African with a 'whole' skin. The gaping sores, the daily suffering that are accepted as a normal condition of life are beyond belief. I shall never be able to forget it."

Heavy hearted though they must have been at times, the medicine scouts went on with their work. In fact, they worked even harder.

A typical shipment to New York consisted of sixty-eight sets of herbarium specimens, forty-nine samples of seeds for assay, six sets of cuttings of various species for propagation, and twenty-five soil samples for antibiotic screening, dispatched air express. They tried to collect five of each herbarium specimen, two for the expedition and the others to be distributed to Kew Gardens, the New York Botanical Garden, and the National Herbarium in Washington. They were severely handicapped from the beginning by having to use shredded newspaper instead of peat moss for the cuttings and by not having any wax paper. Also, the corrugated cardboards in the original shipment were cut with the corrugations running in the wrong direction—vertical instead of horizontal as ordered. Supplies were requested repeatedly, but the shipments were lost. Drying the Strophanthus seeds was a problem, too, until a tailor made little bags of mosquito netting, which they filled with the seeds and hung all around the outside of the trucks. Even allowing for sudden tropical storms, this proved to be the best method. A basket-and-swizzle-stick arrangement, dubbed "The Little Wonder Strophanthus Cleaner," was found to be much faster than picking seeds out by hand.

The explorers took advantage of the jungle "telegraph system" when they needed native collectors, or when their collectors were out in the forest and they wanted them to return. The messages were sent via big wooden drums, which were usually set up on a tree stump—once even with a truck tire underneath, presumably to improve acoustics and tone. They became so accustomed to hearing the drums that they could tell whether a message was being tapped out or someone was just keeping his wrists limber.

Sometimes, in order to avoid censorship, their reports to the States were sent by diplomatic pouch. They also sent coded cables, using Brooklynese, because anyone could buy the contents of a telegram for a dollar. As they traveled eastward, they found that more and more officials knew about The Great Search for Cortisone from Strophanthus. Local newspapermen sought them out, and when the reporters were given minimum statements, they revealed that they knew a great deal about the business of the Expedition. In Angola the plant hunters learned that the local botanist had received requests from Spain and Mexico for five tons of Strophanthus seeds. He mentioned an article in a scientific journal that discussed the possibility of making cortisone from tropical yams of Dioscorea species. The Americans showed no great interest in pursuing the subject because they had for some time been collecting yam samples. In fact, they were very anxious to know what, if anything, the chemists at home had found in them.

In April they doubled back into the Belgian Congo. The roads were terrible, with water up to the hubcaps. But on the twenty-second, they had their first hot baths since arriving in Africa, a memorable event. After Léopoldville, (where

Woodward noted: "Saw a nice looking European woman on the street today—after how long?") they heard nothing more about the other expeditions. When they made inquiries, they found that they were the first Strophanthus seekers in most places. In Northern Rhodesia the roads were excellent and they hit fifty miles per hour for the first time, quite a contrast with sixty miles per day in Gabon.

However, the petty officials were the same all over. Upon entering Tanganyika it was observed: "Immigration was simple, then came customs! An extremely meticulous Indian clerk obviously had sat up all night reading the book. He made a number of entries in four ledgers, in two colors of ink, using three special pens, as well as making several other documents in multiple copies. He thoroughly enjoyed officiating at our entry and he received six pence as overtime pay because he was entitled to it—he had continued working until 12:30 to put the final stamp on the proceedings. . . . All this was done with much palaver and hissing through his teeth."

The native boys were suffering from bad colds after the Angola heights and rains. The explorers concluded that it was sometimes a mistake to transport natives beyond the borders of their own home territory because it was a shock to their systems.

An entry on May 5, at Bahi, Tanganyika: "This is another place found on few maps, about twenty-six miles NNW of Dodoma on a strictly bush road. *S. eminii* is so abundant, at one place pictures were taken through 360 degrees of the circle because the plants were too numerous to count. This makes six species we have seen which could be collected to the extent of a few tons a year, at least."

They continued collecting through the season of "the long rains," not having much luck in getting things dry, sometimes not being able to travel at all. The trail was at an end, finally, when it was time for Brass to return to the Archbold Expeditions on May 22. After he left, Woodward, driving through an almost continuous game preserve from Moshi to Nairobi, wrote of the Africa of the movies—herds of zebra, Acacia trees, all that. And of being lonely.

On June 3, in Nairobi, the trucks and equipment were advertised for sale in the local paper, and safe passage to the West Coast was arranged for the boys. The only hitch was Thomas, who, wishing to "dress" for the occasion, found that he couldn't get his feet into shoes. About a year later, he had a multilingual scribe in his home town write for him: "Dear Mr. Woodward: With much affection to suplicate a few lines of mine before you. I beg to let you know about our journey. We travel very sound and safty. I hope your are quite sound all so with house whole at home? I should be very pleased to hear from you, because I am still suspending waiting your arrival here. Except my compliment of the maintenance which have obtain from you through all the days of our voyage. Your humbel servant, Thomas."

Penick's pharmacognosist also received in New York a letter from Valentin, which said in part: "I want to get married to a girl in my country but I do not have the money to pay for the bride. If you ever come to Africa again, and want me for a 'boy' I will meet you whenever you wish."

The last letter Woodward sent from Africa was dated June 7, Nairobi, and it speaks for itself: "Sold the pickup to a farmer, I think his wife liked the blue color. The Department of Agriculture bought the other truck. All being well, I'll see you in New York on the twentieth, *after* breakfast; a 5 A.M. plane is too early for anyone to meet. I am basically fine, except for the stubborn dysentery. Sold the camping gear to a safari firm. After delivering the truck, I had to take a taxi back to the hotel. It gave me a peculiarly empty feeling: one day you have two truckloads of supplies, a fellow scientist

William Laurence, Science Editor Emeritus
of the *New York Times*.

Leonard Brass in the field.

Edson Woodward in Africa.

John Baldwin
in the Great Dismal Swamp of
Virginia and North Carolina.

Strophanthus sarmentosus vine, fruits, leaves, and flowers.

Upjohn-Penick

Yakuna Indian demonstrates bone and wood snuff tube for Richard Schultes of Harvard, whose arms have been painted for participation in tribal dance.

Natural History Magazine

Massachusetts College of Pharmacy

The late Professor Heber W. Youngken breaking ground for the Medicinal Plant Garden at the Massachusetts College of Pharmacy, Spring, 1941.

E. W. Smith, Harvard Botanical Museum

Profile of Richard Spruce, drawn from a photograph in the Gray Herbarium (Harvard U.).

Bruce Halstead putting plants in press at Neavati Mission, Peru.

Don Ollis

Maria Theresa, Campa Indian witch doctor with "headache plant."

Don Ollis

Margaret Kreig tape-recording interviews, first night at Neavati.

Don Ollis

Where the big trees are kings . . . on the Rio Neavati, Peru.

as a companion, and three native helpers. The next day, you find yourself with a suitcase, a couple of pieces of paper, and that's it. Felt somewhat let down, so took in a movie with two ex-servicemen who are now electric-meter readers here."

After nine months, thirteen thousand miles, eight African countries explored, and twenty-three different Strophanthus species collected, what was the result?

It would take Penick chemists working under Dr. Bywater's direction, several years to get the extractives out of the plants and to modify them. The comment was made about this exciting type of laboratory exploration: "One of the greatest thrills, after you've been plugging away at a problem for six months and it seems fruitless, is to see that first white crystal emerge from the mass of black tar—that is the moment of truth."

At the New York Botanical Garden, the late Joseph Monachino was hard at work on the taxonomy of the genus. When he began, he had not one Strophanthus fruit; now he had 2,000 from twenty-five herbaria collections. In the October, 1951, issue of *Phytologia,* he wrote: "The best collection examined by the writer was that of the Upjohn-Penick Expedition for Botanical Exploration."

Important botanical contributions were made by this group in an area never before studied. Does this mean that Strophanthus seed became an important source of cortisone? Unfortunately, the high hopes of so many were not realized. The difficulties of collection, the distance involved, the problems in cultivation, and the uncertainty of obtaining sarmentogenin from any given sample caused Upjohn and others to abandon their concentration upon Strophanthus research shortly after the expeditions returned home. Techniques for making cortisone from animal products were improved and almost all of the interest in plant precursors for cortisone was subsequently directed toward the yams in Mexico. In 1955, the following statement was made in the October/December issue of *Economic Botany:* "At present there is a diminished, if not a complete lack of interest in Strophanthus as a practical source of cortisone." It was interesting, therefore, to find out what the principals in The Great Strophanthus Search of more than a decade ago now have to say.

William Laurence, the New York *Times* science editor, feels that Strophanthus is still a "Cinderella plant." "I am convinced that there is a lot yet to be found. I know all about the difficulties involved, but I still think they should pursue it. I am, naturally, disappointed that they dropped it."

Dr. Leonard A. Scheele, now senior vice-president at Warner-Lambert Pharmaceutical Co., commented: "When the Strophanthus hunt of Dr. Baldwin started, I thought it would be just a matter of weeks before there would be shipments of seeds and extraction could begin at the National Institute of Health. In fact, we were so enthusiastic that we borrowed Dr. A. Katz from Reichstein's laboratories for six months to work on the problem. When chemical work indicated that our prime objectives weren't going to be met, I was terribly disappointed. But I knew that the road to successful results is usually paved with many failures. Fortunately, the Strophanthus hunt had other successes. And the work on yams rapidly provided the necessary short cuts to cheaper, more adequate supplies of arthritis drugs.

Merck's explorer, B. A. Krukoff, was interviewed on one of his rare visits to the United States from Guatemala, where he now owns an experimental plantation. His search for Strophanthus began on November 24, 1949, and ended January 10, 1950, during which time he collected chiefly in French Cameroun and Gabon. He sent back samples of nine species, but when things did not look too promising the project was abandoned. When asked if he therefore considered the trip fruitless, he replied: "Botanists never consider a trip of this sort fruitless. As scientists, negative results or positive results are all the same to us. I was interested in the field investigation of the plant for its own sake. I personally am much more interested in the herbarium specimens themselves than in what becomes of them. And I hope to be judged by my scientific monographs in the botanical literature. Will they be considered useful by future monographers? That is the only question which concerns me."

Dr. John T. Baldwin, Jr., returned to teaching genetics and systematic botany at the College of William and Mary, after almost a year of collecting in Liberia, French Guinea (now the independent state of Guinea), the Gold Coast, Nigeria, British Cameroons, French Cameroun, and the Belgian Congo. He collected yams in West Africa and continued collecting them in Mexico the following year. In addition to the Strophanthus seeds sent back from Africa for chemical analysis by the United States Department of Agriculture, cuttings for more than thirty species of the plant were started at the Federal Experiment Station in Mayagüez, Puerto Rico, to serve as a germ-plasm repository in case interest in the plant is ever revived. Baldwin, as a cyto-geneticist, is primarily interested in research on the chromosomes of various plants, many of which he collected incidental to his search in Africa. In the dozen and more papers he has published in recent years, not one has to do with Strophanthus, "due," he said, "to the pressure of other things, like the book I am writing on The Great Dismal Swamp."

In the summer of 1962, Florida State University awarded the honorary degree of Doctor of Science to Leonard J. Brass, associate curator of the Archbold Collections at the American Museum of Natural History. In the long citation of accomplishments, no mention was made of his part in the Strophanthus hunt. But attention was drawn to the fact that his "botanical collections from New Guinea have resulted in more than 150 papers by specialists all over the world. The studies of these collections are far from complete, but they have produced descriptions of 1,362 species of plants new to science, 147 of them named in honor of Dr. Brass.

While I was writing this chapter, I paid a visit to the New York Botanical Garden, hoping to see Strophanthus firsthand. Not only was it not in bloom, it was nowhere to be found, even though the obliging gardeners searched overtime. It had been growing there years ago, but now it seemed that the Cinderella plant had disappeared.

In a final interview, I called on Edson Woodward in his office at S. B. Penick in lower Manhattan. He had spent the past decade exploring in twenty-eight countries, including Ceylon, India, Mexico, and also in Central America and Africa. His particular forte is looking after the commercial end of things—investigating his company's sources of supply and scouting for new supply areas as the world picture changes. When his articles appear in scientific and technical journals, they are often accompanied by maps and up-to-the-minute reports on how a Congo skirmish has cut off certain raw materials or how the Aswan Dam may cause prices to rise with the waters. The pressures in the botanical export-import business are fierce; wars, pestilence, strikes, threatened export bans, and a dozen other factors create frequent crises. At any moment, Woodward may find himself on a plane headed for the wilds. The rest of the time, as a businessman— or, more specifically, as an "economic pharmacognosist"—he solves problems from his office. Because he is concerned with the practical commercial applications of botanical exploration, when I first questioned him about the Strophanthus search he laughed and said, "That was just a lot of roaming around in Africa from here to there and back with nothing."

After a few thoughtful moments, he added something that could be applied to other searches for drug plants: "As with so many research projects, unexpected benefits sometimes outweigh the sought-for ones. One of the soil samples we sent back contained an organism that proved valuable to Upjohn in their pioneering work with steroids in fermentation chemistry, with the result that cortisone and related products became available in quantity and at reduced prices. As for Strophanthus, this was an example of all the projects that never directly bring a pill to a patient. And it demonstrated most beautifully what happens when the chemist knows what nature holds . . . but doesn't know just where or how much."

Later he said, "There can always be a P.S., of course. Professor S. Morris Kupchan of the University of Wisconsin has just presented a paper at the International Symposium on the Chemistry of Natural Products in Prague. He described an interesting piece of work in fermentation chemistry in which he changed the cardiac drug strophanthidin (related to strophanthin) into a new and very unusual steroid."

Are we at the end—or a new beginning?

The Professor, the Primitives, and Their Plants

IT WAS COMMENCEMENT DAY AT HARVARD UNIVER-
sity. Nevertheless, Dr. Richard Evans Schultes, Curator of the
Botanical Museum and Lecturer in Economic Botany, granted
an interview between the morning exercises and the afternoon
program. In this busiest of weeks, he was serving on the committee organizing the twenty-fifth reunion of his own Class
of 1937. He also had to present a paper, "The Role of the
Ethnobotanist in Drug Plant Exploration," at the annual
meeting of the American Society of Pharmacognosy at the
University of West Virginia. A few days later, he was scheduled to leave for Colombia, where he would be engaged in
studies of the educational system at several universities.

When he finds time, he works on four books: a definitive
study of wild rubber of the genus Hevea; an encyclopedic
treatment of the derivation of all the names in orchidology,
the largest of the plant families, with over 25,000 species; the
first translation of the Spanish journals of Ruiz and Pavon,
the early Amazon explorer-naturalists; and one on his specialty of specialties, native narcotics of the New World. In
addition, he serves as editor of two scientific journals.

Yet Dr. Schultes had not seemed to be an unapproachable,
cloistered scholar when I called him from New York. As I

climbed the Museum stairs to his fourth floor office, past the exhibits of drug plants dating from prehistoric times and the famous Ware collection of glass flowers, I recalled the remark of a newspaperman who had written several short articles about "the boom in botanicals": "There's a treat in store for you—go up to see Schultes of Harvard. He is one of the most complex and fascinating scientific personalities of our time."

I knew that Schultes had spent from 1941 to 1954 living with various wild Indian tribes of the Amazon in South America. He was alone in the field for as long as fourteen months at a stretch. As a taxonomic botanist, specializing in the classification of plants, he had sent back nearly 24,000 specimens, over 300 of them new to science, and the basis of more than 100 scientific papers. As an ethnobotanist, or one who studies the relationships between primitive people and their plant environment, he believes in friendly participation as well as scientific observation: I had seen a picture of him, bearded and barefoot, his chest and arms painted with intricate designs, sniffing a narcotic snuff in preparation for a Yacuna Indian dance in the Colombian Amazon.

When I entered his office it was, therefore, something of a shock to meet a tall gentleman in a full-dress suit, holding a top hat—the traditional Harvard uniform for class marshals at that afternoon's ceremonies. The morning's crimson doctoral gown and mortar board were on a chair nearby. Schultes is a big, husky man in his mid-forties with a greying crew cut and an engaging grin. He wears sturdy, steel-rimmed spectacles which he laughingly said are hard to replace since "they seem to date from Ben Franklin's day."

His office is basically austere, with white brick walls, a cluttered laboratory sink, and plant specimens in various stages of analysis. But the decorations dramatically illustrate his many interests: jungle photographs hanging on the walls are interspersed with gorgeous lengths of hand-woven fabrics, blow-guns, basketry and other mementoes of the tropics. Behind glass-covered bookshelves are old and rare leather-bound volumes which he eagerly brings out so that visitors may share his delight in the colored plates and quaint descriptive passages. In fact, he is working on a fifth book, a labor of love in which he matches these quotations from early explorer-naturalists with photographs he has taken himself on the scene. Everywhere—on his desk, on top of the files—is a thick overlay of manuscripts: his own scholarly works, articles for the journal he edits, theses of his graduate students, and the writings of friends which he kindly reviews.

The telephone rang and still another facet of Schultes was revealed. His wife, the opera and concert singer Dorothy Crawford McNeil, was preparing for the soprano role in the Boston Handel and Haydn Society's *Messiah* and she was faced with a rather unusual babysitter problem. Since their marriage in 1959, the Schultes' have had three babies, now under the age of three. (Richard Evans II, two and one-half; Alexandra Ames and Neil Parker, year old twins.) No wonder Schultes has written, "My family has replaced my former hobbies of photography and gardening"!

Soon apparent to all who meet him is the Schultes brand of rugged individualism. A New Englander and proud of it, he says exactly what he thinks, and what he thinks is sometimes rather startling. He has observed: "A sympathetic understanding and tolerance of his beliefs and ways and participation in his customs do more than anything else to win the Indian's respect and confidence. . . . I naturally learned to chew his toasted coca leaves and, finding it to be a most helpful custom when one must work hard and there is little food, I used coca for eight years while in these remote areas, with absolutely no desire to continue upon my return. Cocaine, the powerful alkaloid extracted from the leaves is, of course, a very dangerous addicting drug. But coca leaves, as they are used by the South American Indians, particularly in the bleak Andean heights, are not addictive and they do serve a useful purpose, enabling undernourished, debilitated persons to do a day's work and thus, at least, survive. The energy expended upon punitive international legislation against coca leaves might better be supplanted by an all-out attack upon the basic problems of malnutrition, disease, and a system which in many respects resembles paid slavery. . . .

"I found that because I accepted coca as a fact of life, and went along with its use, the Makunas along the Apaporis River in Colombia told me of an isolated group of Tanimukas who prepared a superior type of coca. These important tribes are not even mentioned in anthropological handbooks, by the way. Pursuing this lead, I learned of a most ingenious method of infusing into coca powder the acrid incense of the resin of the tacamahaca tree, one of the very few variations found in the preparation of this narcotic plant."

Schultes feels very strongly about what he calls "the wormlike boring into private lives that is placing the whole idea of personal freedom in jeopardy." He spoke of a trial of three Navajo Indians, belonging to the 200,000-member congregation of the Native American Church of the United States, a religious sect that worships peyote cactus. "As used by these people in their religious rites, peyote seems to be innocuous, yet there are those who would deprive the Indian of peyote. Alcohol and tobacco are truly narcotic, but they are legally used in our country. The term 'narcotic' has, unfortunately, been twisted by misuse to mean only the dangerous and addictive ones, which are few indeed."

When Schultes first went to South America in 1941, he was on a one-year National Research Council Grant. When, in his second year, he contracted to work for a government agency, he was asked to fill out reams of forms. He completed these with his usual signature, Richard Evans Schultes. They were sent back with the terse notation that no one in government service was permitted to use three names; he was to call himself "Richard Schultes" and that was that. He responded: "How does Franklin Delano Roosevelt get away with it?"—then plunged into the Colombian wilds where there were convenient six-month lags in the mails and handy waterfalls for filing "letters to be answered."

"I went to Colombia for a year and I stayed thirteen . . ." Our interview time ran out as Schultes made this offhand remark. To paraphrase this comment, I went to Boston for perhaps an hour's interview and I stayed for several weeks . . . to obtain the rest of Schultes' story and to use the research materials at Harvard, particularly those in the Oakes Ames Library of Economic Botany. What follows are highlights from our many talks together, from his unpublished field notes, and from his other writings.

As with every other scientist interviewed for this book, Schultes insisted from the beginning that he had no "adventures" worth describing. "If an explorer is *always* meeting unusual obstacles or having hair-raising experiences, he probably shouldn't have ventured outside a large city. It's a fairly good sign that his expedition was poorly organized or that he is just not adapted for exploration. The pathetic aura of heroism fabricated around those who brave the so-called 'green hell' can many times be traced to sensational writers who grind out books on 'exploration.' They are often full of errors, misrepresentations, and misconceptions."

A book and a college biology course were the two greatest influences on Richard Schultes' choice of a career. As a boy he read *Notes of a Botanist on the Amazon and Andes, Being Records of Travel on the Amazon and its Tributaries, the Trombetas, Rio Negro, Uaupés. . . . During the Years 1849–1864* by the Yorkshire botanist, Richard Spruce, Ph.D., whose extensive collections and meticulous work have prompted Schultes to call him "the greatest botanical explorer ever to have gone into South America, and one of the most careful and inquisitive botanical collectors of all times."

Schultes became the first scientist to retrace most of Spruce's itinerary and to re-collect many of the plants he discovered in the wilds of the Amazon a century earlier. Somewhere on the upper Rio Apaporis in 1951, Schultes wrote a series of articles as a tribute to the man who had so inspired him. Published in an English horticultural journal, they end with the statement: "Richard Spruce still lives, and will live on to fire the heart and shape the thoughts of many a plant-explorer as yet unborn, who will tread Spruce's trail to carry forward his great, unfinished work."

As a college student at Harvard during the depression, Schultes was urged by his parents to study something practical, like medicine. He stayed with the pre-medical program for three years, concentrating on biology, chemistry, and languages. During his third year, he took Harvard's course in economic botany, which he now teaches. In those days there were only six in the class, and the late Professor Oakes Ames, who was the world's leading authority on orchids, didn't really lecture to his students. He sat on the corner of a desk and "chatted." These chats caused Schultes to abandon medicine forthwith in favor of the plant kingdom.

He soon became interested in a curious member of the cactus family, which has 1,300 species, all native to the New World. He chose to investigate and eventually to write his bachelor's honors thesis on peyote, *Lophophora williamsii,* a cactus that grows only a few inches above the ground in northern Mexico and Texas. Its fleshy grey-green top is covered with tufts of white hairs instead of spines, and underground there is a long carrot-like root. Peyote grows in clusters that resemble buttons; in the United States the dried disk-like tops of the cactus are commonly called "mescal buttons." This is misleading because mescal is a fermented drink made from one of the Agave species related to the century plant, while peyote is non-alcoholic.

The effects that come from taking peyote are far more mystifying than those from alcohol, for the cactus produces one of the most highly complex forms of intoxication known. The most spectacular phase consists of a kaleidoscopic play of brightly colored visual hallucinations, which is attributed to one of the alkaloids contained in peyote—mescaline. The seven other known alkaloids in peyote have, like mescaline, now been synthesized. Psychiatrists and other mental disease investigators no longer have to use the dried, leathery "buttons," because mescaline in pill form is supplied to qualified scientific researchers by several ethical drug firms.

In 1937, when Richard Schultes first became intrigued with the possibilities in the narcotic plant, no drug company was interested in his research. Peyote was something "those Indians out West use to get high on." But Schultes knew there was more to peyote than that. He had the continuing encouragement of Professor Ames, who obtained a small grant which permitted him to make his first field trip. He went to Oklahoma with an anthropology student, Weston LaBarre, (now a professor at Duke University) to live with the Kiowa Indian tribe and to observe their uses of plants. In this study he participated in their peyote ceremonies. Not often had scientific investigators made such a thorough field investigation of peyote, including taking the drug in its native environment. This trip set the pattern for his professional life.

Before he left Harvard, Schultes read everything available on peyote, from the chronicles of the conquistadores, who called it a "diabolical root," to the turn-of-the-century experiences of the English psychologist Havelock Ellis and the Philadelphia psychiatrist S. Weir Mitchell, who tried it in their own homes and described beautiful visions, fields of precious gems, and luminous Gothic towers. William James, another who tried it, got nothing but a stomach-ache and was violently ill for twenty-four hours. Schultes learned, however, that the literature was not all reliable. Some of the most distorted, non-factual, and biased accounts in print came from white doctors, missionaries, and travelers who claimed to have inside information on the peyote cult.

Schultes feels that the Indians are sincere in their belief that the plant serves as a divine messenger enabling them to communicate with the gods without the medium of a priest. Or, as the Articles of Incorporation of the Native American Church of the United States read, through the use of peyote the worshippers are "able to absorb God's Spirit in the same way that the white Christian absorbs the Spirit by means of sacramental bread and wine." The peyote plant is ritualistically collected, and the participants in this form of all-night worship purify themselves through special diets and sexual continence before eating the cactus; the more devout cross themselves before using it. Those who feel it necessary discharge arrows to the right or left to ward off evil spirits.

Schultes came away impressed with the reverence and seriousness of the peyote-worshippers. In the perennial peyote trials which have been before our courts for the past half-century or more, scientific testimony has never shown peyote, *as used by the Indian in his religion,* to be morally, socially, or physically of any great danger. It is not under Federal narcotic legislation, but some states prohibit its use. Meanwhile, Schultes feels that peyote still offers a vast field for study. "What should concern us," he said, "is the advisability of intensive chemical and pharmacological investigations of the cactus family, especially the genera related to peyote. There has never been a concerted screening of this family for potential medicinal properties."

Peyote was, and still is, used by the Indians as a general medicine. Schultes wrote that powdered peyote was put into arrow wounds; freshly cut peyote was packed around aching teeth and rubbed into the skin to ease rheumatic pains and to soothe burns. One of its most important native uses was in the treatment of tuberculosis. Pharmacologists have noted that some of its alkaloids act as cardiac and respiratory stimulants, but, although its value as a therapeutic agent has not been completely explored, it is likely that these native medicinal uses are based on magical or mystical beliefs. The only modern follow-up has been in the field of mental illness. In pre-Columbian times the Indians found peyote useful for severe insomnia and mental disturbances; clinical investigators are now using it in a limited way to try to determine the causes of these afflictions.

After he completed his thesis on peyote in 1937, Schultes knew that he wanted to specialize in the study of primitive uses of narcotic, stimulating, and intoxicating plants. In the course of translating sixteenth-century accounts of the Aztecs written by the Franciscan priest Bernardino de Sahagun and by Dr. Francisco Hernandez, physician to the King of Spain, he learned that the Aztecs had called peyote *peyotl* and had also used it as a religious narcotic. But in the moist central regions of Mexico, where the cactus did not grow, they had a plant which they valued even more. This was a twining vine called *ololiuqui,* or snake plant. Hernandez was the first white man to record its use in a Latin Codex, *Nova plantarum, animalium et mineralium mexicanorum historia,* written between 1570–1575. Along with such details as "When the priests wanted to commune with their gods and to receive a message from them, they ate this plant to induce delirium. A thousand visions and satanic hallucinations appeared to them. . . ." was included a stylized drawing of the plant itself.

After studying this drawing, Schultes became convinced

that it represented a plant of the morning-glory family. Was it possible that these innocent ornamentals harbored a narcotic-producer among them? There were hints of this all through the old manuscripts he consulted. A Father Alarcon wrote: "It is remarkable how much faith these natives have in *ololiuqui* seed, for when they drink it, they consult it as an oracle to learn . . . things beyond the power of the human mind to penetrate. He who drinks *ololiuqui* to excess loses his mind. They venerate it so much that they do all in their power so that the use of the plant does not come to the attention of the ecclesiastical authorities." The Spanish priests, putting the use of such plants on a par with cannibalism, asked during the confessional, "Have you eaten the flesh of man? Have you eaten the flesh of the sacred mushrooms? The seeds of *ololiuqui*?" An editor of the Hernandez account, in an attempt to shield the reader or thwart the further use of the powerful plant, inserted the comment, "It would not be wrong to refrain from telling where it grows . . . for it matters little that Spaniards be made acquainted with it."

In 400 years no narcotic morning-glory had turned up in Mexico, although a Mexican ethnobotanist had insisted that Hernandez must be right. An American botanist, the eminent Dr. W. E. Safford, had looked into this drug and its identification in 1915, and had written in the scientific journals that no morning-glory could possibly contain narcotic substances. He felt that the effects described in the early chronicles were the result of taking Datura, one of the deadly nightshades, a quite different plant altogether. Safford insisted, "A knowledge of botany has been attributed to the Aztecs which they were far from possessing. . . . The botanical knowledge of the early Spanish writers, Sahagun, Hernandez, etc., was, perhaps, not much more extensive: their descriptions were so inadequate that even to the present day, their chief narcotic, *ololiuqui* . . . remains unidentified."

This was a challenge to Schultes. In his work in southern Mexico, he conferred with native plant experts and witch doctors, and eventually he found *ololiuqui* growing in the dooryard of a woman witch doctor, a *curandera,* in the state of Oaxaca. It was a vine with a woody stem and beautiful white flowers, funnel-shaped like our morning-glories, but only about an inch long. Its leaves were heart-shaped and pointed. The small, dried fruit that followed the flowers contained single, lentil-like seeds. These the *curandera* used as a sacred, divinatory narcotic.

Long before the conquest, Aztec priests had gathered the plants and repeated the ritual, "Come hither, thou, come and expel the green pain, the brown pain, which now wishes to take away the life of the son of the Gods!" After the Spaniards came, Christian influences appeared: for example, the dose selected was thirteen seeds, that being the number present at the Lord's Supper. Because of their very hard coating, the seeds were soaked in water, then chewed and swallowed. Unlike peyote, *ololiuqui* traditionally has been taken in private, with only the witch doctor present. It is considered best not even to hear a cock's crow. Some natives still believe that in a little while the spirits of the plant, thought to be children, come out and tell the communicant about the future, the whereabouts of lost property, and anything else he wants to know. This occult use has remained unchanged.

But *ololiuqui* has also been highly prized for its pain-killing properties. In the high, cold regions of Oaxaca where rheumatism is rife it is considered a blessing. The early writers said that when the seeds were pounded into a salve, it had a numbing quality. Was there an analgesic, as well as an active hallucinogenic principle in the plant, Schultes wondered? He wrote, "Perhaps the *ololiuqui* of the ancient Aztecs may yet serve mankind in a less satanic way than that which so sorely bedeviled the church fathers of old."

He returned to Harvard with high hopes. His carefully collected botanical specimens enabled him to identify the plant as *Rivea corymbosa* of the Convolvulaceae, or morning-glory family, which contains 1,100 species, including the closely related genus Ipomoea, to which our cultivated, ornamental morning-glories belong. Schultes was anxious to find someone to do the chemical and pharmacological work on Rivea, but American drug companies still were not interested. "We are trying to get away from the plant kingdom," they told him. The accent in research was on producing new synthetics. It didn't help to stimulate interest when a Mexican doctor published a paper in which he said that he had tried eating a "handful of the *ololiuqui* seeds" and nothing had happened. That there was a good reason for this was not explained until later.

Finally, Dr. C. G. Santesson, an aged, retired pharmacologist in Sweden, became interested in working on the seeds. In tests with frogs, he found evidence of narcotic action. He thought the active principle might be an alkaloid (complex organic compound containing nitrogen) combined with a glucoside; then, unfortunately, he died and no one else continued his experiments for many years.

In the late 1930's, Schultes made a second trip through Mexico and Guatemala and wrote his doctoral thesis on *The Economic Aspects of the Flora of Oaxaca*. And it was in Oaxaca that he found a third Aztec hallucinogen, the most improbable of all: a sacred mushroom called *teonanacatl,* meaning "God's flesh" in Nahuatl, the Aztec language. Dr. Safford had had his own somewhat unorthodox views about the mushrooms, too, back in 1915; he insisted they were really peyote. But by getting to know *curanderos* who ate the fungi in their practice of medicine and divination, Schultes and a Mexican physician, Dr. B. P. Reko, were able to obtain specimens which Schultes identified botanically at Harvard as mushrooms of the genus Panaeolus. The botanical knowledge of the ancient Aztecs and early Spanish writers was vindicated again. Pictures of the mushrooms had been drawn and the clerics had written that they "are harmful and intoxicate like wine." According to the Aztec historian, Tezozomoc, inebriating mushrooms were part of the coronation feast of Montezuma in 1502. Dr. Hernandez had mentioned three different kinds and described their special effects.

After he returned to the United States, Schultes published several scientific reports on the mushrooms and an exhaustive illustrated monograph on the narcotic morning-glory, which he modestly titled, *A Contribution to Our Knowledge of Rivea Corymbosa*. One would have thought that the finding of two similar hallucinogenic properties, in such widely separated members of the plant kingdom as a lowly fungus and a twining green vine, would have caused a sensation in botanical circles, at least. But Schultes says with a grin, "My papers were so very earth-shaking when published in 1941 that they gathered dust on my shelves for almost two decades." The strange way in which these fascinating new drug leads were finally picked up and turned into useful pharmaceuticals rivals the exotic botanicals themselves for sheer incredibility —involved were a poet, an international banker, a pediatrician, a French professor, a Swiss chemist, and a Saskatchewan psychiatrist. (This story will be told in a later chapter.)

Meanwhile, for thirteen years Schultes was deep in the heart of the Amazon basin, completely unaware that very slowly, but very definitely, a resurgence of interest in natural products was occurring in the pharmaceutical industry. A steady procession of revolutionizing botanicals with a history of native use—muscle relaxants from curare, antibiotics from fungi, reserpine from Indian snakeroot, cortisone from yams, to mention a few—would usher in the day when research directors might listen with interest to what a botanist had to say.

Early in 1941, the newly-minted Doctor Schultes went to Colombia on a grant of a few thousand dollars. He planned to collect all the native narcotic and poison plants he could find—Colombia and Mexico being the two countries that make the greatest use of these in day-to-day life. When news of Pearl Harbor reached him in the wilds, he returned to the American embassy in Bogotá and was assigned to a government agency to search the Amazon jungles for supplies of rubber from the wild trees. Before he was through, he collected seven tons of rubber-tree seeds, each one about the size of a pecan, which were used for root stock for grafting rubber in plantations in Colombia, thus helping to assure us of a rubber supply in this hemisphere.

It is probably safe to say that Schultes knows more about the classification of wild Hevea rubber trees than any man alive. As for his search for drug plants, the rubber assignment, lasting from 1941 to 1954, provided an unexcelled opportunity to collect these and to investigate the general flora. Few modern botanists are fortunate enough to remain in the field for so long and not all of them would if they could. It is rugged and lonely work; at times miserable and dangerous, although Schultes would discount these aspects.

Let us see what it was like.

About 3,000 miles due south of Harvard Square lies Bogotá, Colombia's capital, a center of culture and intellectual ferment since the 1700's. But the country is little known and poorly understood by Americans who read about barbaric bandits slaughtering busloads of people in politically-inspired vendettas. The land is divided physically, too. Three mountain ranges chop the northern part into a series of cold, damp peaks. Life at these altitudes is uncomfortable, but almost 98 per cent of Colombia's population resides here. It is a rich land of immense potential, wild and beautiful, with orchids, emeralds, and coffee on the slopes and in the valleys. But few of its people are educated; most of them are wretchedly poor.

Over half of Colombia's land area is composed of tawny plains, or *llanos,* and soggy, impenetrable jungles, the *oriente,* where the remaining 2 per cent of the population is scattered. For thirteen years one of these few was Schultes, an adopted son, who now holds an honorary degree from Colombia's leading university and membership in its Academy of Sciences. Devoted to this country and its people, he returns almost every year. He knows and respects hundreds of Colombians, from highly placed church and government officials to the Indians he lived with in the rain forests. In fact, he quickly and emphatically pointed out that without the help of Colombians—especially the outstanding botanists there— he could never have done his work.

Schultes also tried to become acquainted with as many of the estimated 50,000 plants that grow there as he could. When he returned to Harvard, he did bring back over half that number of botanical specimens for a lifetime of study. On his very first day in Bogotá, he chanced upon a species of orchid new to science, growing on a tree on a hillside above the city. It measured less than half an inch, including root and blossom. He was off to a good start!

Schultes did not linger long in this city of a million people. He was anxious to get on with his first project—traveling the length of the Putumayo River that forms the boundary of Colombia and Peru. One lesson he learned early was that much of the paraphernalia usually lugged along on jungle expeditions is quite unnecessary: high boots, fancy hammocks, complicated tents, and such. He always picked the lightest possible canoe; on later trips he used an eighteen-foot, fifty-three-pound aluminum one with a five-horsepower motor. The native log dugouts were too heavy, for they required the help of many men in order to pass the rapids. A large crew meant problems with food, clothing, and money. Schultes seems to have had a horror of anything that might have distracted him from his work. When a choice had to be made between dreaded complications and giving up his own comfort, he chose the "simplest" way out: paddle your own canoe, if you have to. Most of the time this approach paid off, and he still swears by it. But once in a while he was forced to drag himself, fever-ridden and exhausted, to the nearest help at an army outpost, mission station, or Indian campfire.

At the start of each trip he carried only a few tins of emergency rations. (Once he and a guide lived for four and a half days on a can of condensed milk after they lost everything else in some rapids.) He took his plant-collecting materials, a machete, a small medicine kit, and a change of clothing. That was it, except for his camera, which hung around his neck. Fitted inside of the camera case was a hypodermic syringe and snakebite serum, ready to use. But he saw only a dozen snakes in a dozen years, and not one was interested in biting him. Once, though, while he lay desperately ill with malaria, twenty-five wasps did a thorough job of stinging his face and neck; in the jungle he now respects these insects more than he does snakes. On his first trip he took volumes of Dickens, Virgil, Ovid, and Homer, and a Latin dictionary; the peace and quiet of Amazonas was conducive to this kind of reading.

What, really, is "Amazonas"? Looking at a detailed map of South America, one sees that there are separate provinces in southern Colombia, southern Venezuela, western Brazil, and eastern Peru, all called Amazonas. Taken collectively, they comprise Greater Amazonas, the largest forested region on earth. These vast reaches are interrupted only by rivers feeding into the world's greatest waterway. (We are speaking now of river basins.) The Amazon basin covers 2,053,318 square miles; the next largest, the Congo's, is 1,339,923 square miles; then come the Nile and the Mississippi-Missouri. As to length, the Amazon measures 3,900 miles, exceeded only by the Nile which is 245 miles longer.

To get a rough idea of Schultes' area of concentration, visualize a triangle with the city of Manaus, Brazil (halfway down the Amazon), as one point of the base, and Iquitos, Peru (up near the headwaters) as the other. The northern peak of the triangle might be placed at Puerto Carreno, where Colombia projects into Venezuela and touches the Orinoco River. He made many side trips into Colombia and south of Manaus, as well, but this gives a general idea of his range.

One might ask, is it really necessary to spend fourteen months at a stretch in the jungle? Schultes feels that this is the best way to know the plants. "A botanist literally must live with them to be successful in his efforts," he said. "He must study them throughout the year to obtain both flowers and fruit, watch changes in the leaves, and evaluate the effects of high and low water. Only through long and intimate association with a particular plant can he really come to understand it." In his collecting he was particularly happy when he could obtain a century set from the type locality, (100 identical specimens from the exact area where a species of plant was first discovered). The duplicates were distributed among the leading herbaria of the world.

While he is vague about the dangers of rapids, hostile Indians, and bouts of disease, he still remembers his depression after he lost all of the material collected in one particularly inaccessible area. He had "preserved" it with formaldehyde which was weak or impure, and the specimens had rotted away. Another time, in a canoe mishap, he sustained one of his great losses when a large bundle of plant material for chemical study of a new narcotic, the plant having been described by Richard Spruce and never seen since, floated over a waterfall. For the record, the plant was used in the making of *ayahuasca,* the hallucinogenic drink of the Amazon, though it was not of the usual species of Banisteriopsis but a new species of a related genus which Schultes named *Tetrapterys methystica*. He did not lose his single pressed specimen and was thus able to identify it. On another occasion, he was attracted back to camp by a wisp of smoke and found that several months of hard work had been destroyed by fire— cardboards, plants, presses, and all.

Schultes subsisted mostly on farina, a dry, pulverized product of the poison yuca, or tapioca plant, the main source of carbohydrate in the area. The poison is leached out in two or three washings and the violently poisonous water is boiled down to a molasses consistency. The heat breaks down the toxins, and the resultant syrup, *tucupí,* is delicious, Schultes recalled, when spread on meat or fish as a condiment.

He drank whatever was handy. Often this was *chicha,* a slightly fermented potion derived from fruit in season and brewed in a dugout. After he got an aluminum canoe the old women in the villages where he stopped made him uneasy as they eyed his treasure speculatively, as though they might like to spirit it away as a vat for their *chicha.* Civilized whites have difficulty getting used to the idea of this drink, for it is prepared in the manner popular with natives in the tropics. The brewmasters first thoroughly chew the starting materials, their saliva enzymes turning the starch to sugar. Then the bacteria in the air complete the fermentation process.

"I preferred not to dwell on this aspect," Schultes said. "I had to think that the alcoholic content was probably sufficient to eliminate any risk of infection. The stuff has a surprisingly refreshing taste and I do believe that it is nourishing, for I managed to live on it at times."

There was not much meat in his diet, and although he took vitamins and gave them to his helpers, he did contract beriberi. He thought his hands were getting numb from the formaldehyde at first, but then his feet were affected. It took him forty days to paddle to Manaus. Schultes recalled, "the moment I appeared in the doctor's doorway he said, 'Come in, you have polyneuritis, I see,' and he gave me B-vitamin shots. There are still a few lingering effects."

At times there was surprisingly little game or fish to be had. And he did not carry firearms. "Twice I came face to face with jaguars, but they were as surprised as I was; if I had had a pistol, I would have been too startled to use it. To carry a pistol to protect oneself against the Indians is the most ridiculously childish attitude an explorer can assume. You have to sleep sometime and all they would have to do is club you. You have to depend upon them for food, so you could easily be poisoned. And besides, there is the bother of cleaning the gun every few days because of the humidity."

Friend of the Indians though he is, even Schultes admits that he knows of instances in which boats carrying whites were mysteriously "lost in the rapids," or otherwise vanished. He feels it is surprising there is not more of this when one considers the cruel exploitation of the Indians as rubber workers only a few generations ago. "I have talked with older Indians," Schultes said, "who had their ears and fingers lopped off for being just a few pounds short in their latex collection. The Witoto tribe numbered around 15,000 in 1900. By 1914, when the atrocities were ended by the collapse of the rubber trade, there were only 2,000 Witotos left in the Putumayo. And yet I never had an Indian try to wreak vengeance upon me as a solitary symbol of the white man. For one thing, word travels fast in the jungle—they knew that I was not armed. For another, I was searching for plants to use as medicines. And they respond in kind when treated as human beings."

Schultes feels that a botanist is in a better position to get along with the natives than other explorers are because he shares a common interest with them. He found them very curious about why he spent all of his time collecting and studying plants, but despite language barriers—there are at least sixty different dialects in Colombia alone—as soon as he made them understand that such-and-such might be "good for treating disease," they seemed pleased. "So many natives have experienced the white man's patronizing or even deprecating brush-off, so far as their medical practices are concerned, that they are naturally reticent, at first. But when they find that you are sharing their views, some lively discussions ensue. I frequently was permitted to watch the treatment of disease by witch doctors; this led to information about plants employed as styptics, as snakebite remedies, in treating eye diseases and burns, in loosening teeth—even plants which they believe are effective as oral contraceptives. Within the sphere of certain missionary influences or commercial centers, it is absolutely impossible to discuss such plants, although I strongly suspect that many of the civilized natives use them."

The following statement seems to sum up Schultes' working methods and beliefs: "Much can be accomplished if the ethnobotanical investigator treats natives as a gentleman should. He must realize that, far from being a superior individual, he—the civilized man—is in many respects far inferior to the native in the native's own environment."

It took him seven months to make that first trip down the Putumayo River; when he finally arrived at the Brazilian border and staggered into a Colombian army outpost, perhaps he felt particularly inferior. For although he was alive, he was half-starved, barefoot, and with just a few shreds of clothing. When he finally gained an audience with the commanding officer, Major Gustavo Rojas Pinilla, who later became President of Colombia, his explanations were cut short by the comment, "I know who you are; it's my business to know." Schultes hoped to stay here temporarily, mosquito-infested swamp though it was, on the chance that he could ride back to Bogotá on one of the ancient, three-motored

Junker planes Colombia had bought from the Germans for their war with Peru.

"I have just one question," the Major said. "Can you play chess?"

Schultes could, and did, for days on end. The Major was obviously in no hurry to lose the first chess partner he had met in this wretched tour of duty.

Schultes had other encounters with the military over the years. Once in 1950 when he and a Colombian botanist, Dr. J. M. Idrobo, were in the Macarene Mountains, some planes suddenly appeared and began to drop bombs all around. Unknown to the plant collectors, soldiers were entrenched on the other side of a small hill. This was part of a civil war which was to last for eight years; there were frequent border incidents, too. When Schultes finished one phase of his work in 1948 and had to get to Bogotá, the country was torn apart by uprisings and there were no military planes to the forests. So he and an Indian helper paddled day and night the 1,200 miles down to Manaus, where he took a Brazilian plane, finally reaching Bogotá the long way around via Lima.

In time, he persuaded the Colombian air force and Don Miguel Dumit, owner of the private airline A.I.D.A., to co-operate with him. They dropped him at locations otherwise completely inaccessible and picked him up on pre-arranged dates. But on one occasion when they were busy with the current war, he had to wait for exactly sixty-two days in one isolated hut near where the plane was to land. "I couldn't roam far from the clearing for fear the plane might come any day," Schultes recalled, "and it was driving me crazy with frustration because the surrounding forest was full of new species."

What were some of the species that Schultes collected? What were some of his accomplishments in the Amazon rain forest?

When Schultes first went to the Colombian Putumayo area in 1941, he was anxious to botanically identify yoco, a liana or thick vine employed by the Indians as a sort of "benzedrine breakfast." Yoco rates next to food in importance, and every household keeps on hand a large supply of the stems, which seem to retain their stimulating properties for a month or longer. In the preparation of the beverage, all bark and softer tissues are scraped off and the sap is squeezed from this material into cold water. The cloudy white or light brown liquid is taken every morning between five and six o'clock instead of breakfast. No food is eaten until noon by the Indians.

"I have tried yoco on many occasions," Schultes said, "and was able to make long trips through the forests feeling neither fatigue nor hunger. The effects are rapid. A tingling of the fingers and a general feeling of well-being are noticeable within ten minutes after drinking a cup or two of yoco."

After a year of persistent but vain searching for flowering or fruiting specimens, Schultes was forced to go to a small naval base on a river to wait for a plane to fly him back to civilization. Constant wading in flooded forests had caused deep ulcers to form on his legs and feet. He recalled that the clean accommodations offered on a navy gunboat at the base were so pleasant that when an Indian came paddling downstream to tell him about a flowering yoco, he was reluctant to leave. Yet intuition forced him to go back. Two days upstream and one day through an inundated swamp-forest brought him to a 100-foot climber. Strewn on the ground beneath were very tiny white flowers. After felling seven trees to bring the giant vine to earth, he was rewarded by being able to establish the identity of the elusive yoco as an undescribed species of the genus Paullinia.

It was later found to contain in its bark almost 3 per cent caffeine, and possibly it has other constituents not yet discovered. It is, apparently, the first plant used for this stimulating alkaloid in which the bark is the source, rather than the berries, beans, or leaves, as in coffee, cocoa, and tea, respectively. (The coffee tree, discovered in Abyssinia and not brought to Brazil until 1774, is by no means the most potent producer of caffeine, its berries contain only about 1 per cent.)

A near-relative of yoco, *Paullinia cupana,* or guarana, contains up to six times as much. Hundreds, perhaps thousands, of years before the white man came to the Amazon, the Indians of the Tapajós are said to have cultivated this woody climber in order to harvest its cluster of tough seeds containing the caffeine. The native preparation of the stimulating beverage is ingenious. Because the seeds quickly become moldy if stored, they are instead ground up and mixed with cassava flour. This is shaped into sticks that become dry and hard, easily taken along on canoe trips or jungle treks. When it's time for a "guarana break," the Indian uses the rough, file-like tongue of the *piraracú,* the largest fish in the Amazon. With this six-inch, flat grater, the guarana is prepared—about half a teaspoon to a cup of water, either hot or cold. During the enslavement of the Indians at the height of the diamond and rubber booms, guarana was an indispensable energizer.

Schultes' discovery of this plant demonstrates the interest and loyalty which he found among the Indians of the region. He said, "I really cannot subscribe to the widespread belief that the Indian jealously guards his plant lore . . . that civilized man must resort to ingenious duplicity in order to pry it from him. I had alerted Indians far and wide to my need for flowers of yoco, which are sporadic and capricious in their appearance. As soon as they were discovered, I was informed."

In his studies of native narcotics, Schultes did not neglect the Western Hemisphere members of the Solanaceae or nightshade family which has over 3,000 species distributed throughout the world. The nightshades have a lurid past dating from antiquity. While they include the prosaic potato, tobacco, eggplant, and tomato, they achieved notoriety because belladonna (*Atropa belladonna*), henbane (*Hyoscyamus niger*), and species of Datura contain such powerful alkaloids as atropine, hyoscyamine, and scopolamine. These plants were staples in poison potions and witches' brews, bringing on fits of madness with delirium—or death, according to the recipe.

Several modern analyses of witchcraft drugs have proven that those muttering old hags with their boiling caldrons knew very well what they were doing. Mixed with eye of newt and wool of bat was the equally ridiculous toe of frog. A most potent modern hallucinogen is *bufotenin*. Where did our scientists discover it? In toad skin.

Recently a German professor, Dr. Will-Erich Peuckert of Göttingen, mixed an unguent of belladonna, henbane, and Datura from a seventeenth century formula and rubbed it on his forehead and armpits and had colleagues do the same. They fell into a twenty-four hour sleep in which they dreamed of wild rides, frenzied dancing, and other weird adventures of the type connected with medieval orgies. A pharmacological explanation for these sensations: irregular heart action when one is falling asleep produces the feeling of dropping through space. When combined with drugs which enhance this irregularity and also cause delirium, one might well believe it possible to fly like a witch on a broomstick. So much for Satan's simples.

When the early settlers landed at Jamestown and began to search for "pot herbs," they had some fatal experiences with *Datura stramonium*. Ever since, this noxious weed has been commonly called Jamestown or Jimson weed and it still causes many accidental poisonings. Other Daturas are strikingly beautiful and are grown as ornamentals for their huge trumpet-shaped white flowers. Because they have spiny seedpods, a common name for this genus is thorn apple.

Daturas are used extensively as narcotics by the Indians in

southwestern United States and Mexico, where the plants are usually herbaceous, meaning they die away to the ground each year. In the Andes from Colombia to Chile, the genus is composed of trees. In both areas, they have been an important part of the magico-religious rites since earliest times. *Datura fastuosa* is a species found growing around the sites of ancient Inca temple operating rooms. The priests are thought to have used concoctions of the plant in their surgery as an anesthetic which numbed the patients or, in stronger doses, put them into a coma lasting several days. Datura was also used by the ancient Chibchas, a Colombian tribe, who gave it to women and slaves to induce stupor before burying them alive with their departed husbands and masters. In Central America, in Darien and Choco territory, children were made to drink a decoction of *Datura sanguinea* seeds and then walk about during the primary stage of excitement. It was believed that when this wore off and they fell to the ground, gold would be found there. Since there was a large quantity of gold in that soil, this frequently paid off.

The Jivaro Indians of Ecuador and other tribes still use Datura to correct very unruly children. The harassed parents hope that during the hallucinations the spirits of their forefathers will step in and admonish the incorrigible ones. This is a drastic cure with overtones of our "civilized" shock treatments, because during the initial stage of excitement there is such violent agitation that the partaker must be held down. And the visions which follow can be extremely terrifying. Schultes found that Datura was most commonly administered in the form of ground-up seeds mixed with *chicha.*

In 1942, while studying rubber trees, Schultes entered the strange, isolated Valley of Sibundoy in the Andean heights of southern Colombia near the headwaters of the Putumayo. Here he found the silted-up bed of an ancient lake, 7,000 feet above sea level, surrounded by bleak, mist-shrouded moors and still higher mountain peaks. And here he also found two extraordinarily "narcotic-conscious" Indian tribes, the Kamsá and the Ingano, who, he feels, possess more knowledge of narcotics than any other natives in the New World.

They cultivate a number of previously unknown narcotic plants, such as a beautiful twenty-five-foot tree with enormous, fragrant flowers, called locally *culebra borrachera.* The leaves of this ornamental in the gardens of witch doctors contain alkaloids far more potent than the closely related Daturas. After Schultes discovered this botanical and studied it for fourteen years, he gave it the name *Methysticodendron amesianum,* the first part from the Greek, meaning "intoxicating tree," the second in honor of Professor Oakes Ames.

The witch doctors "own" this tree, and pass it and the knowledge of its lore on as hereditary property. Young boys aspiring to become sorcerers must undergo a long apprenticeship and become intoxicated with *culebra borrachera* many times in order to learn its secrets. The drug is taken only during the moon's wane, in the form of a cold-water infusion of leaves, freshly picked within the hour. As with so many of these intoxicating, hallucination-inducing drug plants, its chief use is in divination. While under its influence, the witch doctor "discovers" stolen or mislaid articles, predicts the outcome of tribal projects, detects hexes, or diagnoses diseases.

The plant is also used in treatment. The leaves and flowers are applied in poultice form to reduce tumors and swellings, especially of the joints. Persistent aches, chills, and fevers are common in these high altitudes, and patients are frequently bathed with a warm decoction of the leaves for a pain-relieving effect, followed by a lamb-fat rubdown.

The Indians of the Sibundoy Valley go far beyond the mere harvesting of drug plants, however. What makes them really remarkable is that they keep and reproduce clones—cuttings from the same parent plant—with definite objectives in mind, objectives which rival in importance those of our scientifically-trained geneticists and other plant specialists. The Indians, in their experiments, have developed what seem to be "virus-races," clones of Datura plants so attacked that they grow to monstrous, almost unrecognizable forms and may have chemical alterations. The witch doctors insist that infected Daturas cause stronger, or weaker, or entirely different reactions in their patients than the healthy Daturas, thus permitting a wide range of individualized treatment. Schultes commented: "Here is a problem never before investigated but surely worthy of research. Are the infected clones really chemically different? And if so, is this due to the virus?"

The nightshades have provided us with useful modern medications, despite their lurid past and questionable employment in recent times as a kind of "truth serum." They served during the "twilight sleep" era of childbirth anesthesia and are still used as pre-anesthetics in surgery, as anti-spasmodics, and as a cure for motion sickness. Belladonna, which made the eyes of Renaissance Italian ladies more beautiful, dilates our pupils during examinations for glasses. The important drug atropine, a respiratory and circulatory stimulant, comes from this family. Stramonium from Datura eases choking attacks of asthma; thus, even the lowly Jimson weed makes a contribution, and has, in fact, a long history of use in folk medicine.

But do the deadly nightshades hold still more fascinating secrets? Could modern medicine make wider, better use of them? Fermentation chemistry, through the use of bacteria acting upon Strophanthus, has provided new leads for research on that lately ignored drug plant. We already have several useful drugs derived from a fungus blight on rye, the ergot alkaloids. There are scattered reports about various plant diseases causing illness in man—the red rust that produces severe reactions in the skin of celery pickers, for instance.

A reporter on the trail, Margaret Kreig.

Bassett Maguire
of the N.Y. Botanical Garden
in the field.

Robert Raffauf with a map of his 10,000 mile "commute" to work in the rain forest.

Siri von Reis with herbarium sheet in Harvard's Gray Herbarium.

Maynard Quimby asking Birom girl
about local herbal remedies
on the Jos Plateau, northern Nigeria.

Georgia Persinos testing Nigerian folk remedies at the Massachusetts College
of Pharmacy.

Cleopatra's Aloe plant now used for radiation burns.

Doctors Bobbitt, Schwarting, Rother, Collins, and Kelleher (left to right) of the University of Connecticut with the extractor invented by Dr. John Uri Lloyd, a vital piece of equipment used to separate active from inactive parts of a crude drug by a process similar to percolation.

Might not these effects somehow be reversed to our advantage? Moldy bread used by Middle European peasants to cure infections in wounds was an unlikely lead for scientists to follow; yet if we had followed it, the blessings of the antibiotic era would have been ours much sooner.

Daturas collected and identified by Schultes are undergoing chemical analysis at the Massachusetts College of Pharmacy. Methysticodendron is being grown at London's Kew Garden and at Longwood Garden in Pennsylvania. Its alkaloids have been identified as belonging to the tropane series. Meanwhile, presumably, the Kamsá and Ingano Indians of the Valley of Sibundoy are carefully cultivating and observing—as they have since time out of mind—generation after generation of diseased Daturas.

While exploring the Rio Apaporis in Colombia in 1951–1953, Schultes added another new drug to his growing list of native narcotics and stimulants of the New World. This was the intoxicating snuff *yákee*. That this discovery should be connected with the following miscellaneous items is intriguing.

In the "Nutmeg Islands" of the Indian Ocean, the musklike smell of the flowering trees is said to be so overpowering that the birds of paradise fall to the ground. . . . Old ladies in times gone by used to carry nutmegs in silver graters, convinced that this would insure sound sleep. . . . Prison officials are clamping down on nutmeg "jags" from smuggled spices. . . . Nutmeg grated with a heavy hand into a small cup of eggnog may well contribute a "kick" of its own. . . . The widespread, dangerous, and false belief that nutmeg possesses abortifacient properties has caused serious poisoning and fatty degeneration of the liver in its victims.

The common chemical denominator here is myristicine, a phenolic ether found in the volatile oil of the nutmeg seed. It also exists in the seed coat, which is processed separately to become the spice we know as mace. As commonly used in our kitchens, these are of course harmless. Among the oldest spices in use, being mentioned by Plautus about two centuries B.C., they come from an aromatic evergreen tree, *Myristica fragrans,* native to the Spice Islands, where, strangely, they are never used as condiments by the inhabitants.

The essential oil was formerly used in medicine as a stimulant and tonic for the stomach, but more pertinent here is a quotation from Richard Banckes' *Herbal,* printed in London in 1525: "To cleanse the brain of superfluous humours, take a quantity of maces and chew them well . . . hold them there awhile, and that shall loose the fumosity of humours that rise up to the brain, and purge the superfluity of it."

For over a hundred years, it was known that Indians of the northern part of South America used snuffs, some reputed to be violently intoxicating. But the botanical identification of the sources of these snuffs was in a state of extreme confusion. Local Indian names varied widely from tribe to tribe, or the catchall term *paricá* was applied. Sometimes the snuff described by travelers as being especially exotic was nothing more than common tobacco, a species of Nicotiana.

The first clue Schultes had in solving this riddle came to him when he began translating the writings of Dr. Adolpho Ducke, the great Brazilian botanist who worked for half a century in the Amazon. In Ducke's 1939 paper on the bean family of Brazil was a footnote implying that *paricá* powder might come from a species of Virola of the Myristicaceae, or nutmeg family, the first and only reference in scientific literature. The 1949 edition of his book eliminated this footnote as unimportant, or possibly because the leaves of the Virola were said to be used, when actually, as Schultes later found, the Indians use a blood-red resin that oozes from the inner surface of the stripped bark. The resin is scraped off with a machete and boiled in an earthen pot until a thick paste is left. It is allowed to dry, and then pulverized and sifted through a fine bark-cloth strainer. An equal amount of ashes from the stems of a wild cacao species is added to give the snuff consistency to withstand the excessive dampness which might otherwise quickly melt the powdered resin paste.

It was eight years before Schultes was finally able to prove that *yákee* could be prepared from any one of three species of Virola and that the active principle was, therefore, undoubtedly the same essential oil, myristicine, which makes nutmeg a dangerous narcotic when taken in excessively large amounts. Work on samples that he brought back from the Colombian Amazon has not yet been completed. But we do have his account of taking the narcotic snuff:

"I took about one-third of a teaspoon of yákee in two inhalations, using the characteristic V-shaped snuffing tube made of hollow bird bones—you put one end in your mouth to blow on and the other in your nostril. The snuff is inside, of course. This was about one-quarter of the dose a medicine man would take. The dose was snuffed at 5 P.M. Within fifteen minutes, a drawing sensation was felt over the eyes, followed very shortly by a strong tingling in fingers and toes. Then came a severe headache. Within half an hour, my feet and hands were numb. Walking became almost as difficult as when I had beriberi. I felt nauseated until 8 P.M. when I took to my hammock, overcome with a drowsiness. Strangely, this was accompanied by muscular excitation, except in my hands and feet. About 9:30 P.M. I fell into a fitful sleep which continued with frequent awakenings until morning, when a strong headache continued until noon. A profuse sweating and, probably, fever persisted throughout the night. My pupils were strongly dilated during the first few hours of the intoxication. Though performed under primitive conditions in the jungle, this experiment does, I think, indicate the great strength of the snuff. The larger dose used by the witch-doctors causes them to see visions in color, which I did not experience. During their dreams, they emit wild shouts that are interpreted by their assistants. They admit that using this substance is a dangerous practice, one of their number from the Puivave tribe having died during *yákee* intoxication."

Schultes classes tobacco and alcohol—independently discovered in both hemispheres and prepared from a host of plant materials—as narcotics, a word which he noted as having taken on a very sinister meaning in American culture. In its classic sense, from the Greek "to be numb," it applies broadly to any substance, however stimulating in one or several stages of its physiological activity, which may benumb the central nervous system. All narcotics, he pointed out, have at some point in their history been linked to religion or magic. And when problems do arise from the employment of narcotics, he added, they arise after the narcotics have passed from ceremonial use to purely hedonic or recreational use.

None of the New World narcotics, except tobacco and coca, have become important in modern civilization, and in the Old World there is chiefly opium. The new plants just described await a considerable amount of chemical and pharmaceutical investigation. Many others remain to be discovered and botanically identified. "Here," Schultes said, "lies one of the most promising fields for research. We know that tropical America still holds many secrets in connection with medicinal plants. But I should like to emphasize the importance of doing the basic botanical studies before medical research is begun. Much of the excellent European chemical work of the past seventy-five years is worthless today because it cannot be repeated. No authenticated herbarium specimens backed up the botanical determination of the material under analysis; therefore, we cannot go out and obtain these plants again. The so-called 'determination' was often done, not by a botanist, but by a chemist or even an office employee working only from the plant's common name. We have learned today, fortunately, in most cases to avoid this error."

Schultes is one of the few ethnobotanists in this country; and the Harvard Botanical Museum is one of the even rarer institutions where one may be trained in this specialty. Today he spends much of his time in teaching and guiding students and post-doctoral fellows and in working up the extensive materials already collected, for he believes that a botanist would be remiss in his professional obligations if he did not publish his findings for others to build upon. The field work may be exciting, but it is only the preliminary part.

One wonders, though, whether those long years in the jungle made Schultes dissatisfied with civilization. His journals carry many descriptions of the beauty and fascination of those primitive surroundings. Here is just one, chosen at random: "November, 1947, Upper Rio Negro. Tonight we had a most wonderful twilight and sunset. Brilliant scarlet . . . grey and black streaks, nothing else. This truly would be laughed off as an exaggeration in 'civilized centers' if shown in a painting." He has said that his sentiments are like those of the English traveler Charles Waterton, who wrote 150 years ago: "Gentle reader, after staying a few weeks in England, I strayed across the Alps and the Apennines and returned home but could not tarry. Guiana still whispered in my ear and seemed to invite me once more to wander through her distant forests." Amazonas frequently whispers to Richard Evans Schultes.

When M.D.'s Consult the Witch Doctors

DOZENS OF PLANT EXPLORERS HAD PATIENTLY TRIED to answer my questions: Do you recall your first time in the jungle? How did you feel? What is it really like? How did you prepare for that expedition? Have you changed your procedures? And as I noted their responses, I was also aware, almost unconsciously, of how *this* man, *this* method differed from all of the others.

In the case of Bruce W. Halstead, M.D., director of the World Life Research Institute, a non-profit scientific organization, the answers became dramatically evident, for I was able personally to observe him collecting medicinal plants in the Peruvian rain forest for Chas. Pfizer & Co. This chapter, then, is a subjective detailed account of what it is like to go on one's first expedition.

I first heard of Dr. Halstead when he was teaching at the School of Tropical and Preventive Medicine, College of Medical Evangelists, Loma Linda University. Here the Seventh Day Adventists train their doctors and nurses who do such vital humanitarian work in 196 countries, the largest Protestant medical mission program. Halstead had been a United States Public Health Service officer and he was also, according to an article in that organization's *Reports,* "the world's leading authority on poisonous marine animals." He published a basic text on the subject in 1958 and is expanding this into an encyclopedic work for our Department of Defense.

The first time I talked with him on the telephone, I asked him how it happened that a physician with such a strong zoological orientation became involved with the plant kingdom. His answer: "If you ask professional pharmacognosists, they'll say they never heard of me. I am not a botanist. I'm not a chemist and I'm not a pharmacologist. I probably shouldn't even be in this field, except that I am personally dedicated to the development of impoverished countries through natural products. Two-thirds of the world's population revolves around natural products, but tragically, I think, the potential is not being tapped. I am interested in developing new drugs; also better, cheaper sources of protein for the starving; even potential capsule foods for space travel. What I believe that I can contribute is this—a botanical collecting approach, utilizing missionary contacts and witch doctors, that enables me to move rapidly through language, ethnic, political, and other barriers. My method of logistics telescopes years into hours and minutes."

I wanted to hear more about this, but Halstead was then on his way to Wake Island. Previously he had been skin diving for marine specimens in the Red Sea, and, before that, investigating promising anticancer plants used by witch doctors in the head-hunter country of Ecuador—all in a period of six months or so. His logistics system certainly seemed to be functioning.

Next I read an announcement in the October 30, 1961, *Oil, Paint and Drug Reporter*: "The World Life Research Institute is launching a new exploratory undertaking to cover the less-advanced sectors of the earth. Crude drugs found in those parts will be passed on to a sponsoring pharmaceutical company for practical consideration. The sponsor will be given all commercial rights that the drug may present." I knew that in order to achieve his personal objectives, Halstead worked through grants-in-aid from government agencies and companies such as Pfizer, Pitman-Moore, and others.

When I was in California in February, 1962, I visited Halstead at the Institute he established on a sixty-acre tract in the San Bernardino Mountains, forty miles west of Los Angeles at Colton. In the central building were his offices and one of the most complete marine biotoxicology libraries anywhere. In the laboratories, where experiments were being conducted, there seemed to be tons of frozen specimens of all kinds in the walk-in freezer rooms, and many sea creatures were preserved in huge bottles.

Halstead is a lean and lanky six-feet-four, built like a college basketball player. He bears a strong resemblance to the late Dr. Tom Dooley, both in his facial appearance and in his evident concern over the plight of the sick and malnourished. Because of the tremendous enthusiasm that he pours into this work, he seems younger than his forty-four years.

I asked him to explain his "missionary approach" to drug plant collecting. He told me that the missionaries, many of them his former students or lifelong friends, "bridge a gap between cultures." By making use of this bridge, he finds it unnecessary to live for long periods of time with the native witch doctors in order to gain their confidence; the medical missionaries have established this rapport for him. As doctors and nurses, they are also in an excellent position to observe and evaluate native medicines.

"They have taken care of these people for years, and they have demonstrated that they love them—there is no commercialism connected with it. Our missions stress healing and cleanliness—clean bodies, clean food, as well as decent living. Over a period of years, this brings such beneficial results even the witch doctors are converted. Once they become Christians, they want to help the missionaries in any way they can."

Witch doctors had been mentioned so frequently in connection with Halstead's work, I was surprised to hear him say: "Many so-called miracle cures attributed to witch doctors have no basis in fact. They first make their patients sick with powerful poisons of short duration, then claim a cure when the effects wear off. On the other hand, there *are* certain discoveries that modern medicine cannot explain—these are the mysteries we are exploring. Botanical explorers basically are looking for just one thing: physiologically active properties. Actually we don't care if plants cure diarrhea or cause diarrhea, produce a headache or take it away. We are interested in anything that will cause anything in the human body and it doesn't have to be a spectacular reaction. We have found that the quickest route to active plants is through native remedies. Humans survived all these years because they carefully noted these reactions."

He explained that although he was interested in how the plants were used and for what, native usage was only a clue. The plant might turn out to be more valuable in modern medicine when used in an entirely different way—the leaves instead of the root, for instance, or for another disease altogether. "Modern applications must be worked out over a period of testing by pharmacologists in laboratories and by doctors who do the clinical trials," Halstead added.

As we talked about the book I was preparing, he commented: "I wish you could have some firsthand experience on a collecting trip. A lot of the questions you keep asking are so basic that they are almost impossible to answer—some things you just have to experience yourself before you can understand them. After a couple of expeditions, they become second nature to you and when you are asked to describe them, you can't. It's not that we don't want to tell you all these details and anecdotes, we have just forgotten them."

When he said, at one point, "I could show you how this method works in Point Barrow. Tierra del Fuego, and a hundred other places," I couldn't help saying, "I wish you would!" He smiled and said, "In this business, one should always keep a suitcase packed."

Shortly after I returned to New York, I had good reason to wish that I had taken that advice seriously. The third week in February, I received a note from him, obviously written in great haste: "If you can be in Lima, morning of March 6, I'll take you on a Pfizer collecting trip to Neavati. Contact the Inca Union Mission when you arrive. Hope you can make it. Sincerely, Bruce Halstead. P.S. Get shots, yellow fever, etc."

During the next two weeks I had my smallpox vaccination updated and a complete course of inoculations—typhoid, paratyphoid, typhus, tetanus, and yellow fever, all necessarily administered on top of one another. Not having been out of the country before, I needed a passport and, as often happens, I had no copy of my birth certificate on hand. My mother offered to come halfway across the continent again to care for my family, although she had just gone home after staying with them while I was in California. Despite the fact that even the Peruvian consul in New York didn't know where Neavati was—and I had no idea when I would return—my husband and sons insisted that this was the chance of a lifetime and not to be missed.

I called Halstead and learned from one of his five children that he was on another expedition in southern Mexico and would probably go directly to Peru. His wife, Joy, came to the telephone to explain that Neavati was a mission station east of the Andes, deep in the heart of the rain forest and almost impossible to reach.

With ultimate destinations and return dates unknown, I made airline reservations as best I could. The ticket agent urged me to stop over in Jamaica, Colombia, Ecuador, and Nassau. "Might as well, no extra charge. . . . And for just a little more, you could go to the fabulous Inca ruins at Machu

Picchu." As I dashed around getting the necessary visas I felt a little guilty because Halstead had delivered a stern lecture on how he ran his expeditions. It went something like this:

"I seldom take more than four in my group because we often go 'military,' traveling light, by whatever means is available. No one comes along just for the ride; each person must make a definite contribution. There is absolutely no time for sightseeing. I've been to Egypt, but have never seen the tombs at Luxor. I went to Japan three times, but missed Mount Fuji. I could go on and on listing tourist attractions, wonders of the world, that I've had to pass by. When you are on an expedition, there is *work* to do and you *do* it!"

I was finding out about this already. Much as I wanted to buy guidebooks, study the history of the Incas (just in case) and bone up on the Indians of the Amazon, there simply wasn't time. Explorers had explained what they took along on expeditions and why, but there was no time to shop, beyond picking up a poncho and a machete at an Army-Navy store. My sons Ray, Andy, and Larry ran these errands and contributed blue jeans, shirts, and a pair of low gym shoes. By adding a knit dress to the suitcase, I felt pretty well packed. Then Nicole Maxwell, who wrote *Witch Doctor's Apprentice,* the story of her one-woman search for drug plants in the Amazon, told me that I should wear jeans only on the trail; I needed dresses in frontier towns as well as cities. "Lima is one of the most fashionable places on earth," she explained. "Dress as you would on Fifth Avenue." So, I filled another suitcase. Dr. Louis G. Nickell, a scientist who crisscrossed Central and South America many times in his searches for Rauwolfia and other drug plants, warned that the Andean heights could be bitterly cold, even on the equator. I would need warm clothing there; but in the humid rain forest, only the lightest tropical things. With rugged clothes, dressy ones, and in-betweens, for both winter and summer climates, plus all the bottles of drugs supplied by Pfizer and American Cyanamid (to give to the medical missionaries), I had far more luggage than I could handle. But I felt equipped for any emergency. The day before I left I read a travel article in the Sunday paper that outlined the supplies needed for a motor trip to Baja, California—a list almost as long as the one used by the Upjohn-Penick safari. It included, in case anyone should break an arm or leg: "some galvanized quarter-inch mesh chicken wire ($1.25) to use along with a pillow as a splint." That's one helpful hint that was passed up.

I was unaware, settling down for the flight to Lima, that I had forgotten such fundamentals as comfortable shoes. I was wearing pumps with three inch heels and by the time I discovered my oversight it was too late to remedy it. I alternated between two extremes in footwear until the gym shoes fell apart, then hobbled around after long-legged Dr. Halstead in my "spikes." Once he observed absent-mindedly, "You somehow don't seem properly dressed for an expedition —those shoes, are they really comfortable?"

In the frantic packing, unpacking and re-packing before departure, I inadvertently replaced some unlabeled foil-wrapped antimalarials with equally anonymous foil-wrapped antacid pills of the same size. All the time I was in one of the most malarious regions on earth, I placed my faith in the antacids which I never failed to take every Friday morning.

In Lima, when I met Bruce Halstead and Don Ollis, of Santa Barbara, California, the expedition's prize-winning photographer, I found them more harried and exhausted than I was. A travel agent had mixed up their reservations and they had been "stand-bys" sitting around airports in various parts of the Western Hemisphere for the past seventy-two hours. "You haven't heard the worst," Halstead said. "The Inca Union Mission has tried everything to get us on a plane to Pucallpa, east of the Andes, but there isn't a single civilian seat available for five weeks. Landslides have cut off the main roads up there, plane crashes have reduced the number of planes, and, to top it all, troops are being shifted. [The army overthrew the government a few months later.] This is typical of expeditions; the best-laid plans never work out as you expected. You have to be resilient and not let these last-minute roadblocks throw you."

While I was being told all this, we were riding at breakneck speed through Lima in a jitney cab that had lost its hood, fenders, and windows. The doors had to be held shut by hand. This was one of the famous *collectivos* that stop anywhere for as many passengers as can be packed inside or draped on the outside. I didn't know whether we were going over the Andes in this contraption or not. As it turned out, we were headed for San Marcos University, where Halstead interviewed a botanist on the flora of the Neavati region.

Later I was told to be in the hotel lobby at 4:00 A.M. the next morning, as we were going to take the local bus across the Andes, a ten-hour trip. When I met the men at the appointed hour, they were shocked by the amount of luggage I had, but said nothing about it—then.

On the outskirts of Lima we piled into an overcrowded, rickety city bus. The seats were metal, had no springs or padding, were about a Pigmy-and-a-half wide, and allowed knee-room only for Pigmies. But Halstead and I were lucky to squeeze into one of these; Ollis had to sit on a sack of onions in the aisle, along with many squatting Peruvians wrapped in blankets, while babies, farm produce, and household effects were tucked under, around, and over us.

We drove for miles through a wretched *barriada* of lean-to shacks, said by World Health authorities to be one of the worst slums anywhere. Then, leaving the arid coast, we began to climb rapidly until we approached Morococha, which has an altitude of 14,850 feet. Near here, the bus broke down and everyone seized this opportunity for a rest stop. Once outside, I found myself too weak to climb back into the bus, and for a moment I thought that I was going to faint. I didn't know it then, but I had *soroche,* or mountain sickness, which hits most people at heights over 7,000 feet. Above 15,000 feet, few can survive, according to Dr. Herbert Hultgren, a Stanford University authority. Drowsiness, headache, terrible weakness, and some pain are the symptoms. The slightest exertion is unbelievably exhausting. There is no drug to protect one from this and it can be dangerous, especially for people with heart or lung disease. Frequently there is vomiting—all of the children and one or two adults in the bus were sick. Ollis turned a little blue at one time and slumped over for a few moments, missing, to his later annoyance, some beautiful shots of snow-capped peaks. But he simply couldn't lift his camera. No one spoke, for every bit of oxygen was needed to sustain life, and we still had at least another thousand feet to climb. It was very cold. We were passing through glaciers and catching glimpses of blue lakes through the clouds. In the central part of the range there were bleak plateaus, called the *puno,* where only Alpine plants grow among the patches of snow. The few houses were sod hovels, mostly underground.

At our one official stop, I was much too weak to get out of the bus. When a brown hand thrust something that looked like a pastry turnover filled with chopped meat through the bus window, I took it, depositing a coin in the hand. I have no idea what it actually was, but it tasted wonderful. "Sooner or later," my plant-explorer interviewees had told me, "you will find yourself at the point where you'll eat anything." I had reached that stage somewhat sooner than expected.

As we continued on our journey, the road narrowed so that there were only a few inches of unbarricaded clearance between the bus and a sheer drop of thousands of feet to the chasm below. There was a roaring river down there and we passed a number of hydroelectric plants, some of which have since been partially destroyed by Communist-inspired riots. My thoughts were not on the political situation, however; I was wondering what would happen if we met a vehicle on one of the hairpin curves cut into the sides of these peaks. The regulations stated that eastbound traffic used the road on Monday, Wednesday, and Friday; westbound, alternate days. Or was it the other way around? And what happened on Sunday? We soon had an answer when a truck with seven men in it bore down upon us. After some haggling—our driver's argument being that he had more passengers to lose —they backed up a considerable distance before there was room to pull off and let us pass.

Our greatest concern while we were at the peak altitudes was the state of our driver's health: passengers were toppling over, would he be the next? He drove hunched over the steering wheel, never blinking his eyes; partially obstructing his view was an impressive collection of dangling good luck charms. As we began our descent on the eastern slopes, the men said that the road was the most dangerous they had ever seen. There were many roadside shrines with flowers and candles marking the passing of such as we. In a canyon far below we saw the rusting remains of a train, lying like a discarded toy, its tracks torn loose from the mountain across the way. The stretch of road between Tarma and our destination at San Ramon had many fallen rocks to be inched around and small waterfalls that ran across our path, making the stones slippery and undermining the roadbed. In between these hazards, our bus driver pushed the gas pedal to the floor, careening around turns and through murky tunnels with what seemed to be reckless abandon. Halstead explained, "We have to get out of the mountains before dark."

The wildest, most perilous ride was had by the little boy who was obliged to cling to ropes holding baggage on top of the bus. Whenever we came to a low tunnel, he quickly swung himself inside through a window to avoid being decapitated and then, just as rapidly, scrambled topside again to watch over the bundles.

We had lost so much time that we arrived in San Ramon after sundown, and vampire bats were swooping overhead. This was in the *montaña,* as the high jungle is called. It was warm and very humid and we were extremely thirsty, but before we could stop for a sip of water, we had to locate the bush pilot who was supposed to be waiting to fly us into the low, flat jungle called the *selva.* It was at this point that Halstead's logistics system began to operate smoothly. Mission headquarters in Lima had radioed ahead to a jungle army outpost at Puerto Bermúdez, about twenty miles from the Neavati mission. Messages were relayed to the mission and to this pilot, who agreed to fly us over the following morning. The missionary sent word that he would be at Puerto Bermúdez to pick us up when the plane landed. And that is just the way it worked out, without a hitch. We took off at daybreak in a single-engine Cessna 180, all of us leaning over the pilot's back to throw the total load as far forward as possible in order to get off the ground.

While my suitcases were being fitted into the small cockpit, Halstead and Ollis apparently felt that the time had come to straighten me out for bringing so much "junk." They listed what they had brought. Besides the dark, washable summer suits, drip-dry white shirts, and ties they were wearing ("We can go anywhere in this outfit; it's what we wore when we left home and it's what we'll be wearing when we return"), they had sweaters and plastic raincoats ("The plastic stops the wind and keeps the heat in, weighs nothing, takes no space. Cheap, replaceable anywhere"). In their bags they had sport shirts, khaki pants, and swim suits, plus changes of underwear and socks, rolled up tight, navy style.

Each had a pair of old shoes for roughing it, to be thrown away later. Except for shaving kits, that was it. "You don't need a thousand pills and potions," Halstead explained. "You only need anti-malarials and something for diarrhea." Then Ollis showed me his tiny survival kit: packed inside a 35mm film cannister were a miniature compass, a vial of water purification tablets, two Band-Aids, a safety pin, a razor blade, four fishhooks of various sizes, a ten-foot length of braided nylon fishing line, and a book of safety matches cut down to fit in the watertight can. His "medium-size" Swiss Army knife had scissors, auger, saw blade, and a can opener.

I said, rather weakly, "It's a little bit different for a woman . . ." but the roar of the motor carried my words away. We were taking off! As we flew over the vast Amazon basin, almost as large as the continental United States, the treetops resembled a tightly packed, endless crate of broccoli. There were no roads, just brown winding rivers looping back upon themselves, and no sign of life anywhere. About eighty miles away, we approached a cleared patch surrounded by a few buildings—Puerto Bermúdez. As we bumped over the rough ground in the middle of "town," pigs, chickens, and small boys scattered in all directions. A man in sunglasses and a pith helmet smiled broadly and waved as he walked toward us. He was the Pastor, Dwight Taylor, who was in charge of the Seventh Day Adventist medical mission station at Neavati. Halstead wanted to buy some machetes, so we went into a little trading post where huge slabs of crude rubber were piled off to one side. We each bought a nicely balanced twenty-inch machete (made in Brooklyn) for about a dollar. The store was run by a Chinese, and Ollis remarked that no matter where one goes on the world's frontiers, one always finds efficient Chinese shopkeepers.

As we slipped and slid down the muddy Río Pichis' embankment, passing my heavy luggage from hand to hand and stowing it in the boat—then reversed the process some twenty miles upriver at the mission—I made up my mind to get rid of as much as I could and I did, in fact, reduce everything to just one large suitcase while at the mission.

Mrs. Taylor and her three young children welcomed us to Neavati. A pretty woman not yet in her thirties, Betty Taylor was a registered nurse and one of Halstead's former students. As the only person trained in modern medicine for many miles around, she was "doctor" to 1,000 Campa Indians in the nearby forest. A steady stream of them came to the door for advice, examination, and treatment. She said afterward that a lot of the complaints on this particular day were psychosomatic: The Indians were not used to strange white men, having been by-passed by the rubber-boom exploiters and the oil men, and our arrival had upset them.

Until Pastor and Mrs. John Elick, now in Lima, established the mission in 1951, the Campas were very warlike. "They love to fight," Betty Taylor said. "The Elicks used to have to go out in the thick of battle and take their bows and arrows away from them. The women and children fight right along with the men. That's why they want as many babies as they can possibly have. Even today you'll see little five-year-olds shooting sharp arrows at each other as fast as they can; this is encouraged by the parents to develop their skills. We don't have many wars any more, though. The Christian Indians help us to discourage such things."

Taylor said that some of the Campas were frightened because there was a rumor going around the jungle that white men were rendering down native flesh to get oil for their airplanes. When our plane landed, though, a little Indian boy standing next to him asked, "Is that Jesus coming?"

Since we planned to go out on the trail to collect plants first thing in the morning, there were candlelight consultations that night near the huts of several witch doctors who

were persuaded by the Taylors to talk about their plant cures.
The Indians did not speak Spanish, so the missionaries acted
as interpreters. I recorded these interviews with some trepi-
dation, because when I played back the voices briefly in the
beginning to test the machine, several Indians laughed de-
lightedly; but most appeared alarmed. I recalled hearing that
an explorer had been killed after showing an Indian a picture he had taken and developed: the savage thought his
soul had been stolen. But Halstead felt the tapes would be
useful in case he didn't catch everything in his notes.

Later we sat around talking in the house which the Taylors had built entirely of mahogany planks. Some Indians
came in and sat on the floor, while others peered in through
the windows and doors from time to time. Their faces, tat-
tooed by means of thorns and vegetable dyes, were somewhat
startling, but they were basically handsome, with beautiful
bronze skins and thick black hair. We saw no deformities of
any kind. We learned that when twins are born, non-Christian
Indians always place the weaker baby out in the noonday
sun, where it perishes very quickly. "Of course, they try to
conceal these practices from us," Betty Taylor said, "but
when someone is hopelessly ill or injured, we suspect that
he is done away with. Also, they believe that all sickness is
caused by some person casting a spell upon the victim. Last
November we had a whooping cough epidemic and six babies
died. A non-Christian witch doctor was consulted and he
said that one of our twelve-year-old girls had caused the epidemic."

"How did he decide that?" we asked.

"He took the *ayahuasca* vine and boiled it all day; when
he drank the brew it caused hallucinations and he 'saw' the
person supposedly responsible for the illness. This is a common way of dealing with sickness. As it happened, he visualized his own grandchild, a girl of twelve. But the mother

was nonetheless ordered to take her into the forest and strangle her, which she did before we could stop it."

The Taylors said they had been able to rescue fifty-five condemned children by "buying" them with large metal cooking pots and placing them in the "protective custody" of Indians belonging to the mission's church. When they went to school their young male teacher was the first child "bought" by the Elicks years ago when they came to Neavati; he had been sent away to be educated and was now serving also as the assistant minister. "Everything the wild Indians do is for the sake of the tribe as a whole," the missionaries explained. "In order to save the others, they feel it is right to kill one child. Ignorance and the brutality that it fosters—that is what we are struggling with here. The Campas are basically a very clean, hardworking group."

The talk turned to wildlife in the forest. One day a full-grown panther had wandered in and then out of the house. Another time a giant boa constrictor had come up the stairs (the house rested upon eight-foot stilts) and killed a pet toucan. A large, venomous snake had recently struck a three-year-old Campa child, killing her instantly.

A tepid shower from the barrel of rainwater outside did little to soothe my nerves after these bedtime stories. The second important thing I had forgotten to bring, besides comfortable shoes, was a snakebite kit. Soon after we all retired for the night, a violent storm suddenly drenched me through a nearby window. I jumped up to move my cot, and the moment my foot touched the floor I felt a sharp pain under my heel. With my flashlight, I saw two punctures about half an inch apart. Convinced that a deadly snake had bitten me, I sank down, calling for Dr. Halstead, who was sleeping on the floor in the next room. He did not respond, but another tired voice said, "Go to sleep, these storms sound worse than they are." The disapproval I had felt from the men over my excessive luggage, the strain and exhaustion caused by the ride across the Andes were taking their toll. I began to weep, feeling very sorry for myself indeed.

But I didn't quite manage to die. For, as the morning light revealed, I had not stepped on a venomous fer-de-lance, but on two strong staples that were stuck together, prongs upturned, in one of the cracks between the floorboards. When I told of my encounter with the "deadly staple snake" at breakfast, chiding Halstead for not taking night calls, we had our first good laugh of the expedition. This scare seemed to act like a shock treatment which somehow had the effect of removing undue apprehensions for the rest of the trip.

From reading the field journals, diaries, and letters of quite a few plant explorers, I knew that they had moments of homesickness and self-pity, too, especially on their first expeditions. In the writings of many men, contemporary and historical, one encounters such phrases as "Today is Mother's birthday and I doubt that I shall ever see her again," or "Everything is going wrong here, and I'm feeling very ill, besides," or, even, "Why did I *ever* . . ."

We were up at the first rooster's crow the next morning, and after the services in the chapel we had a hearty breakfast of fried strips of cooking bananas, boiled and mashed yuca root, and *cherimoyas,* a tropical fruit with a custard-like filling.

It was the height of the rainy season, and on the trail to the river the slime was ankle-deep, with water sometimes up to our knees. Even barefooted Indians took occasional spills. The jungle had looked flat from the airplane, but it was not. We seemed to be dragging ourselves up hills or half-way falling down them all day. Even in fairly level spots, hidden roots tripped us, causing painful wrenchings. I could see now why I had been advised not to wear snake boots— the mud would cling to them and make them too heavy.

With gym shoes, I could squish through anything. As one botanist had told me, "Don't worry about needing high top boots for protection against snakes. Any snake down there that doesn't strike above the boot tops isn't half trying; besides they drop from trees."

Augusto, a solidly built Campa, led the way, whacking with his machete at the underbrush. Behind him was a woman witch doctor, Maria Theresa, short, wizened, looking sixty, but only in her thirties. She was wearing a handwoven sacklike garment called a *cushma*. Felix and Eduardo, her only surviving children from a family of seven, followed close behind.

The entire success of this trip depended upon Maria Theresa's good will. She knew where the healing herbs grew and the deadly ones, too. The question was, would she tell?

Taylor, following her on the narrow path, was confident she would because she had recently become a Christian. For five years he had worked patiently for that. She no longer seemed to relish bloodshed; it was months since anyone had been put to death by witchcraft. Taylor said he was sure that she would not trick him, that she really intended to show us where she found the plants she used in her secret remedies.

Ollis, with cameras draped around his neck, walked behind Halstead, ready to photograph the plants in color in their natural setting. I stumbled along behind with my tape recorder over my shoulder, a camera, and a notebook, protected by a suffocatingly hot poncho. The sudden drenchings were wild and punishing, almost like walking under a waterfall; the other members of the party simply got wet, dried off in the blistering sun in the open places, and got wet again.

The path ended at the Río Neavati, a fair-sized but apparently unmapped river, which empties into the larger Río Pichis some twenty miles away. This, in turn, pours into the Pachitea, that becomes the well-known Amazon tributary,

the Ucayali. The land across the river from the mission and
beyond is known as the *Gran Pajonal*. Even the Campas
never venture into that territory because of the ferocious
tribes. It had been impossible, so far, for anyone to establish
mission stations there.

In a dugout canoe, we were poled upstream by Augusto.
Heavily loaded, the canoe had only an inch or so freeboard
above the water. I tried not to dwell on the fact that this
river was known to contain that favorite fish of adventure-
story writers, the small red-throated piranha (whose little
teeth are supposed to strip bones bare in a matter of minutes),
as well as caimans (a type of crocodile), and water boas that
may reach thirty-seven feet in length. Halstead had written
an article for a medical journal on *Urinophilus,* a miniature
catfish native to these waters, which seeks out orifices in the
human body. Because this fish is equipped with backward
running barbs, it has to be "surgically" extracted. We noticed
that the natives were extremely clean and took several baths
a day in the river. They were just careful not to go in when
they had cuts that might ooze blood and attract the piranha,
and they instructed their children never to *psindaitea* (uri-
nate) while submerged, lest the *Urinophilus* seek them out.

The trees that came right to the water's edge were magnificent. They had the light, smooth bark characteristic of
the rain forest, and their branches were hung with huge ant
nests and long, funnel-shaped baskets woven by a species
of blackbird. But only once were we aware of birds: when a
treeful of raucous-voiced parrots objected to our passing. Bril-
liantly colored macaws and tiny green parakeets were kept
as pets by the Campas around the mission, but they were not
seen in the forest. Disappointingly, the strange animals hid
from sight, also. We had been told that there were many
types of monkeys, ranging from marmosets no bigger than
a mouse to the booming-voiced howlers that could make the

very earth shake, as well as sloths, coati-mundis, and tapirs. Later on, a *tigrillo,* or small spotted jaguar, took one look at us and disappeared faster than Alice's Cheshire cat.

We traveled close to shore because the water was high and the dugout could not be poled against the midstream current. On the opposite side was what looked like a solid wall of green reaching up 150 feet or more. Beyond lay one of the world's last stretches of true wilderness, with an incredibly rich flora. The naturalist, Louis Agassiz, recognized 117 different species of trees alone in an area half a mile square. To look at this "green curtain" from the river was to comprehend for the first time the meaning of the word "impenetrable." I thought of a Joseph Conrad description in *Heart of Darkness*: "Going up that river was like traveling back to the earliest beginnings of the world, when vegetation rioted upon the earth and the big trees were king."

After several hours we turned off into a side stream where the dugout was tied to a tree. There was no perceptible footpath but Maria Theresa seemed at all times to know exactly where she was going, and we followed, sometimes crawling on our hands and knees through the lush undergrowth near the water's edge. Once we were away from the sunny riverbank it was surprisingly dark under the canopy of leaves high overhead. Here the low-growing plants were starved for light and nourishment in the leached-out soil. There were no exotic tropical flowers, only a few washed-out blossoms on spindly stems. And the forest was silent. Where were those insane bird cries that are heard in the background of every jungle movie? We looked in vain for sky-blue Morpho butterflies with eight-inch wingspreads. Once in a while, a blaze of orange fungus caught our eye or a shaft of slanting sunlight glanced off a beetle's iridescent back, giving the impression that it was jewel-studded. We also saw heavily burdened leaf-cutter ants and some fat-bodied black ants.

Clouds of tiny gnats stuck in our eyelashes and were inhaled when we gasped for breath after stumbling. Biting, stinging pests raised welts through clothing and insect repellant; this was more or less expected. But I had not thought that we would tramp for hours and never stop to rest. There isn't any place to sit down in the rain forest, and, as Don Ollis told me, everything is always go-go-go on a Halstead expedition. If you need to rest or eat or stop for other reasons, there is obviously something wrong with *you*. At times, I was so far behind the others, I thought I was lost for good. But the harder I ran to catch up, the more I tripped and fell down, so it was best to pick my way carefully.

At last, just when I was convinced that Maria Theresa and Augusto were enjoying a primitive joke at our expense, the first medicinal plant was pointed out. It wasn't much to look at, about a foot or so high with a few dangling leaves that were used as a poultice in severe burns. Taylor said: "When our baby burned his hand so badly, we couldn't get it to heal and it became infected. We were really worried. Then we tried applying these leaves and the pain must have subsided right away because the baby stopped fussing. We couldn't get over how fast that burn began to heal." The plant was photographed with flash bulbs because of the gloom; then leaves, stems, and roots were given a collection number corresponding to the number in Halstead's small notebook and put into separate plastic bags.

We pushed on. The next plant was a climber said to be good for making a solution in which to bathe broken bones. Supposedly, it also helped if you drank it. This seemed unlikely, but samples were taken nevertheless. Another plant, we were told, yielded a red resin which, when cooked down to a thick gluey consistency and applied while still warm to a broken limb, hardened into a plaster-like cast. Farther along we were shown botanicals recommended for pains in general, one to reduce fevers, another with a root that Indian women chewed during childbirth. In all, about twenty specimens were collected that first day.

I raided a bush with huge heart-shaped leaves that were supposed to cure a headache if you placed them on your forehead. By now it was late afternoon, and the combination of hunger, altitude-sickness hangover, and jungle heat made me the ideal experimental subject. Unfortunately, I can write no testimonial, though I think I gave those leaves a fair trial. It wasn't easy to keep them in place; in fact, it was a nuisance. If anything, the effort made my headache worse. But maybe they'll turn out to be good for something else, like the common cold.

Halstead told Taylor, "We have no secrets; if any of these plants prove out, we will relay the information to you so that the natives can use them more efficiently in taking care of themselves. In fact, my goal is to develop 'cash crops' of crude drugs in mission stations like this one. If Pfizer's natural-products experts feel that these plants have commercial value, they will want them in quantity, paying so much per pound for them." He suggested that Taylor might consider setting up papaya plantations. The dried latex produces an enzyme called papain, which is medically important in the treatment of bruises and in cleaning up wounds. It is also used to aid digestion and, in industry, to tenderize meat and chillproof beer. Similar enzymes are being obtained from pineapple plants and species of fig trees.

Taylor said that there was some small-scale trading in achiote berries, which the Indians used to dye their skins and keep them disease-free. Neighboring Amazon tribes spread the berries under the hammocks used for childbirth, hinting at some germicidal property. (I was surprised to find a fifteen-cent bottle of achiote berries for flavoring on the spice shelf of my Manhattan supermarket when I returned home.)

On the way back to the mission in the dugout, I saw a snake, coiled and drowsing on the riverbank an arm's length away. It was almost as big around in the middle as a tire tube and it was beautifully camouflaged; its rough, mud-colored skin and darker, diamond-shaped markings blended so well with the dappled background that not even the Campas noticed it. What people say about wild things—just leave them alone and they won't bother you—seemed true. I tapped Taylor on the shoulder to ask what kind of snake it was, and Augusto, seated behind me, followed my gesture.

"Maranki!" he shouted, jumping up and striking the snake with his paddle. Maria Theresa and her children took up the cry, "Maranki! Puyeri!" ("A snake! Kill it!") Suddenly the snake thrust itself across the dugout between Taylor and me, lashing this way and that. As the Indian struck it again and again with the paddle, trying to beat it down into the water, the dugout was all but swamped. For a moment it seemed that everyone would soon be thrashing in the water with the snake. Then it stopped fighting, turned its lighter underside up, and was carried away by the current. It was between seven and eight feet long.

"That's a *shushupe,* a bushmaster," Taylor said, "the same kind that killed the little Campa girl. That's why Augusto was so excited. They get to be up to twelve feet long, very large for pit vipers, and they carry so much venom you might as well forget about using serum. Which reminds me, tomorrow we'll go out and get the snakebite plants. Old Jonas is a specialist in that line; he'll be pleased to show them. . . . Well, now you can relax; you have probably seen your first and last dangerous snake. This is only the third one I have seen in five years."

That evening at the mission, while helping prepare a dinner of breadfruit, yuca soup, and banana pudding, I learned about some of the primitive customs of the forest Campas;

for instance, marriage takes place when a boy presents food to a girl he fancies and she cooks it for him. Girls become marriageable one month after their first menstrual period —having spent the time in a small hut weaving a *cushma*. These Indians, by the way, have discovered that the leaves of a certain plant when taken as a tea cause sterility for about three years. But because so few children, out of all those born, survive death by disease and witchcraft, the potion is taken only under special circumstances. (If a woman is very frail, for instance.) "If the Campa men ever found out their wives were taking these leaves, they would probably beat them to death," I was told. "Fathering a lot of babies is a masculine status symbol."

(Dr. Saul Miller, of the Museum of the American Indian in New York, later told me that little is known about the Campas. They belong to the Arawak language group and have a loosely organized tribal system with no chieftains. One or two families of fifteen to thirty persons live together, with considerable distance between settlements. The population density has been estimated at one Indian per square mile.)

It was tedious work putting the plants into the plant press, and as I helped Halstead that evening he explained that we had to be careful not to have any soil clinging to the specimens or they might be destroyed by the United States Department of Agriculture to prevent the possible entry of pests. For this reason no living plants could be shipped. While we were busy with this task it grew dark and we continued by candlelight. It seemed incredible that we had journeyed so far and in just a few hours had collected twenty drug plant specimens. "That's the way it is," the doctor said. "Getting to the collection site is really the major ordeal. Once you arrive, things move very fast."

We were interrupted by the arrival of a messenger saying that an Amuesha Indian family some distance away was sick and needed Mrs. Taylor right away. Using flashlights, we all picked our way through the forest. As we came close to the hut, we saw cockroaches as big as mice and heard other creatures slithering in the grass. A starved-looking dog jumped at us, snarling and snapping. We found the family silently gathered around a young woman on a platform of woven rushes, just outside the doorway. Her eyes were wild with pain and she moaned as Dr. Halstead gently examined her and Betty Taylor talked to her soothingly in a mixture of Campa, Amuesha, and Spanish. From inside the hut we heard another sound, hardly a human cry; there we found an old woman, near death from tuberculosis, sharing a filthy mat with a little boy who had a high fever. Halstead said that the young woman was suffering from toxemia of pregnancy, anemia, possibly diabetes, and probably tuberculosis and syphilis. (We had passed through a village in the highlands where 90 per cent of the inhabitants were said to be syphilitic, and the condition was not unknown here.)

I could understand Halstead's anger and frustration at being able to do so little to help these people. On the way back to the mission he punctuated his remarks to me by slashing at the foliage with his machete: "Now you know what we are up against in the tropics. I can see that these three cases have upset you, but they are the first you've seen. I have seen hundreds. Babies have died in my arms because I didn't have the dime's worth of vaccine needed to save them. Right now we don't have a few cents worth of chemicals to make a urine test. I can't take that young mother's blood pressure because a couple of months ago the ants ate up the Taylors' blood pressure cuff. There's no use trying to combat her anemia without doing something about the parasites that are causing it. Go to work on them and she'll be reinfected as soon as you stop."

At the mission, he and Mrs. Taylor carefully went through

all of the medicines stored in a footlocker. They thought the young woman also had malaria, and the little boy's eyes were badly infected. But there was only a dab of eye ointment left in a tiny tube. I knew that they were out of analgesics and anesthetics because Taylor had pulled molars that day without them. "There just never are enough drugs to go around," the Taylors said. All of us were glad to contribute our drugs but we could see that even a suitcaseful would be gone in no time.

Something had been bothering me about jungle medicines. "Why," I asked, "if these areas are so rich in useful drug plants are so many of these people sick? Why . . ."

". . . aren't the natives all healthy, wealthy, and wise?" the doctor finished bitterly, then got up to pace back and forth. "That is a fool's question. I'm sorry, but it is. That young woman you saw tonight would tax the facilities of the finest medical center. A native remedy, no matter how good, even a modern 'miracle drug,' simply cannot do a job on a body that is starved for protein and riddled with parasites. These are your number one threats in the tropics. My ultimate goal is not only to collect plants but also to try to do something about these basic problems. We just can't come into these places and *take*; it's got to be a two-way proposition. Explorers and other foreign-based representatives of American pharmaceutical companies are in an excellent position to investigate ways to aid sick and malnourished peoples. It's a challenge we simply have got to face.

"And there are other reasons why native remedies are not as helpful as they might be. The obvious one is, they are hard to get. These people use cotton all the time to weave their *cushmas,* but in thousands of years it has never occurred to them to cultivate the things they need. They gather wild cotton, hit or miss. They only began to have little garden plots, or *chacaras,* after the missionaries came. When illness strikes, they have to get up, go out, search for the plant—as we did today. If you're flat on your back, I don't need to tell you it's not easy."

Mrs. Taylor added: "There's also the matter of dosage. The latex from the *ojé* tree, a species of fig we have here, is a valuable vermifuge, but several Campas died recently because, unless exactly the right amount is taken, the parasites form a bolus that obstructs the intestines and can be fatal. Some natives think 'if a little medicine is good for you a whole lot will be even better,' with disastrous consequences."

Her husband pointed out still another factor. "Sometimes, very good remedies and important foods are not used because of religious taboos or superstitions. For instance, we do not have much fish or game here, but the Campas will not kill the best source of meat, the red deer, because they believe that the souls of their dead relatives reside in the deer's body."

We stayed on at the mission collecting and preserving plants in the manner described earlier, which need not be repeated, until it was time to go to Puerto Bermúdez to meet the pilot who had brought us. We were going to stop briefly in Pucallpa, about 140 miles north, and then go on to Iquitos, 600 miles further north, on the Amazon. There, we had confirmed reservations to fly back to Lima on Faucett Airlines, a reliable line, about ten days hence.

After making the long, hot river trip to Bermúdez and waiting all day, it was obvious that our pilot wasn't coming. There was no place to stay, so we all returned to Neavati. This happened three days in a row. Unfortunately, the army radio sending set was not functioning properly, so Halstead could not get in touch with alternate pilots. But both he and Taylor felt confident that the mission headquarters in Lima would send someone to get us out; we just had to be there on the spot and ready to go.

By the afternoon of the third day, Halstead had considered the river route to Pucallpa but decided against it because it would take anywhere from five to fourteen days. He had instead made an arrangement with the Peruvians to get us back to San Ramón and from there we would take the bus, returning to Lima over the same route we had come and giving up our trip to Pucallpa and Iquitos. While we were discussing this, some hysterical Spanish suddenly blasted from the receiving set: "Derrumbe monstruoso!" the voice kept saying. "Well! That takes care of that little plan," Halstead said. "A quarter of a mile of the road we crossed between Tarma and San Ramón just fell into the valley!"

"Derrumbe monstruoso!" was as bad as it sounded. But Halstead was already making new plans. The harassed radio operator knew a pilot who might be persuaded to fly to Pucallpa. When this young man eventually showed up in his small plane, he seemed very nervous about the whole prospect and insisted that he could only take two of us. He also said it was necessary to take off immediately so he could rendezvous at some point with another plane, going over the jungle. Never having flown to Pucallpa before, he needed a guide, apparently. He was also making sure that if we had a forced landing, another pilot would know where to send help. He finally agreed to take the three of us for all the cash we had, but he drew the line at baggage. Halstead managed to convince him that the plant press and his and Ollis' small satchels weighed next to nothing, but when it came to my big suitcase it was either me or my luggage. I managed to grab some of the things packed on top, and the rest remained behind. Thus I learned my lesson about traveling light.

The pilot seemed to be operating on a learner's permit, his radio didn't work, and he had no map. He was trying to follow the other plane which was following the winding river system. Before I left New York, my oldest son, a map buff, had dashed down to the Customs House to get World

Aeronautical Charts for the areas we might cover. When I now pulled W.A.C. Number 1072 from my handbag, it was snatched from my hands by the pilot sitting next to me.

Stepping out of the plane in Pucallpa, we were almost flattened by the heat; after cashing traveler's checks at the bank, I began a fruitless search for a ready-made dress. There was beautiful yard goods from Switzerland, Japan, and England, brought up the Amazon and Ucayali, but not a single finished garment was available. I finally had to buy a blouse off a salesgirl's back and have her stitch up a length of material on a waistband for a skirt in order to continue the journey with a change of clothing.

Our object in stopping there was to confer with the doctors at the Albert Schweitzer Hospital Amazonicas and at the hospital run by the Summer Institute of Linguisticas, a non-denominational Bible translating group. These stops were about ten miles out of town, but a bus driver cheerfully went miles off his regular route in order to drop us at the door . . . imagine a Fifth Avenue bus driver telling a passenger, "Sure, on my way up from Washington Square, I'll be glad to drop you off at La Guardia." A few standees in the bus called out *"Vamanos a Pucallpa"* ("Let's get going," or words to that effect), but the majority of the passengers didn't mind at all.

After Halstead made notes on the native uses of local medicinal plants, as observed by the physicians and nurses in these hospitals, we returned to Pucallpa, noticing on the way many *"Castro, si, Yanqui, no"* signs painted on buildings. At dinner there was almost an international incident involving an item on the menu called *Huevos Cubanos,* or Cuban-style eggs. When I decided that I would prefer fish, the waiter glowered and said in Spanish, "So you don't like Castro, eh?" Hoping to avoid possible reprisals in the kitchen, we quickly reassured him with *"Castro, si, huevos, no,"* feeling like traitors. We saw no other *Norteamericanos* as we began an after-dinner walk around town, and we terminated this stroll when a passerby spat in our faces.

Having completed our interviews, we took a cargo plane the next morning to Iquitos, on the banks of the Amazon. The skillful Peruvian air force pilot brought the lumbering aircraft in to a safe landing under a violent tropical storm, and although our expedition leader discouraged sight-seeing, he seemed just as thrilled as the rest of us were as we stood on the banks of the mighty "ocean river," 2,300 miles from its mouth. On the edge of Iquitos was a floating village on rafts which reminded the men of Indonesia; in the heart of the city were the splendid remains of the rubber boom—palatial old hotels covered with Spanish tiles and a building made entirely of molded iron imported from Europe.

In addition to trips out of Iquitos into the jungle, we interviewed missionaries, anthropologists, and "civilized" witch doctors who were sophisticated enough to charge for samples of the *ayahuasca* liquid we had heard about at Neavati. (This was the vision-producing brew used by the witch doctors who condemned the children to death; it was made from the vine *Banisteriopsis caapi,* first identified in 1852 by the great English botanist Richard Spruce.) Halstead naturally was alert wherever we went for new methods of preparing *ayahuasca* and for botanical specimens of the vine. I recorded on tape a number of these native recipes, all highly contradictory, and wondered whether the Pfizer researchers would make any use of them. We learned that the immediate result of drinking the potion was vomiting, followed by characteristic blue aureoles around the fantastic visions. The effects are not lasting and when the forest Indians take the drug during their ceremonials, such as the brutal whipping rites used to initiate boys into manhood, they may consume five or six doses during an evening, becoming ill each time. One hundred years ago, Spruce regretted not being able to make a complete analysis of this plant. Recently, Schultes of Harvard, said, "We stand merely on the threshold of our investigation into the botany, ethnology, history, pharmacology, chemistry, and therapeutics of that complex of intoxicants known as *ayahuasca, caapi,* or *yajé.*"

At Iquitos, our expedition broke up. Halstead was anxious to fly his plant specimens back to the World Life Research Institute, where they would be accurately identified by taxonomic botanists and given preliminary tests in his laboratories. Then the promising ones would be sent on to Pfizer for further work. I knew full well that it might be years before any findings could be made public; or, as so often happens in pharmaceutical research, all the work done on this expedition might come to naught. Now that I was personally involved with Maria Theresa's curatives, I was beginning to understand the tremendous amount of hope and enthusiasm that drives the drug plant explorers and researchers.

As we said goodbye, Halstead commented, "You know, each expedition is a synthesis of all those you've been on before. I remember my first one—I had a trailer load of stuff intended for my own personal use and I never even looked at half of it. Huge containers. Microscopes. Enough drugs to stock a small pharmacy. I could have outfitted two expeditions for six months and had plenty left over. We *all* have to learn from our mistakes!"

The basic ingredients of the boom in botanical drugs are search and research. I had been in on the search in the field, and when I returned I wanted to see the follow-up—the laboratory research and testing. I was particularly interested in following through on *ayahuasca.*

For this part of the story I went up to the newest of Pfizer's Medical Research Laboratories, which overlooks the Thames River in Groton, Connecticut. Dr. Frank A. Hochstein of Pfizer, a tall, friendly Canadian and a leading natural-product chemist, had published the most recent work on the chemical constituents of this botanical. He explained that *Banisteriopsis caapi* had been examined many times. Three names—telepathine, yageine, and banisterine—had been assigned to the alkaloids isolated from the plants studied by early workers. But several subsequent investigators concluded that harmine was the sole alkaloid, identical with the other three.

"Undoubtedly, some of the early inconsistencies resulted from errors in botanical identification," Hochstein explained. "The plant cultivated by the witch doctors is cut back so frequently that it never flowers, and the wild plants flower rarely. Spruce found flowering specimens on the Río Uaupes, but since then no one else has. All the work has been done on sterile samples, which accounts in part for the confusion in the literature on this plant. But the modern investigational techniques that you will see here today, especially paper chromatography, have enabled us to extend the earlier work. We have found that harmine is the major alkaloid, but it seems likely that two lesser alkaloids may have substantial hallucination-producing activity in their own right. We have tested these two new drugs on dogs and the results suggest, please note, *suggest,* that the dogs do have hallucinations. These alkaloids are being used in the experimental study of mental diseases in New York State, under the personal supervision of Dr. Paul H. Hoch, commissioner of mental hygiene. Some improvement in patients has been noted after treatment with *ayahuasca*'s derivatives. The effects are similar to those caused by mescaline, from peyote cactus, and by LSD, the ergot fungus derivative that has been the object of so much research in this field."

There is a temptation to try to describe exactly what happens to a drug plant from the moment it arrives as a bale of crude leaves or a bundle of vines until it emerges in pill or capsule form. But it is neither practical nor possible to do this for many reasons. Whole textbooks are devoted to explaining just part of this process. And, of course, procedures as well as products are patented by all pharmaceutical manufacturers. The one thing that can't be patented is the wild-growing drug plant itself.

Briefly, though, when a botanical arrives at the laboratory its parts are usually ground up separately in a Wiley mill or an ordinary food blender, and percolators turn it into extracts. This material is then freeze-dried. In working on *ayahuasca*, Hochstein utilized the countercurrent distributor, an ingenious device made of hundreds of elongated, glass test tubes which must be kept scrupulously clean—a bottlewasher's nightmare. This equipment separates mixtures of very similar materials according to their slight differences in solubilities. Rocking back and forth for twenty-four hours a day, it may subject a mixture to as many as 10,000 individual extractions in a day or two. Formerly, this procedure would have exhausted a bevy of laboratory assistants for months.

The technique of paper chromatography is a powerful tool for separating and identifying very small amounts of pure substances. If you have ever looked closely at a large ink blot on a blotter, you will recall that the dyes in the ink separate into different zones. In the early 1940's, the application of this principle resulted in a procedure that has now become routine for the separation of complex mixtures. At Pfizer, 10,000 chromatograms are made in an average month. A drop of a natural or a synthetic substance is placed on a sheet of filter paper, one edge of which is suspended in a suitable solvent. As the fluid flows over the drop being tested, different pure ingredients in that drop move at different rates of speed and come to rest in varying positions, leaving their distinctive "chemical fingerprints." Unknown substances can be identified by comparison with known ones; mixtures can be separated into components; minute amounts of pure materials can be obtained for further study. With their delicate colors, chrom-atograms look like pale finger-paintings. Quite often they are viewed under ultraviolet light, where some of the compounds fluoresce brightly, giving another clue to their identity. The ingredients isolated are also checked to determine the nature of their infrared spectrum. In the case of *ayahuasca,* natural harmine and a synthetic form proved identical when compared by these methods.

I never did ask Hochstein whether he wanted to listen to the tapes of the witch doctors' recipes. Even if I had brought back a jug of *ayahuasca,* it was obvious that the expensive and time-consuming process of screening could not have been set in motion until the plants were scientifically identified and some assurance was given that additional quantities of the same material could be collected. Five pounds or more of crude botanicals are usually needed before a drug company can begin to do any extensive screening. The lead must be very promis-ing before they can afford to do this, for it has been estimated that the average new product requires five years of preparation and an investment of around $5,000,000. The cost of an expedi-tion to the ends of the earth to collect the plant specimens is only the beginning.

But, as Dr. Ernest M. Weber, Pfizer's research director, explained, "Pfizer has a continuing interest in botanical re-search. Many naturally occurring molecules are so complex that duplicating them synthetically constitutes an intellectual challenge; however, this type of work does not always yield practical applications. It is usually more rewarding from a useful-product point of view to extract and purify the active ingredients from a natural plant then, by chemical alteration, improve potency or reduce side effects. To us, plant hunting constitutes an important source of potential new products. Some of our most valuable drugs have been derived from bo-tanicals—others equally valuable may yet be discovered."

Variations on the Theme:

- *Back to the Lost Worlds*
- *The Taxi to the Jungle*
- *The Botanist from Bonwit's*
- *Kitchen Midden Housekeeping*
- *The ABCDEtc. Approach*

INVOLVED IN BOTANICAL DRUG RESEARCH ARE OTHER men and women whose approaches or working methods demonstrate that there can be endless variations on this basic theme.

Back to the Lost Worlds

Plant explorers employed by botanic gardens spend a large share of their time collecting plants that are purely ornamental, beautiful in themselves. They are also asked by drug companies to "Look around for some so-and-so while you are on your next expedition," and being seasoned field botanists, they do an excellent job. But they often share the sentiments of Dr. Richard Spruce, who, despite his many contributions to economic botany, was basically interested in the Hepaticae, relatives of the mosses. He wrote: "I like to look on plants as sentient beings which live and enjoy their lives—which beautify the earth during life, and after death may adorn my herbarium. When they are beaten to pulp or powder in the apothecary's mortar, they lose most of their interest for me. It is true that the Hepaticae have hardly as yet yielded any substance to man capable of stupefying him or of forcing his stomach to empty its contents, nor are they good for food; but if man cannot torture them to his uses or abuses, they are infinitely useful where God has placed them, as I hope to show; and they are, at least, useful to and beautiful in themselves—surely the primary motive for every individual existence."

Millions of visitors know the New York Botanical Garden as a delightful park with a towering central greenhouse that features a mountain waterfall spilling through lush tropical foliage. Outside there is the herb garden in the form of an intertwined knot, a fragrant reminder of the physick gardens of the Middle Ages. All botanic gardens owe their origin to the needs of medicine and probably all of them still make important behind-the-scenes contributions to that science. For instance, the telephone number of the Garden's reference librarian, Elizabeth Hall, is one of those most frequently called by more than one plant hunter in this book, and the three million plant specimens classified in the herbarium constitute the first stop of many an outward-bound expeditioneer. The late Dr. Henry H. Rusby initiated the Garden's interest in drug plants as a result of his early explorations in Bolivia. Dr. Rusby discovered the botanical *Guarea rusbyi,* whose bark provides cocillana, a soothing ingredient in cough syrups. And today the *Journal of Economic Botany,* published by the staff, frequently contains articles on new medicinal plants contributed by scientists working the world over.

One of the most interesting contemporary botanic garden explorers is Dr. Bassett Maguire, head curator of the New York Botanical Garden, a veteran of some fifty expeditions. When he was a boy fifty years ago in Alabama City, Alabama, young Bassett had two favorite books, W. H. Hudson's fantasy *Green Mansions* and Sir Arthur Conan Doyle's pseudoscientific thriller *The Lost World.* Both of these books are highly imaginative accounts of life in the South American jungles, but they are based upon the reports of two famous

German explorer-naturalists, Baron Alexander von Humboldt and Robert Schomburgk. Bassett Maguire was out of his teens before he chanced upon a rare copy of Schomburgk's *Travels in Guiana and on the Orinoco during the Years 1835–1839*. In fact, he was well on his way to becoming a physician; but he took a botany course and abandoned his pre-medical studies. He was forty years old before he picked up Schomburgk's trail in Venezuela.

In his office Dr. Maguire presents a trim, scholarly appearance, but photographs taken in the field show a man who might be mistaken for Robinson Crusoe. There is the same peaked hat turned down all around, trousers torn off at the knees, and a full red beard. Mark well the beard.

When this plant explorer first ventured into the remote area in southern Venezuela that Schomburgk described, the natives began to celebrate. Maguire knew that he was the first white man any of them had ever seen, but this was an extraordinary reception. Then, little by little, he learned that Schomburgk had established a reputation for being able to work miracles. His legendary feats had been re-told for generations and were even carved on rocks jutting from a precipice nearby. The natives insisted that he, Maguire, was the returned spirit of Schomburgk: they were both white-skinned and they both had magnificent beards. There was little that the guest of honor could do to persuade them that this simply wasn't true, so he joined in the dancing and merrymaking.

But the Indians proved unpredictable. When he wanted to collect some specimens of bamboo that grew fifty feet high, they became very difficult. It mattered little then that he was a celestial spirit returned to earth; they were worried about the bamboo god. Finally they agreed to permit him to take the bamboo and other plants, but he had to insert a stake in the spot vacated so that the gods would be appeased.

These Indians were the Maquiritares and they proved to

be a troublesome lot when hired as helpers, too. Maguire and his party wanted to scale the great mountain called Huacha-macari, but the Indians used every ruse to cause the white men to become lost, delayed, or otherwise thwarted in their efforts, because Huachamacari means "house of the gods" and the Indians feared reprisals if they permitted this sacri-legious intrusion to occur.

Maguire was not intent upon scaling the mountain "just because it was there," nor was he in Venezuela merely to satisfy a boyhood whim. He and his colleagues, Dr. Julian A. Steyermark of the Chicago Natural History Museum and Dr. John J. Wurdack now of the Smithsonian Institution, wanted to fix accurately the geographical position of a large system of mountains and to inventory rare plants on them.

This area, the Guiana Highlands, lying south and east of the Orinoco River, is one of the oldest geological regions in the Western Hemisphere. Some hundred million years ago, it was one vast sandstone mass, possibly related to trans-oceanic sandstone plateaus in western Africa. But the annual rainfall of 200 inches gradually cut canyons into these rocks, and as torrents of rushing water widened them, isolated mesas were created. Some of these flat-topped mountains are 9,000 feet high; their range extends in an arc from Surinam westward to the foot of the Andes. Because the divides be-came too broad for insects to fly across and the sheer sides of the cliffs prevented animals from going up or coming down, evolutionary contact with the rest of the earth was cut off.

These mist-shrouded, eerie plateaus are much the same today as they were a million years ago. They are truly named "lost worlds." Because Maguire and his associates had avail-able every modern means of access, they were able to be the first men, white or native, to set foot on many of these pre-historic terranes. The combined top area of these mountains probably totals 50,000 square miles, and hundreds of them remain to be explored. The exciting thing is that they are by no means all alike.

The highlands to the east in Guiana were first noted by white men when sixteenth-century adventurers traveled up the Orinoco in search of "El Dorado," a legendary golden king who bathed in a mythical lake filled with golden nuggets. In southern Venezuela Maguire found streams with gold and diamonds being taken from them, but for a botanist the true El Dorado exists in the fantastic plant life around these plateaus and on them. He has, for instance, seen pitcher plants twelve feet high with as many as thirty enormous pitchers on them, each holding a quart and a half of sticky, insect-trapping fluid. There are sunflower relatives five feet thick and up to seventy-five feet high. A palm leaf thirty feet long and six feet across—undoubtedly the largest leaf of any kind in the world—was found at the base of Duida, the mountain mentioned in *Green Mansions*. Attempts to grow these plants in the New York Botanical Garden greenhouses have not been successful so far, but research on collected specimens continues. Pictures of these marvels growing in the wilds are prized additions to the Garden's already fabulous collection.

According to Maguire, this area has the largest contiguous tropical flora in existence, far larger in the biological and physical sense than any other. Study of this flora will shed light on the origin and dispersal of vegetation in the Western Hemisphere and on the rate of the processes of evolution. Here there are breathtaking waterfalls with a rebound higher than Niagara's. There are tribes like the Guaicas, who are ritualistic cannibals, wear no clothing, make fire by friction, have no well-developed agriculture, and do not even build dugout canoes. Maguire said that they seem to lack certain human emotions; when a child tumbled into a stream, adult Guaicas watched stone-faced as he was swept to his death, never lifting a finger to help. When Maguire fell ill with malaria he kept a gun at his side, for otherwise he felt sure that his guides would abandon him. Once he stayed with a missionary for three days; the day after he left, the missionary was shot in the back.

Before he even sets out on one of his frequent treks, Maguire has the job of fund-raising to face, as do most of his colleagues who work for botanic gardens, museums, and noncommercial organizations. This excerpt from a New York newspaper cites typical sponsors: "Dr. Bassett Maguire and three staff members of the New York Botanical Garden will leave today on an eight-month expedition to Venezuela. . . . With the addition of native boatmen, hunters, and porters needed to transport three tons of gear and five tons of food, the party will eventually number about thirty persons. The National Science Foundation and Forestry Colleges of Yale and Syracuse Universities are participating. . . . The Explorers Club is supporting the geographical phase and the Eli Lilly Company is underwriting the investigation of new plants as possible drug sources."

Also received, and greatly appreciated, are transportation assistance by various steamship or airline companies, housing provided by friends or government agencies in South America, and trade goods by the courtesy of Sears, Roebuck and Company and others. Maguire puts great store in having large quantities of lice combs, mirrors, needles, belts, lengths of cloth, and blue glass beads to trade with the Indians for services. His bearers especially like to get percussion caps to use in their old-fashioned shotguns. They use the same shells repeatedly by recharging. Since some of their equipment dates from the flintlock era, Maguire also brings along flints. The trade goods are carefully wrapped in brown paper and packed in waterproof bags and boxes to protect them during the long haul upstream through rapids.

"I have done a considerable amount of expedition organizing," Maguire said, "and I do not believe that one can do effective work without the support of people. The problem of logistics is the most difficult one and you don't solve it by striking out alone with a knapsack, in my opinion. I line up helpers for the next expedition at the end of a previous one."

The New York Botanical Garden groups usually have several principals with technical or scientific training, plus up to sixty-seven bearers. Seldom is the party less than fifteen. Often it includes Dr. Maguire's wife, Celia, and their son, Bassett, Jr. I asked Maguire if it were true that he takes along such things as a silver tea service and tablecloths. He good-naturedly replied, "Oh no, not silver—stainless steel! Yes, we take tablecloths and anything else to add to our comfort. If you are going to live in the forest from three to five months, you must have sufficient facilities so that you can rest and relax in the evening. You must also construct the camp so that you can care for your plants properly. We do not take portable laboratories because we do no field testing, but we need a lot of surveying and other scientific instruments. Since we are exploring virgin territory of an especially inaccessible type, we also gather data for sciences other than botany. We have studied the biological significance of the uplifting of the Andes, for instance."

The Indian helpers can hardly be expected to grasp the importance of this work, however. Maguire returned to camp one evening to find that several dozen carefully numbered and measured blocks of rare wood, which he had managed to preserve from termites for months, had provided the heat which cooked his supper. Since he had gathered the wood in an area not likely to be re-visited, he understandably lost his appetite that night.

But in this part of the rain forest, he usually ate heartily and well—tapirs, guinea pigs, peccaries, and armadillo, which he considers the sweetest and most delicate of all bush meats. With fifty hungry Indians, he sometimes has to store as much as 600 pounds of meat at a time, in addition to beans, rice, flour, cases of canned goods, and other staples.

One time he and his son, Bassett, Jr., who was then a college student, went out on a long trek with a party of Indians. They left food in caches several days apart, but on the return trip they found that these had been stolen. After existing on palm buds for several days, they got hungry enough to eat an eight-inch bird spider that looked like a giant tarantula, but tasted like a hard-shell crab. While the Indians hurried on ahead to an abandoned native hut to dig for yams that might have been overlooked, the Maguires ate a few dried kernels of corn and some grubs.

When they caught up with the Indians in the clearing, the men were holding some snake-like creatures they evidently considered a great delicacy. These giant earthworms, which were five feet long and as tough as garden hose, were cut up, cleaned, and stewed with a few yams. Maguire recalled the reaction of Dr. Waldo Schmidt, curator of the Smithsonian Institution, when he heard about this: "He was horrified. He made me promise to go right back there and find some of those worms for him on my very next trip. It seems that there isn't a single specimen, alive or pickled, in any museum in this country. And *I* had to go and *eat* them!"

These explorations have produced several hundred new botanicals that have been examined by Eli Lilly researchers. A company spokesman said, "A few have shown specific activities which warrant further investigation and new collections are being made to verify our original observations." As this is written, Dr. Maguire is in the field once more gathering these fabulous plants that may well contain unique compounds—new chemical structures with effects as extraordinary as the lost worlds from which they came.

The Taxi to the Jungle

In contrast, Dr. Robert F. Raffauf, natural products field representative for Smith, Kline & French, prescription drug producer, said: "I look upon my trips much as any traveling businessman does. The fact that I may commute 10,000 miles round trip does not really alter the picture very much. I fly in comfort on jets, and when I return to my wife and children in the Philadelphia suburbs I am wearing one of the suits I normally wear to the office. My luggage, except for a small medical kit, is about what I would take to Paris in the summertime. I don't expect to get sick and I never have. My health, if anything, seems to improve. Have I had any 'exciting adventures'? Yes, I have. But they have all been of the mind, intellectual adventures, you might call them."

As an organic chemist who spent two post-graduate years in Switzerland as research assistant to the Nobel laureates Reichstein and Paul Karrer, Raffauf has ranged somewhat far afield. But the useful techniques he learned from them in handling minute amounts of plant constituents have served him well, both in the laboratory and in the rain forest. Just as botanists like Schultes and Maguire, basically interested in pure science, have made contributions of economic value, so Raffauf, commercially oriented, has helped the field of botany.

Since 1951, when he first came to work for Smith, Kline & French, he has circled the globe three times, searching for new drug plants. Before and after this, there were four- and five-month trips to Southeast Asia, Africa, and South America. He now feels that shorter, concentrated efforts are more productive. For instance, a recent objective was a patch of jungle about forty kilometers from Manaus, Brazil, that fascinating city of almost 170,000 halfway down the Amazon. During the rubber boom, it had more millionaires per capita than any other city in the world and its opera house attracted European divas of the Gay Nineties. Although Raffauf believes it may be in for a renaissance, the paved streets still end abruptly on the edge of town. Old logging roads continue a little further and then the leafy green curtain drops down.

Raffauf began one typical Manaus working day by having a pleasant breakfast chat with his table partners at the air-conditioned Hotel Amazonas. They were an English couple who had traveled all this distance "to see what the jungle is like." Very well, why not come along with him? He couldn't offer them transportation because the local botanist's jeep was loaded with collecting equipment, but their taxi could follow along behind. And when they got into the forest, they could help with the machete work if they liked.

It was a sticky business, they learned, and the insects were unbelievably bothersome. But they all came back in time to freshen up before tea. Perhaps the tourists were disappointed, but Raffauf had found what he had come down for: some new plants containing alkaloids. About 10 per cent of all plants have them. He was not interested in any other kind. "This is not to say that glucosides, saponins, and other constituents are not important," Raffauf explained. "They certainly are. But some alkaloids, such as morphine, have proved to have such striking biological effects when administered as drugs that we are limiting our investigation to them at this time. We are seeking plants which have not been examined and reported on in the literature of science. These might serve as new drugs themselves, or new drugs might be synthesized from them. Basically, what we want are new chemical structures."

How Raffauf determines what is "new" is a story in itself, one which reinforces this plant hunter's image as a businessman-scientist. In a sense, one might say that he has arranged for an IBM machine to do his exploring for him before he even leaves the office. In the Science Information Department, employees are busy transferring to punched cards data on all of the alkaloids that have ever been found in any plant at any time by anybody—a monumental task. But it is scarcely any trouble at all to run these cards through the electronic sorters and tabulators, once the material is coded. The job of searching through botanical, chemical, and other technical journals for this basic information each time it is needed is eliminated. To date, about 15,000 species of plants have been assayed for the presence of alkaloids by Smith, Kline & French and the results tabulated. They are screening about 4,000 plants each year, and chemical and pharmacological studies are made on about one-third of those which are alkaloid-positive.

Needless to say, such streamlined office procedures leave little time for pondering the exotic use of plants by witch doctors. When Raffauf is in the field, he would rather methodically collect one sample of each plant in the area than cultivate the friendship of the local medicine man, who probably wouldn't know an alkaloid from an astronaut. He can be this independent because he carries in his pocket a small bottle of a modified Dragendorff reagent (for alkaloids) and some filter paper. When a likely plant is encountered, he cuts away a piece of it, squeezes it between the paper to extract a drop of sap, applies a drop of reagent, and presto! The presence of an alkaloid is accurately disclosed eight times out of ten. Since he is something of a one-man literature retrieval system himself, carrying his files in his head, Raffauf wastes little time and few motions out where it's hot and humid.

There are even further refinements. Certain families of plants are comparatively well known chemically, and closely related genera may be expected to contain similar chemicals. These already familiar groups may thus be eliminated. Raffauf always tries to have a well-trained botanist at his side to assist in these botanical determinations.

In addition to this very selective screening, Smith, Kline

& French are making collections of every plant that grows in a given area—again, testing only for alkaloids. They started in their own back yard, Pennsylvania, where they found an indole alkaloid, gramine, in the silver maple, and unclassified alkaloids in sassafras root. No one is willing to commit himself on whether tropical plants really offer more prospects for drugs than those in temperate regions; but this study, now being undertaken in Florida and California, may provide some answers.

These answers would not only have commercial value but would also contribute to our basic understanding of chemical processes within plants. Scientists still don't know why plants produce alkaloids. Because Smith, Kline & French tests all parts of the plants at different times of the year, when these findings are tabulated new information of use to plant physiologists and geneticists may be revealed. Also, some plants were found to be inaccurately placed in the taxonomic scheme; the company's compilations helped botanists to classify them properly. Thus, basic scientific contributions have already been made by a program that set out to find marketable pharmaceutical products.

To those of us who do not routinely travel to far-off lands, Raffauf's trips may seem to be adventures—but to him, the excitement lies in making additions to scientific knowledge.

The Botanist from Bonwit's

Dr. Siri von Reis, a Harvard Botanical Museum Research Fellow, is probably the only botanist in the world who was a high-fashion model while preparing a doctoral thesis (on *The Genus Anadenanthera; A Taxonomic and Ethnobotanical Study*). It was a case of being in the world of Christian Dior and Balenciaga by day and delving into the literature of *paricá, yopo,* or cohoba snuff at night. Dr. von Reis has never been to the Amazon jungle and has no burning desire to go, but as a graduate student she became fascinated with the study of native drug plants of the New World. Particularly interesting was the centuries-old but little-known West Indian and South American narcotic made from seeds of the mimosa-like tree *Piptadenia peregrina* (formerly known as Anadenanthera). Called cohoba in the West Indies, this snuff was first described by Ramon Pane in 1496 when he sailed with Columbus on his second voyage.

In partial fulfillment for her degree requirements, she combed through 450 sources and corresponded with sixty authorities in plant chemistry, pharmacology, and experimental psychiatry. Although the intoxicating properties of this plant were reported by many explorers, the active constituents remained a mystery until National Heart Institute scientists began to probe its secrets in 1954. In that year, bufotenin was isolated from the seeds and it is now being used in the experimental study of mental disease. Drs. W. J. Turner and S. Merlis, writing in the January, 1959, *Archives of Neurology and Psychiatry,* described the use of this compound in treating schizophrenics at a New York mental hospital. In reporting the results in a very withdrawn, hallucinating woman, they wrote, "The whole experience had a salutary effect upon the patient. At the time of writing there is a virtual cessation of translation of her thoughts into physical sensations and perceptions."

In their references they stated, "The literature on Piptadenia is very extensive but generally either confused or repetitious. We have searched this rather thoroughly, aided in part by Miss von Reis, who permitted us to read the manuscript she is preparing for her Ph.D. thesis. This is the most complete and authoritative work on the subject we have seen." Seldom is an academic thesis so quickly translated into a practical application.

While Dr. von Reis remains interested in New World

narcotics, she has another project that absorbs all her professional time now. The botanist from Bonwit's has devised a unique method of drug plant exploration especially suited to her feminine outlook. In a paper titled "Searching Herbaria for References to Folk Medicine," she described her new work to colleagues at the 1962 meeting of the Society for Economic Botany. Some men in the audience may have doubted, momentarily, that such a delicately chic young woman would actually spend her days shut up in the Harvard University Herbarium, turning over its 2,000,000 sheets one by one. But that is essentially the task she has taken upon herself, hoping to discover data useful in modern medicine.

When asked about this chore, she said, "Oh, it's fun—it really is. Some of these collections are over a hundred years old and you never know what you'll find in the faded, handwritten notes accompanying them. It seemed a shame that most of these meticulous entries never saw the light of day. I have pulled out specimens which may not have been examined by anyone since they were first collected. After you read dozens of entries by the same man, you begin to feel that you know him and you find yourself reliving moments of discovery in all the world's wildernesses. It is not the same as being in the field yourself, but it has a vividness all its own. The joy and curiosity of many a frontiersman are still very much alive in his yellowing and fragile notes."

But isn't it dusty, dirty work?

"I never thought of it that way. There is a mingled fragrance of plants, papers, and preservatives peculiar to herbaria, to which one with botanical experience becomes almost sentimentally attached. It's not just the odors of cinnamon, cloves, or lemon grass, but the exciting sweetness of life itself, plucked from out of time and space and laid aside for the instruction and pleasure of posterity."

Despite her lyrical description, this work is hardly on a par with sniffing scents at a perfume bar, nor is it merely clerical. As she records the notes on local medicinal usage made by the botanists who collected the plants, there is a great deal of selection and evaluation involved which only a well-trained taxonomic botanist could do. One also needs an ethnobotanical orientation in order to understand the ways in which primitive peoples made use of the plant materials. Accuracy and attentiveness to details are also requisites for this task, which will take three or four years to complete. No systematic herbarium search of this magnitude has ever been carried out anywhere before. It is hoped that this project will serve as a pilot study and that eventually all of the major herbaria will be included, with the data acquired assembled in some central location for correlation on IBM equipment.

Why should this be done—aside from the facts that it has never been done before and that, at last, there is a qualified scientist willing to do it?

Ancient literature is being read and re-read in the hope of finding clues to new sources of drugs. But the information on herbarium sheets has been largely overlooked, and seldom has it been published. Yet it is an excellent source because the notes made by the botanists are first-hand and scientifically accurate, and there is a specimen of the plant attached, with all the pertinent botanical data so that new collections can be made. In addition, these notes may provide the only clue to the materia medica of extinct peoples.

So far, Dr. von Reis has notes on 3,700 species and she estimates that possibly 10 per cent of these may have some value in medicine. The National Institute of Mental Health is now supporting her project and that of Dean Heber W. Youngken, Jr., who is evaluating her drug plant leads in his laboratory at the University of Rhode Island College of Pharmacy.

Several plant explorers mentioned that Dr. von Reis's summary of the ways in which medicinal plants are used by natives is the first to be based on such extensive research, and that it seems to follow the pattern they noticed in making their collections in the field. This breakdown of information is in itself an important contribution. She has found that primitive peoples use drug plants as follows: out of a hundred species, about eighteen would be used for ailments of the digestive tract; about sixteen for relief from pain; about eleven for the treatment of cuts and wounds; another eleven for specific illnesses; nine for pulmonary diseases; eight for skin problems; six for fevers; another six for circulatory difficulties; five for irregularities of the female reproductive system; and the remainder for a variety of ailments.

Special notations were made on the ritualistic, magical, or religious uses of plants with stimulating, narcotic, or poisonous effects. Another category consisted of plants that attract or repel animals, since this might give a clue to chemical activity.

About 32 per cent of the native medicines were made from leaves. Of the rest, 26 per cent came from bark, 19 per cent from roots, 7 per cent from fruits, another 7 per cent from sap or latex, 5 per cent from stems, and 4 per cent from flowers. On the basis of the data given, 83 per cent of these folk medicines are mixtures or infusions and 17 per cent consist of plant parts employed directly. About 64 per cent of the substances are taken internally and 36 per cent are applied externally.

"I really enjoy bringing all this information together in more readily available form," she told me. "It is a way of furthering work already done, because each herbarium represents a great deal of field exploration, time, and money. We should make use of the materials resulting from such investments. We never know when we might run into a cure for cancer or heart disease or mental illness."

As for the closeted atmosphere in which she works alone each day, it may sound paradoxical but Dr. von Reis said,

"I'm not really alone and I'm having some wonderful adventures: this is the way I prefer to make my rain forest expeditions. Working with such constant reminders of the essential ephemeralness of flowers and men and of the limited earth over which they seasonally pass, one cannot help developing an increased awareness that one is a part of it all, not only in the herbarium, but vitally in the world at large."

Kitchen Midden Housekeeping

What were the first drug plants used by prehistoric men? Histories of medicine usually dismiss this question with a variation of the phrase, "This knowledge is lost in the mists of antiquity." Or they fall back upon Sir William Osler's 1895 observation, "The desire to take medicine is one feature which distinguishes man, the animal, from his fellow creatures," following this up with a discussion of sorcery and magic. They do not begin to name specific plants until they reach the period of recorded history, about 5,000 years ago.

According to the potassium-argon form of dating, Zinjanthropus, an early form of man, lived in East Africa 1,750,000 years ago. New techniques of X-ray examination prove that ancient people suffered from many afflictions that plague mankind today. Even dinosaurs are being diagnosed by paleopathologists, who shed new light on old diseases. Bacteria have been brought back to life after being sealed in Siberian salt deposits for 650,000,000 years; when they were injected into mice, the animals died of a generalized bacterial infection within twelve hours. Seeds of the opium poppy were discovered in Swiss Lake Dweller sites, and stoneseed, *Lithospermum ruderale,* was abundant at the ancient Lodaiska site near Denver. This plant, still used by American Indians for fertility control, is currently being investigated by pharmaceutical companies.

Many scientists interviewed made "educated guesses" that

cave dwellers used direct-action drugs such as purgatives and emetics. Cave men probably discovered that when they were bleeding, certain leaves (containing tannin) would stanch the flow of blood. A number of scientists agreed that alcohol from fermented fruit juices might well have been the first painkiller.

But I still sought a specialist in the botanical field who was actually working with prehistoric medicinals, and such persons, I knew, were very few. Dr. Margaret A. Towle, a research fellow in the Harvard Botanical Museum, is one of them. She is first of all an economic botanist with a doctorate in anthropology, but her specialty is paleoethnobotany.

The day I visited her, she was busy with housekeeping chores in her office down the hall from Dr. Schultes and around the corner from the Peabody Museum. A gracious woman with a charming Southern accent, she might well have been fixing dainty tea sandwiches or canapés for the freezer as she worked with aluminum foil and plastic wrap. Actually, she was storing away bits of vegetation excavated from archeological sites in the Central Andes.

"These specimens may be several thousand years old, but the mice and insects that plague museums find them especially delicious," she said with a smile, as she put some tiny ears of prehistoric corn scarcely an inch long into small, glass fruit jars. She went on to explain that some of her treasures came from the Temple of the Sun at Pachacamac, twenty miles south of Lima in Peru. Because this strip of the coastline is very arid, leaves and roots and seeds and other perishables simply do not perish, but remain in millennia-deep refuse heaps (kitchen middens) to give us a surprisingly full account of life in prehistoric times.

In the Foreword to Dr. Towle's book *The Ethnobotany of Pre-Columbian Peru,* published in 1961, the comment is made that there were so many peanut shells scattered around the dig at Pachacamac that it looked like the main entrance to

Yankee Stadium after a Saturday game. The litterbugs were not contemporary workmen, but Peruvians who lived at least 500 years before the Incas. The lack of rainfall in the area makes it possible to identify accurately the genus and species of many intact plants which elsewhere would have vanished in a season.

There is something very touching about a little bracelet of seeds buried with a baby to ward off illness in the other world or a bag of coca leaves packed in a mummy bundle to insure freedom from care. Anthropologists and paleontologists have disproved the theory that our ancestors invariably were a ruthless group who abandoned the old and sick and weak. Their burial mounds show many indications of tenderness, and, thanks to these expressions of human concern, scientist-detectives like Dr. Towle have valuable clues.

"As a woman," she said, "I find the curative element in my work very satisfying. No matter how professional or in what a masculine field, I think we tend to be drawn to nurturing and treating." I asked how primitive women managed to care for themselves and their new babies without our modern necessities. She said that they turned to the vegetable kingdom, using kapok from Ceiba trees, milkweed floss, and absorbent mosses. "Young mothers today may think that the diaper service is preferable to disposable Sphagnum moss, but really, is it?" she asked. Having done field work among Indian tribes, she cited many such ingenious applications of nature's bounty.

It is difficult to separate the earliest use of plants as foods, as medicines, and as magical charms, she pointed out. But she has found that the ancient Peruvians definitely cultivated *Erythroxylon coca,* for instance, from which we now obtain cocaine, so valuable in eye surgery. Some of the old Inca coca plantations are still in use. "It is interesting," she said, "that the strange properties possessed by the leaves were attributed to divine origin, and coca was therefore restricted to the ruling class. After the Spaniards destroyed the Inca society, the use of coca spread to the common people."

The ceramic jugs of this region are especially rich in their representation of specific plants; also, some of them are fashioned to resemble the faces of coca chewers with a wad of leaves packed into one cheek. It is from such artifacts, cave paintings, and vegetal remains that scientists are slowly reconstructing the medicinal practices of prehistoric cultures.

In some cases the "educated guesses" are being confirmed: the ancient Peruvians used the pulverized seeds of a woody vine, *Mucuna elliptica,* as a purgative; the seeds and bark of *Andira inermis,* a tree, as a vermifuge and emetic; and the seeds of *Aniba Puchary-minor* for dysentery. The first two plants belong to the pulse family, the last one to the laurels. Other drugs were obtained from the peppers and nightshades.

In this work there is always the exciting possibility of turning up a lost remedy of great importance. Man has been around—and ailing—for a long, long time. One estimate says that some 77,000,000,000 persons have come and gone in the past 600,000 years. Did some good uses for botanicals disappear with them? Quite likely. But Dr. Margaret Towle and a few other scientific sleuths are on their trail.

The ABCDEtc. Approach

*A*nthropologists, *b*otanists, *c*hemists, *d*irectors of research, *e*xplorers—all these and a dozen other disciplines or specialties are involved in a co-ordinated effort which is the brain-child of a young pharmacologist at the National Institute of Mental Health. Dr. George J. Cosmides works at the Psychopharmacology Service Center, where the emphasis is on drugs used in mental disease. But a few years ago he became very concerned about certain problems in natural-product research of all kinds.

He felt that something should be done about the wasteful duplication of effort, the lack of communication between the various specialists involved, and the growing dissatisfaction with results of many botanical drug projects. There is no large, formal program at the National Institutes of Health devoted specifically to this field; rather, it is a case of individual scientists or isolated groups working here and there within the various agencies. The plant-screening systems set up in the Heart and Cancer Institutes, for instance, have their own well-defined goals, their own special problems to solve.

What was needed, and badly needed, was a good hard look at the over-all picture. Dr. Cosmides interested his superiors in calling a conference in May, 1961, at which these matters could be discussed informally by experts from all over the country. He well knew that sparks might fly as drug company representatives pointed out the deficiencies in the botanical-collecting techniques of, say, behavioral scientists. And anthropologists might complain that teams of efficient pharmacognosists working in an unspoiled primitive village would destroy cultural patterns. Despite these calculated risks, politely warring factions were invited to the meeting.

It has for some time been apparent to those involved in the botanical boom that all is not coming up Rauwolfia. For example, the lead paragraphs in a good many newspaper and magazine articles on this subject have dealt with a major drug company's expenditure of hundreds of thousands of dollars on a botanical exploration and screening program. It always reads like a big success story. At least one university, a number of botanists, missionaries, and witch doctors were involved. The outcome? Hundreds of plants were collected over a period of years and yet, according to the company's top executive, who opened a confidential file to prove his point, "We obtained not a single botanical worth more than preliminary testing." He added, philosophically, "It's all in the game, though. Millions of dollars are spent on synthetic compounds that don't prove useful either." Still, it was obvious that this firm is not likely to favor this method of investigation soon again, nor are the reputations of the professionals involved enhanced by having their monumental labors classed as failures.

On the very day that these field men returned from their lengthy collection trip abroad, they kindly granted me an interview. Their hopes were high, despite the fact that they had suffered all the usual discomforts and illnesses. They felt that they had done a good job, and certainly they were highly qualified. How sad to learn a year or so later that it all had come to naught. Those who arranged the program say now that the laboratory screening system was "full of holes." They believe that excellent new drug leads have been overlooked. Both sides are disappointed and patients will get no medications, which, after all, was the prime objective for all concerned.

A transcript of the NIMH meeting at which Cosmides presided as chairman shows that this is by no means an isolated instance. But more to the point, the reasons behind such misunderstandings and failures were examined and plans were made for circumventing them in the future. The aim of this preliminary session was to explore a "cross-cultural, interdisciplinary approach to drug plant research," but instead of this official tongue-twister it seemed simpler here to call this the A.B.C.D.Etc. method. Present at the meeting were a number of men and women mentioned in this book, among them Ethnobotanist Schultes of Harvard and Chemist Raffauf of Smith, Kline & French. Anthropologists, psychologists, physicians, psychiatrists, sociologists, pharmacologists, and pharmacognosists rounded out the roster.

Dr. Raffauf, the only industry representative invited, gave a very detailed statement of what his company requires from botanical collectors: adequate documentation of the source, above all. This means that the family, genus, and species of the plant must be confirmed and the location of the herbarium making the confirmation given. The company wants to know the plant number and the name of the botanist who classified it. The collector should make a note of the season, the state of the plant's development, and the nature of the soil and climate. Vague comments about local usage, such as "They say it's good for pain," are of little value, in his opinion, and giving only the native name for the plant is worthless.

It was stressed by several that methods for the proper preservation of plants collected be defined since certain adverse conditions could easily destroy drug properties. Yeasts, bacteria, and molds all secrete enzymes that alter constituents. High temperatures are especially disastrous. Acids, alkalis, water, and sunlight all cause decomposition. As with corn on the cob, there are actual chemical changes which come with standing. Housewives know that they must blanch and freeze their garden produce immediately to preserve its color, flavor, and nutritional ingredients; the same is true with drug plants. Ideally they should be freeze-dried immediately—but the conference members did not come up with a practical way to do this in the jungle.

Even with perfectly preserved and identified botanicals, there are other problems that make test results inaccurate. Professor Norman R. Farnsworth of the Pittsburgh College of Pharmacy reported such an instance. Tiny bits of metal from a grinder became mixed with plant material being ground and affected certain active substances in the botanicals. Professor Maynard W. Quimby of the Massachusetts College of Pharmacy suggested that plants should be tested with all their constituents in one extract first, because one of the active principles might augment another, acting as a synergist. Conversely, however, opposite acting substances in the same plant could counteract each other and an essentially negative effect could be noted. Also, chemists can seldom be absolutely positive that they have isolated all of the constituents; someone is sure to come up with another fraction. And biological screening results themselves are extremely hard to evaluate: What an extract does to a fairly large, healthy animal is not the same effect one might obtain, for instance, with a small, sick human baby.

In view of all this, the wonder is that we have had any success at all—but we have, of course, as Part II of this book will demonstrate. Especially heartening are the various steps being taken to improve the training of future drug plant experts. For instance, the October 7, 1963, issue of *Chemical and Engineering News* described a unique program at the University of Connecticut in Storrs, which integrates the disciplines of chemistry, botany, and pharmacognosy. Five Ph.D's have been granted, so far, to students who majored in one of the fields and obtained extensive research experience in the other two areas. The NIMH has awarded a grant to help support this training program, which is directed by Dr. James M. Bobbitt of the chemistry department. Working closely with him are Dr. Ralph F. Collins of the botany department, and Dr. Arthur E. Schwarting and his colleagues at the school of pharmacy. Dr. Schwarting, who, in addition to teaching, edits *Lloydia,* a quarterly journal of pharmocognosy, said that graduates trained in this program will not only know where a drug fits into the botanical scheme of things, but will also know how to isolate plant and drug constituents and will be able to characterize them chemically. Other educational advances have been reported at meetings of the American Association of Colleges of Pharmacy and in such periodicals as the *American Journal of Pharmaceutical Education.* (Pharmacognosy, by the way, is far from being an overcrowded field. A 1962–63 analysis of graduate programs showed that thirty-nine universities in the United States and Canada offered at least a master's degree in the specialty, but fewer than fifty students were enrolled in the advanced courses.)

However, such conferences as that held at the NIMH have stimulated interest in many circles and there have been some practical results. The first expedition to be sent into the field under the program co-ordinated by Dr. Cosmides went to Nigeria in 1962. Dr. Quimby, who was in charge, was following up botanical leads on almost fifty different crude drugs supplied by an anthropologist, Dr. Stanley Diamond, who spent a year studying the customs of the tribes there. He had observed the natives using these botanicals to treat gonorrhea, relieve stomach disorders, and reduce pain, among other things. Two methods of preparation were predominant: boiling and pulverization. The bark of a thorny shrub, *Dichrostachys nutans,* for instance, was pounded to a powder, mixed with porridge, and eaten for the purpose of increasing fertility.

Performing the taxonomic studies and preliminary phytochemical screening in the new laboratories at the Massachusetts College of Pharmacy, was Miss Georgia J. Persinos, an attractive brunette in her early twenties. She began the work in the fall of 1960 under Quimby's direction, following the completion of her undergraduate work and registration as a pharmacist. Today, with a master's degree earned as a result of this research, she is concentrating on the most promising specimens of leaves, stems, roots and barks, while working towards her doctorate. An exceptionally bright Nigerian boy of sixteen was trained to collect, preserve, and ship additional material as needed.

When Quimby returned from collecting and pressing voucher specimens in the field, he had well over one hundred native drug plants packed in five cardboard cartons. Chemical screening is being carried on and extracts for pharmacological use are being prepared and preliminary tests are being carried out. While in Africa, he found the native tribesmen, chieftans and witchdoctors "unfailingly cooperative." Also involved in this pharmacognostical "farmer in the dell" were a

Canadian physician and a number of missionaries and government people. If all of this does not bring a new pill to a patient, it will not be because the various disciplines did not do their jobs expertly. It just might happen that the active ingredients are already well known from other sources, or that there are better drugs to treat the same conditions. Sometimes that's the way it is and it is no one's fault. But there may well be a happy ending this time. Preliminary results seem most promising.

Once a weary and possibly discouraged young pharmacognosist scribbled a memo to himself, a memo forgotten among his field notes until I chanced upon it:

"I wonder what's around the bend?
         said the explorer.
I wonder what that plant is?
         said the collector.
I wonder what's in it?
         said the chemist.
I wonder what activity it has?
         said the pharmacologist.
I wonder if it will work in this case?
         said the physician.

I hope she lives!
         said the father.
Please, God!
         said the mother.

I think she'll be all right in the morning,
         said the nurse."

2
Biographies of Botanicals

INTRODUCTION

ONE STARTS A BIOGRAPHY AT THE BEGINNING, BUT where is that? In these life stories of some of the oldest drugs known, legends involving animals play a part. Man was supposed to have learned of a plant's miraculous effects by watching a sick mountain lion or a mongoose! Perhaps not so far-fetched because naturalists say that wild creatures have an instinctive hunger for the substances their bodies require; even domesticated animals will seek grasses and leaves of one sort or another to ease distress. We civilized beings may no longer be receiving nature's messages in this vital area. But no authority I interviewed would go on record as saying that he could document the use of a specific drug plant by an animal for a specific condition.

Anthropologist Margaret Mead of the American Museum of Natural History told me that primates will protect their mates and young by fighting, but, in her opinion, the chief thing that separates men from beasts is the desire to nurture others—to gather food and medicinals for other than their own young. An animal collector for a research institution described seeing monkeys in India pulling splinters and making what he concluded were leaf poultices for wounds. An African game keeper wrote that certain baboons served as "healers" to others in their group. Psychologist Harry Harlow of the University of Wisconsin's famous studies on monkey-mothering said that he had heard of this, too, but had not observed it himself. On the other hand, the noted authority on apes, Dr. G. E. Erickson of Harvard Medical School, commented: "For what it is worth, I would judge it extremely unlikely that man learned anything from animals in regard to the use of drug plants."

Because the animal legends are amusing, I have included a few of them, along with some old time herbal recipes, however inadequate they may be when judged by modern standards. Research in this area was a delightful experience, (and shall be a life-long avocation) but my assignment was to report on the uses modern science is making of age-old botanical remedies. The question constantly arose: What is a true drug plant? The banana, for instance, is one of the oldest known fruits and perhaps the first to be cultivated. It has served as a specific treatment for celiac disease since the 1920's, and it is prescribed as a dietary adjunct in cases of typhoid, colitis, and other disorders. It is said to have antifungal factors and antibacterial fractions, as well. Papayas and pineapples may not seem to be medicinal plants, but they provide proteolytic enzymes that are used in a host of new pharmaceuticals designed to reduce inflammation, bruising, and swelling. Their action also intensifies that of antibiotics.

Current research is turning up medicinal properties in everything from lettuce, used by the ancients as a sedative, to apples and onions. A quick sampling to indicate the scope of these investigations shows that: compounds from daffodils may prove effective in treating myasthenia gravis and multiple sclerosis; a neuroactive factor in the perennial sweet pea is now being tested on animals; an extract from lady slipper has been found to exert an effect on high blood pressure; derivatives from the common snowdrop relieve some glaucoma patients not responding to other medication; buttercup juice stops the growth of strep, staph, pneumococci, anthrax, and tuberculosis germs, and that of quivering anemones has similar bactericidal qualities. Research at the United States Department of Agriculture, in England, and elsewhere has proved that antibiotic properties exist in so many plants that it would take many pages just to list their names. New drugs may come not only from rare jungle vegetation but also from the commonest field and garden flowers and everyday foods. We may have the starting materials for tomorrow's wonder drugs growing in our windowboxes!

In writing a book, one must be selective—in this case a painful process in the face of so much rich material. Part 2 begins with a drug, quinine, which has been largely replaced by synthetics in most parts of the world, but its biography contains the essence of the histories of pharmacy and medicine. A roster of the earliest pharmacognosists would include such men as Alexander the Great, who collected curious plant specimens; Marco Polo, who examined the herb garden of Kubla Khan; the Crusaders, who salvaged Arabic botanical lore; Columbus; Vasco da Gama—in fact, all those explorers who searched for spices, and medicinals of times gone by. Pioneers of the Pacific Northwest found Indians using bark, which we know as cascara. In 1753, British naval surgeon James Lind began prescribing citrus juices for his nation's sailors who were, from that day forward, to hear the nickname "Limey" in all their ports of call. Lind didn't know about vitamin C, but he had a horror of scurvy and he found a way to reduce its dreadful toll; as did the Indians in Canada, who used evergreen twigs; old wives in Europe, who relied on rose hips and black currants; and West Indians, who swore by a native cherry—all rich sources of the vital vitamin.

Strange are the ways in which drugs are discovered. It was a dead cow, for example, that opened up a new field of therapy when a farmer appealed to University of Wisconsin researchers for help. They found that animals in his herd had died of internal hemorrhaging after eating spoiled clover. The clover was analyzed and a chemical was extracted and later synthesized. Today, Dicumarol is an anticoagulant medicine for patients susceptible to clots forming in blood vessels.

When Egypt's Queen Hatshepsut sent her plant hunters on the first recorded botanical drug search some 3,500 years ago, she really started something. The end is not yet in sight.

The Incredible History of Quinine

Malaria

THE NATURAL DRUG QUININE, AN ALKALOID EXTRACT-
ed from the bark of the Cinchona tree native to South America,
was the first effective treatment for malaria, the leading killer
among infectious diseases since the dawn of history. Introduced into Europe in the 1640's, quinine remained until a
few years ago the only valid treatment for this scourge which
altered the course of world history, as kings, popes, and military leaders were struck down in their prime.

Sir Ronald Ross, the Englishman who proved in 1897 that
mosquitoes carry the disease, wrote: "Malarial fever is important not only because of the misery it inflicts upon mankind, but also because of the serious opposition it has always
given to the march of civilization. . . . No wild deserts, no
savage races, no geographical difficulties have proved so in-
imical to civilization as this disease."

Have modern chemicals finally conquered this ancient foe?
By no means. United States government doctors report that
new drug-resistant strains of malaria parasites have appeared
in South America and Southeast Asia within the past few
years and may well exist in other areas, threatening to break

the limited control attributed to synthetics. Compounding the danger is the increasing resistance of mosquitoes to the widespread use of insecticides. Health officials are extremely concerned about these ominous discoveries.

Colonel William D. Tigertt, director of the Walter Reed Army Institute of Research, said, "The new strains present one of the most important medical problems in the whole field of infectious diseases. . . . We thought we had malaria under control by the drugs in World War II and here, twenty years later, we again face this problem."

The extent of the menace is staggering. The World Health Organization of the United Nations estimates that more than one-third of the world's population is constantly threatened by the disease. Annual death tolls reach 2,000,000; another 200,000,000 chronic sufferers are only half alive.

But it is difficult, emotionally, to think in terms of millions of casualties and vast regions made uninhabitable by a single disease. What is it like to be just one human being with a case of untreated malaria? At the start there is muscle soreness and backache. Cold chills begin to play up and down the spine, gooseflesh appears, teeth chatter, and limbs shake uncontrollably. Next come violent vomiting, burning delirium, agonizing head pains, and a great thirst. The fever breaks at last in a drenching sweat, leaving exhaustion and depression in its wake.

Is this not torture enough? For malaria, it is not. Relentlessly, seizures return again and again on a schedule prescribed by the infecting parasite's own life cycle. Man learned early to distinguish between continuous fever, as in typhoid, and the intermittent pattern of swamp fever, or ague, as malaria was called, from the Latin *acutus,* meaning sharp. Hippocrates described the different forms of the disease, and the terms he used 2,000 years ago still stand today: the tertians bring acute attacks, or paroxysms, every third day; the quartans, every fourth; and the quotidians, every day, being a mixed infection.

Repeated chills-fevers-sweats, in that order, together with an enlarged spleen, or "ague cake," are basic diagnostic signs. But malaria has many masks: children may suffer from convulsions; some victims appear to be mentally ill, with hallucinations and maniacal excitement; in others, sudden death resembling apoplexy results from the clogging of brain capillaries. Because it is a bloodstream infection involving most of the body's organs, malaria can imitate almost any disease. But today, thanks to Dr. Alphonse Laveran, the young French surgeon who found *Plasmodium malariae* in the blood of dying Algerian troops, the disease may be correctly identified by laboratory tests. Before this parasite was discovered in 1880, the cause of the affliction was nameless, mysterious, and terrifying.

Some scientists believe that malaria's one-celled organism was one of the earliest efforts in the scale of evolution and that it was waiting for the appearance of reptiles, birds, and monkeys, which still suffer from forms of malaria similar to the human variety. Primitive man, contracting the disease and seeing no wounds to cause the illness, must have thought it due to the wrath of avenging gods. Did it not strike down the strongest of men, as well as babes in arms? Did it not capriciously wipe out whole settlements near stagnant ponds while sparing those on higher ground nearby? This was no ordinary pestilence passed from one sick person to another. How could one combat such an enemy?

Thousands of years were spent in fruitless speculation and on worthless treatment. From cave paintings and fossil remains, we know that skulls were opened in trephining operations as early as the Neolithic period, possibly with the idea of letting headache "demons" escape. Healthy fingers were amputated as sacrifices to evil spirits. Blood-letting was the medical treatment of choice for malaria well into the nineteenth century. As families congregated and became tribes, medicine men with their roots and herbs attempted to treat symptoms, as well as placate the All-Powerful One. And we can presume—after observing today's aborigines—that as soon as the chill passed and the fever set in, malaria sufferers from time immemorial stretched their pain-wracked bodies on the cool ground or dragged themselves to icy streams, praying for relief from what the Bible calls "the burning ague that shall consume the eyes."

The ancient Chinese blamed three devils: one with a hammer, one with a bucket of water, the third with a stove. Around 2700 B.C. Emperor Shên Nung prescribed the vegetable drug *Ch'ang Shan* in his *Book of Herbs*. (This hydrangea was tested by Western scientists in the 1940's and found to contain antimalarial properties, but it cannot be obtained today outside of Red China.) But the long list of plant remedies from folklore provides no rival for quinine; by modern medical standards they are considered useless. Even so, what hopes must have been vested in them by countless mothers nursing fast-failing loved ones in times gone by. For instance, there was feverfew, the name a corruption of the word febrifuge, meaning that which drives away fever. We know it as bachelor's-button, *Chrysanthemum parthenium*. Richard Banckes considered it indispensable, writing in his *Herbal* of 1525: "Good to assuage the access [ague], quotidian, or cramp." Other trusted remedies were ague grass, *Aletris farinosa,* and agueweed, *Eupatorium perfoliatum*. One ague prescription called for "Three drops of blood from the ear of a cat, in wine. Must be administered by a lady of high birth."

While old wives concocted these potions, doctors were purging and bleeding at the first sign of the disease. If this didn't work, they repurged and re-bled in an effort to restore a proper balance of solids and liquids in the body. Considering that malaria parasites destroy the iron-containing material in red blood cells, causing anemia and prostration, this "therapy" served only to hasten the end. The poor country folk, who had to get along without physicians, probably fared much better with their innocuous herb teas. If they were going to die, they did so in their own good time, at least.

It was blind faith in Galen, a Greek physician who practiced in Rome about 164 A.D., that caused the medical profession to persist in using these, to us, irrational methods. Galen's system incorporated the earlier ideas of Hippocrates and the ancient theory that all matter is composed of four elements: earth, air, fire, and water. Diseases were thought to be caused by an imbalance of the four humors: blood, phlegm, black bile, and yellow bile. Fever was a bile-caused disorder, and the only hope for a cure lay in bleeding or purging or both. Through the influence of his more than 500 books, Galen succeeded in stifling the scientific investigation of the real nature of diseases for about 1,500 years.

In the case of malaria this was particularly unfortunate because about fifty years after Galen, the Roman scholar Marcus Terentius Varro hinted at the source of infection when he wrote, "Marshes produce small creatures invisible to the eye which fill the air, enter the nose and mouth, and cause loathesome diseases." Later, in the time of Nero, the noted agriculturist Collumella warned that marshes "breed animalcules armed with stings which fly upon us in exceedingly thick swarms and from which are contracted diseases, the causes of which even physicians are unable to understand." Because these ideas did not fit in with Galen's system, it was almost the twentieth century before anything was done about the mosquito menace.

The early Romans did set up a system of swamp drainage, though, because they believed that poisonous vapors arose from stagnant water. This was the beginning of the miasma theory that was popular until just a generation or so ago. An early edition of the *Encyclopaedia Britannica* states: "Attempts have been made, without success, to separate malarious poison from the gases generated by swamps or from the air of malarious localities." An 1890 dictionary contained these "facts": "Malaria: From the Italian, *mala aria,* meaning bad air; specifically, the disease produced by air impregnated with the poisons causing intermittent fever." Dr. Daniel Drake, the pioneer Kentucky physician, attributed the prevalence of shaking fevers to decomposing vegetation under and around dwellings. Night air was considered bad for the health and families were warned to keep doors and windows tightly closed while they slept. Since malaria is transmitted by the genus Anopheles, a mosquito that usually feeds at night or in the early morning hours, the practice probably prevented some infection. The good doctor was right, but for the wrong reason.

The first man seriously to doubt the miasma theory was Dr. John Crawford, a Baltimore physician. In 1807 he published his ideas on the origins of fevers, saying, "Malaria must be occasioned by eggs insinuated without our knowledge into our bodies." This was considered such a wild notion that his patients left him. During the 1840's and 1850's, a French naturalist, an Alabama surgeon, and others argued that mosquitoes, not miasmas, were to blame for malaria, but they lacked experimental proof. In 1882, Dr. Albert Freeman Africanus King, a Washington, D.C., obstetrician, gave the Philosophical Society nineteen well-documented reasons for believing that malaria was transmitted by mosquitoes breeding in the slimy marshes of the Potomac flats. When he suggested that the city could be kept free of this menace if screen-wire as high as the Washington monument encircled it, his audience went away thinking him either a humorist or a crackpot.

Fascinating as the folklore of malaria is, there is a tale to be told about the fever-bark tree itself . . . of courageous explorer-naturalists, antagonistic religious sects, rivalries between nations, commercial greed, and international monopolies. No other drug can rival quinine, because it was *the* entering wedge that brought about the end of Galenism. Cinchona bark, when it entered the materia medica, became the first "specific"—an effective treatment for a given disease, instead of the usual witch's brew containing dozens of useless ingredients.

"A tree grows which they call the fever tree in the country of Loxa [now Loja], whose bark is the color of cinnamon. When made into a powder amounting to the weight of two small silver coins and given as a beverage, it cures the fevers and tertians. It has produced miraculous cures in Lima." So wrote Father Calancha in the *Chronicle of St. Augustine,* around 1633 in South America. This simple message announced that at last a treatment had been found, in what is now Ecuador, for the world's most widespread and devastating disease. As to how the good father learned about the remedy, there is a choice of legends. One begins with a violent storm. Fallen trees lay in a pool of water, making it so bitter that nearby villagers refused to drink it. However, a stranger passing through, being seized with a burning fever and finding no other water, was forced to drink it and he was cured. He afterward prevailed upon his friends who were ill of fevers to travel some distance to obtain this great remedy. (It is true that cold water in which Cinchona bark has been soaking will acquire a bitter taste.)

Another version maintains that the Jesuits, who sometimes chewed the barks of trees in order to differentiate between them, were curious about the extreme bitterness and discovered the medicinal properties in the course of their experimentation. And still another says that a marooned pirate ship's surgeon watched ailing mountain lions seek out this particular tree and chew its bark. The most famous story of all concerns the Countess of Chinchon, beloved young wife of the Viceroy of Peru. It seems that in 1638 she fell ill of a fever so virulent that the court physicians were unable to relieve her suffering. Word of her illness finally reached the Governor of Loja, who sent her a packet of *quinaquina,* the "bark of barks." (The repetition of the plant's name in the Quechuan Indian language indicates medicinal properties.) Promptly recovering, she returned to Spain, where she generously distributed the cure to all who had need of it, and thus it became known as the Contessa's Powder.

There is only one thing wrong with this oft-quoted tale— not a word of it is true, although it has long been a standard introduction to nearly every discussion of quinine in medical texts. In 1941, a report by Dr. W. A. Haggis in the *Bulletin of the History of Medicine* proved that the first Countess of Chinchon died in Spain three years before her husband was appointed Viceroy. The second Countess, according to a very detailed diary discovered in 1930, remained quite healthy until she died in Colombia, without ever returning to Spain. Yet her memory lives on, for when it became necessary in 1742 for the Swedish botanist Carolus Linnaeus (Karl von Linné) to give the fever-bark tree a scientific designation, he called it Cinchona, remembering the Countess of Chinchon but misspelling her name.

Medical historians still cannot agree on whether malaria existed in the New World before Columbus. Some are convinced that the Europeans brought it with them from pestilential cities like Rome and Seville. Others say that Negro slaves were carriers of especially virulent African strains to which they had grown immune, but which wiped out entire settlements in this hemisphere. A few authorities on prehistoric migrations believe that malaria was brought to the Americas by the first Asians to cross the Bering Straits.

One often reads that the Indians did not use Cinchona bark in the treatment of fevers, either because they did not know its value or because they did not suffer from malaria. In *The Conquest of Malaria,* published in 1950, the late Dr. Jaime Jaramillo-Arango, historian, statesman, and former Rector of the National Faculty of Medicine in Bogotá, stated his conviction that the Indians were well aware of the fever bark's curative powers long before the Spaniards arrived. He felt that they merely pretended ignorance in the hope that the conquerors would be killed off by the disease. But, was the fever bark restricted to the use of the Inca royal family? Did only the court physicians know about it? Or was it the carefully guarded secret of a few tribes that were wiped out during the conquest? The answers await further investigation.

We do know this: Catholic missionaries, living close to the people in the remoter portions of the Spanish colonial realm, first observed the astonishing fact that the ague could be treated with fever bark far more effectively than by bleeding the sufferers white in the hallowed name of Galen. That Indian therapies made other ingenious uses of nature's bounty is clear from just one padre's account. He wrote, "From a single plant [not identified] they use: an infusion of leaves for skin disorders; the fresh milky juice of the stems for eye ailments; the dried milky juice for wound plasters and as fillings for cavities in teeth; the resin diluted in water as a laxative; and the dry resin in suppository form for ridding the patient of intestinal parasites. Further, an infusion of the bark is good for reducing swollen legs, and, finally, a branch of the plant . . . is used to clean the teeth."

Pizarro's soldiers are supposed to have preferred the local herb doctors to their own lancet-happy surgeons. At any rate, within sixty years of the discovery of America, Spanish galleons left the New World loaded with balsams of Peru and Tolú, sarsaparilla, and coca leaves containing cocaine, thus starting a brisk trade in crude drugs that continues to this day. This commerce stimulated an interest in natural history throughout Europe. Botanical gardens were started, and in 1568 Nicholas Monardes, a Seville physician, wrote a book about South American plants, referring to these marvels, in the title, as *Joyfull Newes out of the New-Found Worlde*. By 1588 the first natural history of the South American continent had appeared.

In view of all this, it is strange that no immediate effort was made to ship the fever bark—so highly praised by Father Calancha in 1633—back to Europe. In 1643 it was mentioned in the medical literature by a Belgian, but the bark itself did not arrive until around 1645, when it is believed that Father Bartolome Tafur brought some with him to a religious conclave in Rome, one of the most malarial spots in the world. Soon the Jesuits in South America were regularly shipping the botanical to the Holy City. In an early conservation effort, they taught the Indians to plant five new trees in the shape of a cross for every one destroyed in the harvest. Religious pilgrims began to leave Rome with packets of what was now called Jesuit's bark, and knowledge of its curative powers quickly spread through Spain, France, and Italy, although medical men continued to ignore it.

In 1649, Cardinal John de Lugo thought it incredible that doctors had never tested the wonderful Peruvian bark, so he asked the physician of Pope Innocent X to give him a full report. The results were most gratifying. The bark was not only non-toxic; it was the most effective treatment ever tried on the Roman fevers! The Cardinal, although in his seventies and weakened by many bouts with malaria, set about distributing quantities of the remedy to all who needed it. He attached to all samples of the bark a leaflet, printed in Latin and referred to ever afterwards as the "Schedula Romana." It read: "This bark is imported from the Kingdom of Peru and is called china febris. It is used against quartan and tertian fevers accompanied by shivers, as follows: two drams of finely ground and sifted bark mixed in a glass of strong white wine three hours before fever is due. When first symptoms are noted, patient is made to drink the whole infusion thus prepared and is put to bed. In the event of tertian fevers, bark can be administered as stated above when fever has persisted for many days. Constant use of this remedy has cured practically all of the patients who have taken it, having at first well cleared the bowels. For four days after, no other medication whatsoever must be taken. It must be used only on the advice of the physician who may consider whether it is timely to administer it."

To consult a doctor at that time would have meant a veto, so most consumers dosed themselves, found that they were helped, and then passed the good news along. For a short while it looked as though The Powder of the Most Eminent Cardinal de Lugo would be accepted, especially after the Cardinal himself went to Paris and cured the young Dauphin, later Louis XIV, of his fevers.

In the autumn of 1652, the bark was administered to Archduke Leopold of Austria by his physician, who followed the "Schedula Romana" directions. The Archduke was relieved of his symptoms, but a month later he suffered another attack because he had double quartan malaria. The recurrence enraged the Archduke and embarrassed his doctor, Joan Jacob Chiflet, who simply did not realize that it was necessary to administer another dose. This he neglected to do and the Archduke died, but not before ordering Chiflet to write a book denouncing the treatment. Called *The Exposure of the Febrifuge Powder from the American World,* Chiflet's book concluded that the bitter bark had a drying effect upon the internal organs of patients. Doctors who had begun to feel uneasy about their Galenical training now relaxed, as their prejudices were thus reinforced. There was no need for them to experiment further with the substance or to tolerate foolishness from the Vatican. Disparaging statements began to be directed more toward the sponsoring religious order than against the drug itself. Banners appeared in the streets proclaiming that the Jesuits wanted to exterminate all the Protestants in the world with their insidious bark. For the first time in the history of the papacy a Roman conclave (held in 1655) resulted in no ague deaths, but in Protestant countries the bark was virtually unobtainable because the Jesuits found the risk of bringing it in too great. Also, it had been wasted by laymen on every feverish ailment from pneumonia to plague: it had even been quilted into jacket linings.

In England, where the bark was introduced in 1654, things were literally at a fever pitch. The ague was rampant and London was described as one vast infirmary. Oliver Cromwell had become the nation's Protector and the zealous guardian of the Protestant faith. When he succumbed to the fever, it was out of the question to use The Powder of the Most Eminent Cardinal. Cromwell would be the last to allow himself to be "Jesuited to death," and so he died of malaria in 1658.

In 1670, a young apothecary's apprentice and medical student named Robert Talbor, also called Tabor or Talbot, set himself up in London as a "pyretiatro," or fever specialist. He soon thereafter brought out a book entitled *Pyretologia, or A Rational Account of the Cause and Cure of Agues,* said to be something between a salesman's pitch and a reasonably scientific report. In this book, Talbor cleverly disparaged the fever bark, saying "Beware of all palliative Cures and especially of that known by the name of Jesuit's Powder . . . for I have seen most dangerous effects follow the taking of that medicine." His own remedy consisted of two ingredients from England and two from abroad. While he would disclose nothing more, it was said to work like a charm; in no time at all he had the most fashionable practice in London. He charged fabulous fees, but did not bleed or purge his patients in the physical sense; what is more, he cured malaria.

His financial success, his unorthodox methods, his audacity —in short, everything about him—enraged the Royal College of Physicians, who tried to discredit him. Their efforts were in vain, however, for he was summoned to cure King Charles II, and did. As a reward, the ague-curer was knighted in 1678 and became Sir Robert Talbor, Physician to the King. From then on he was very busy ministering to the crowned, but feverish, heads of Europe. When Charles II learned that the only remaining son of Louis XIV was dying of fever, Sir Robert was dispatched immediately to the royal bedside. The French court physicians, expecting to expose his flimsy scientific background, asked him:

"What is a fever?"

"I do not know," he answered. "You gentlemen may explain the nature of a fever but I can cure it—which you cannot!"

He did just that. Louis XIV, forgetting that he himself had been cured long ago by the Cardinal de Lugo, thought this was the most fantastic thing he had ever witnessed. Mme. de Sévigné, delighting in the court physicians' misery, wrote, "The remedy of the Englishman makes them quite contemptible with all their bloodletting."

King Louis XIV finally paid 3,000 gold crowns for the secret of the mysterious remedy and promised not to reveal it while Talbor still lived. Further, its use was to be restricted to Talbor for ten years. When Talbor died in 1681 at the age of thirty-nine, his formula was published in the newspapers:

> 6 drachms of rose leaves
> 2 oz. of lemon juice
> A strong infusion of Peruvian bark.

It was administered in wine. Talbor slyly changed the kind of win from time to time in order to keep his patients guessing.

After his death, Talbor was almost always referred to as an ignorant quack. Quack he was, in the sense that he passed as a doctor without having the proper training, used a secret remedy, disparaged the work of others while claiming that he alone could cure, and deliberately cornered the market in fever bark, causing the price to rise from 25 to 100 francs a pound, while thousands suffered and died for want of the drug. But he was certainly not ignorant, for he knew that a mere apothecary's apprentice could never openly persuade the English to use Jesuit's bark and that secrecy was the only way to get around the prejudices of his day. Medical historians believe that without Talbor the widespread use of this medicine might have been delayed for decades or even centuries.

Dr. Thomas Sydenham, the English "Hippocrates," eventually declared that he had always regarded the drug as harmless and effective, and he took credit for having discovered the proper way of administering it—that is, repeatedly, when the attacks of malaria recur. Mr. Thomas G. Morton (like Sydenham, originally opposed to the use of the bark) had this to say: "Opposition to Peruvian bark was mainly a result of a conspiracy between physicians and apothecaries who resented the cure of a disease which had been for so long an unmixed financial blessing." Peruvian bark finally made the British Pharmacopeia and in 1696 it was introduced into Germany. In 1711 there appeared a treatise by Francesco Torti— the Italian physician who gave us the name malaria—which proved that the bark was useless for all fevers *except* malaria.

As physicians began using the botanical drug regularly and observing its effects, they were puzzled by the fact that even in malaria its action was extremely variable, though different shipments looked much alike. One reason for this undependability was greed; when suppliers could not provide the real thing, they doctored other barks with aloe juice to make them bitter and passed them off as the true Peruvian product. Because of the demand and scarcity, any bark in camouflage commanded a good price.

In North America the colonists were dependent for their bark on the luck of buccaneer doctors like Lionel Wafer, who confiscated Peruvian shipments while raiding the Spanish Main. But most malaria cases remained inadequately treated and the disease continued to plague the early settlers as they made their way West, especially along the watercourses. One pioneer doctor wrote, "Every man, woman, and child within my range shook with ague every other day. Daily life is arranged to allow for attacks."

Almost nothing was known about the origin of the bark or the type of plant it came from. It did not even have a scientific name until 1742, when Linnaeus called the tree Cinchona. Meanwhile dozens of names were used, including "China-China," erroneously thought to indicate its homeland. The English physician Dr. Gideon Harvey and others insisted a few years after Talbor's death that it was an artificially manufactured product of "those clever Jesuits." At one point in Harvey's all-out attack, he wrote: "I wish these Fathers had kept their *Indian bark* to themselves, and sure I am, hundreds would be on this side the Grave, whose bones are now turned into the first element."

Actually, the Jesuits became less and less involved with the collecting and exporting of the product; by the mid-1700's, Peruvian bark was largely the concern of the Spanish government. And yet, one hundred years after Father Calancha's announcement, no European had even reported seeing the fabulous tree, much less published the sorely needed botanical study. It was high time.

The Search for the Fever-Bark Tree

In 1735 two great and ultimately related scientific events took place: Linnaeus published his *Systema Naturae,* revealing the ordered world of botany; and a group of explorer-naturalists, on an expedition sponsored by the famed French Académie des Sciences, opened the vast botanical storehouse that is South America. They are said to have accomplished with their telescopes and sextants all that shot and shell had failed to do.

On May 16 of that year, a quiet, unassuming botanist, Joseph de Jussieu, joined the expedition aboard a man-of-war anchored in the Bay of Biscay. No one could have guessed that he was fairly bursting with ambition; he intended to be the first scientist to unlock the secrets of the fever-bark tree. His eye-witness account would, he hoped, become *the* definitive study and win him membership in the Académie.

The most dynamic member of this group of natural philosophers, as they called themselves, was Charles Marie de La Condamine, third in command. Tall, slim, every inch the aristocrat, he was nonetheless an excellent mathematician and geographer who had become an Académie member at the age of twenty-nine. His enthusiasm for the purpose of this expedition—to make certain measurements at the equator in order to determine the circumference of the earth—knew no bounds. Soon it became "La Condamine's Expedition." From the outset this caused such intense jealousy that one of the members, the gifted astronomer M. Pierre Bouguer, seemed to devote most of his time to undoing all that La Condamine accomplished. He was obsessed by the thought that La Condamine planned to keep all the glory for himself. Only affable Joseph de Jussieu seemed unconcerned.

They set sail for Cartagena (now a Colombian port) on the Caribbean, the first non-Spanish group to be allowed to travel in South America in its 250 years of recorded history. (Permission had been granted on the grounds that the equator near Quito, Ecuador, was the only such accessible spot on the face of the globe.) Cartagena, fragrant with vanilla, balsams, and acacias, overwhelmed Jussieu. He walked through groves of cacao trees; he tasted papayas, pineapples, and other fruits so full of juice they melted in his mouth; and everywhere he went, he feverishly collected specimens of plants, taking care later to preserve them properly so that they could be accurately classified. Already he was living only for the time when he could compile his Great Work.

The expedition next sailed to Portobelo on the Isthmus of Panama, the busiest port of the Spanish Main and the chief target of Hawkins, Drake, and Henry Morgan's "Boyes." Here merchants dealt in gold, silver, and emeralds with seeming abandon, and mule packs loaded with vicuña and crude drugs streamed into the market place. Jussieu was anxious to start the long boat trip down the west coast of South America, but there was a problem in crossing the Isthmus. The watchmaker who cared for La Condamine's eighteen-foot telescope, various pendulums, and octants feared that a hard day's ride "would unseat their correctness." It was finally decided to sail another fifty miles southwest to the Río Chagres, now part of the Panama Canal, and then go by canoe to Venta de Cruces. From there a six-hour mule trip would bring them to Panama City, where on another boat they could sail to the Ecuadorian coast.

They were lucky to get out of Portobelo, the pest-hole of the Americas, alive; but new dangers faced them on the Río Chagres, where the wildly flailing tails of alligators threatened to upset their canoes. After sailing to Manta, a sleepy port halfway between Guayaquil and the equator, the group broke up. Jussieu left for what is now southern Ecuador, and La Condamine and Bouguer headed north to work their way across the mountains to Quito.

For seven years these two dragged their heavy equipment up bleak 16,000-foot heights and apparently they quarreled bitterly most of the way, for La Condamine, in his many letters and Académie reports, complained of the astronomer's independent streak. This got the best of Bouguer in 1743, when he suddenly departed for France, leaving his partner, all unaware, on another mountain peak. It was two and a half months before La Condamine wearily came down the mountainside to check his measurements against those of the other man—and found that he had been working all that time in vain. Two years later he returned to France himself, deaf and partially paralyzed, but probably only too eager to settle the score with Bouguer.

Other members of this group suffered violent deaths in South America and several lost their minds, but the earth-measurements had been sent on to the Academie and technically the expedition was a success.*

After Joseph de Jussieu left La Condamine at Manta in 1736, he began having his own troubles. As he painfully hacked his way through the forest to Loja, piume flies plagued him, sauba ants and flying roaches the size of mice destroyed some of his collections, and microscopic insects, called niguas, burrowed into his toes and made nests that had to be cut out of the tissue. His feet ached as with the gout, but still he trudged on. He lived with the Indians, eating their grilled guinea pig-like agoutis and drinking their evil-smelling fermented brew, concocted from rotting plantains. If he had to sit in the torrential rains unprotected while all available covering was put over his treasures, he did not mind. He was preoccupied with his dream.

We can only imagine what his feelings were when at last he saw the tall, straight quinaquina evergreens—members of

---

* A monument was erected in 1936 at latitude 0'0'0'', high in the barren Andes about eighteen miles north of Quito, one of the most desolate spots on earth. As I read the inscription, which said, in part, "Carlos M. de Condamine, Pedro Bouger [sic] . . . 1736–1744, que Midiendo el arce del Meridiano Equatoriae dedujeron la forma de la terra," a cold, raw wind cut through my heavy clothing, although I was standing on the equator. How those men must have suffered!

the madder family, which includes coffee and gardenias—with their leaves shining in the sun and their white, pink, lavender, and red flowers, faintly fragrant. Jussieu was the first to note that there were different species, with reddish, yellow, or very light, almost white, bark. He prepared painstaking reports, not only on these botanical features, but also on the best methods of cultivation and conservation because he was shocked to find the Indians either chopping the trees down or stripping the bark so systematically from even the smallest branches, that few trees survived.

There were no endless quinaquina forests. They never grew in clumps, but always stood alone on hillsides, sometimes as close to the Andean frost line as tropical trees ever get, 10,000 feet up. They were not found in the plains below and they required abundant rainfall. The leaves on the older trees—those that were eighty feet high with trunk diameters of fourteen to sixteen inches—were fiery red. Some varieties had large leaves, some small, some smooth, some corrugated. The lilac-like flower clusters were followed by a dry fruit about half an inch long that split to release seeds very narrowly winged and so tiny that they ran about 98,000 to the ounce.

No doubt Jussieu thought this the most beautiful tree in the world; many naturalists since have said that this is so and have written enough books about it to fill a good-sized library. Of Jussieu's writings, only a few notes were ever published. A French quinine manufacturer in 1936 commemorated his first hundred years in business with an advertising brochure that included a brief description of the fever-bark tree, written originally in Latin by Jussieu in 1737. Ironically, this was the year that La Condamine made a quick trip through Loja, saw the tree more or less in passing, and dashed off a layman's description to the French Académie, where it was read the following year. He, of course, was credited with the first eyewitness report that Jussieu had so much hoped to give. But the botanist was not embittered; he simply continued his painstaking research.

After almost thirty years in the jungle, Jussieu finally was ready to take to Europe the priceless collection that many had heard about and even a few travelers had actually admired as they crossed his path. But the night before he was to sail from Buenos Aires, a servant who was hired to watch over the mysterious boxes because "they contain objects of the greatest value" disappeared into the jungle with them and they were never seen again. Jussieu suffered this tragic loss in 1761 and for the next ten years he disappeared from sight. Some say that he tried to rebuild his collection; others believe that the shock caused him to lose his mind and wander aimlessly. When he finally arrived in Paris in 1771, his relatives soon had to put him in an asylum, where he is said to have died in terrible agonies of mental suffering.

The Old World was still waiting for accurate, scientific information about the source of the malaria cure. True, Linnaeus had named the tree genus Cinchona, but he had done this believing a fanciful legend, and he had based his description on the report of La Condamine, who admittedly knew nothing about botany. Later, La Condamine tried to bring young Cinchona plants back to Europe so that they might be cultivated. He managed to keep them alive in the intense heat of a 3,000-mile trip down the Amazon, only to lose them when a giant wave washed them overboard as they were being transferred to the ship bound for Europe.

Mrs. M. L. Duran-Reynals commented in her fascinating book *The Fever Bark Tree*: "This was the first of a series of strange incidents which time and again contrived to hinder the development of the new remedy after medical opposition against the drug had at length been defeated. A new element had now come into play, so subtle and elusive that it cannot fail to suggest to the imagination . . . what one's reason is forced to repudiate. As if a malignant spell had been cast on the fever bark tree, every attempt to study it, every effort to acquaint the world with its properties, was doomed to failure and disaster. As if a curse followed those who touched the fever bark tree, Fate, availing itself of uncanny means, repeatedly threw its victims into the depths of strange misfortune and calamity, until the story of their stirring adventure reached the proportions of classical tragedy."

La Condamine and Joseph de Jussieu were only the first of these. In 1761, just about the time poor Jussieu was preparing to sail from Buenos Aires, a young medical-school graduate left Spain for the New Kingdom of Granada, now the Republic of Colombia. Dr. José Celestino Mutis had no interest in the practice of medicine. He was accepting the position of physician to the Viceroy in Bogotá as a means to an end, for he shared with Jussieu and many others a burning desire to produce an exhaustive treatise on Cinchona. So certain was he of success that he impulsively wrote to Linnaeus and promised to send him a most unusual collection in the very near future. Although the eminent botanist had never heard of young Mutis, he encouraged him, and they corresponded until Linnaeus died in 1778.

Unfortunately, Mutis found himself trapped in a fashionable practice that left little time for field trips. When he first began to search in the wilds, it was for something he had never seen; hunting Cinchonas was never easy, because their foliage, high in the forest, was hard to see from the ground, and their barks were usually quite similar to those of the trees around them. However, Mutis was finally able to make an important contribution in cinchonology: he reported that, contrary to general belief, the trees did grow north of the equator, and he sent Linnaeus dry leaves and flowers of this species, named *C. bogotensis*. This marked 1772 as the beginning of direct mass distribution of the bark from many Caribbean ports; formerly, it was either sent around Cape Horn or up to the Isthmus for trans-shipment by mule pack to the East Coast.

Mutis now wanted to found a botanical research center, but all his petitions to the King of Spain were refused. At the age of fifty, he could stand life in the court no longer, so he fled to the forest. But a new Viceroy persuaded him to return by making him chief botanist and astronomer of a provisional scientific commission. There were several assistants, among them artists who worked on illustrations in monk-like silence, reproducing the natural botanical colors exactly. A Cinchona plantation was started as the first step in a detailed conservation program. During this period, Mutis, called "the Prince of American Naturalists" by Linnaeus, accomplished a great deal: he discovered the nocturnal variation in the barometer; he co-authored a grammar of Colombian Indian languages requested by Catherine II of Russia; he obtained financial support for the construction of the first astronomical observatory in the hemisphere, and much more.

But the long years of frustration and the strain of attempting to catch up by working night and day had a telling effect upon his personality. His desire to protect the priceless information compiled, the herbarium specimens, and the illustrations kept him in a constant state of anxiety. The scientists had been working north of Bogotá in Mariquita, a town conveniently on the edge of the jungle but one where the inhabitants were a noisy lot addicted to frequent fiestas, complete with fireworks. On these occasions, Mutis could be seen perched on the roof of the building where his treasures were stored, ready with a broom to beat out flying sparks. About this time, he became increasingly involved in lawsuits and unseemly quarrels with colleagues.

When, by 1793, neither the monumental treatise on the flora of the area nor the complete medical and botanical study of Cinchona had been received, the Spanish government became concerned. It had invested heavily in what was now called The Botanical Institute of the New Kingdom of Granada, installed in handsome quarters in Bogotá with a staff of competent scientists. The German naturalist Baron Alexander von Humboldt, who visited it in 1802, said that its library was the world's richest in the sphere of natural history. In fact, this first center for pure scientific research in America was not to be duplicated until the twentieth century.

Where, then, were the reports that European men of science were waiting for? Spanish government investigators arrived and were shocked to find that the thousands of illustrations and botanical specimens were all scattered and mixed, as if by an evil spirit. Not a single manuscript was in final form, although everyone was working at breakneck speed, especially Mutis.

In 1793 Mutis produced under pressure two short pamphlets. Disappointingly—and some say, by design—they merely reiterated what was already known about the action of the fever bark. Nevertheless, these were the first publications on the subject since La Condamine's brief description of the tree fifty-five years before. But doctors still didn't know whether the particular bark they were prescribing so blindly had medicinal properties or not; some favored yellow bark, others red, and still others the light, or gray. The medical profession could make no further progress until a natural history of the tree was compiled and the differing properties in the various species were spelled out. Mutis was said to have this information ready, on the verge of presentation. But Mutis, from all reports, could not bring himself to share this knowledge: sick and almost totally blind, he died at seventy-six without publishing a word of the colossal mass he had exhausted himself in accumulating.

After his death, Francisco José de Caldas became Director

of the Institute and immediately began to sort out the material for the printers. It was at this point, some researchers say, that the disorder was shown to have been deliberate, rather than accidental. Mutis, before he died, is supposed to have carefully explained to Caldas just how to bring order out of this chaos, designed to conceal "certain secret discoveries." Caldas, at any rate, was the only person who could untangle these records. But, being a native South American and a patriot, when an insurrection against the Spanish ruler broke out he left to fight for his country's independence. After he was captured and condemned to death, he had nothing to say on his own behalf, but he did plead for six months in which to finish his project at the Institute, offering to work in chains if necessary. His request was denied and on October 29, 1816, a firing squad shot him in the back. Caldas is remembered for many scientific contributions, including his discovery of the method for determining altitude by the temperature at which water boils. He constructed his own delicate instruments for these experiments, which grew out of one of his immensely important projects—charting the geographical distribution of Cinchona. He left diagrams of the chief locations of the different varieties, plus information about their growth and the required climate, moisture, and sunlight.

The following year the material in the Institute collection was shipped to Spain, arriving safely at the Botanical Gardens in Madrid. Because of a shortage of space it was stored in an abandoned shed, where it remained forgotten for decades. Eventually, two copies of a Mutis treatise on Cinchona, with 122 colored drawings, were readied for publication in Cadiz, but during an insurrection the manuscripts were destroyed. However, the famous plates were salvaged and finally published less than a decade ago.

Even before the Bogotá Institute was established, the Spanish government had a number of independent expeditions scouring the jungles for Cinchona. Each team had its share of discomfort and misfortune in the by now familiar pattern, but Hipólito Ruíz, José Pavón, and José Dombey had an experience that was somewhat unique. They began to gather the usual enormous amount of material on the fever-bark trees in 1777, in Peru, only to lose the collection eleven years later while it was being transported to Spain. "Shipwreck" was listed as the cause. In 1852 their magnificent assortment of barks was observed in the British Museum and traced to an auction of booty from a Spanish transport which had been preyed upon by English pirates. The Ruíz-Pavón-Dombey saga has a modern sequel, according to Dr. Richard Evans Schultes of Harvard. During World War II, Dr. Jaime Jaramillo Arango, then Colombian ambassador to Britain, explored the bombed-out basement of the British Museum for quinine lore. He found the original Ruíz and Pavón manuscript, which has since been published in Spain in two beautiful volumes. Dr. Schultes is now translating this into English and is also working with the Bogotá Institute on a volume of Mutis.

It was Baron von Humboldt and the French botanist Aimé Bonpland who finally resolved much of the confusion about the different types of Cinchona bark. The results of their observations in South America from 1799 to 1804 were published in twenty-nine volumes. Among other things, Humboldt proved that *quina de la angostura,* discovered by the Capuchin monks and reputed to have value as a febrifuge, was a "false" Cinchona and of no use in the treatment of malaria. (Today angostura is indispensable to bartenders, however.) He also demonstrated that the system of classification based upon leaf characteristics was unreliable, because there was great variation in the leaves on a single branch of these trees. Humboldt, of course, was influential in many fields, inspiring both Charles Darwin and Simón Bolívar. One of many persons deeply concerned about the wanton destruction of the fever-bark trees, he made this prophetic statement: "If the governments in South America do not attend to the conservation of the quina, either by prohibiting the felling of trees, or by obliging the territorial magistrates to enforce the cutters to guard them from destruction, this highly estimed product of the New World will be swept from the country."

Quinine from Cinchona

Two French pharmacists of extraordinary generosity gave the world Cinchona's chief antimalarial agent—quinine—in 1820. This marked the turning point in the story of the fever-bark tree.

In 1816 a Portuguese naval surgeon named Gomez obtained a substance from the gray bark that he called *Cinchonino*. Four years later Joseph Pelletier and Joseph Caventou isolated from the same material an alkaloid soluble in acid and alcohol, cinchonine. After experimenting with yellow bark, they learned that its crystals were also soluble in ether, while those from the gray bark were not, and thus quinine, a much more powerful alkaloid, was discovered. Since then almost thirty different alkaloids have been obtained from Cinchona.

Pelletier and Caventou decided not to patent their method, and after they published their findings manufacturers immediately began to produce quinine sulfate, a purified product of standard potency still employed today. The only reward for the discoverers, who unraveled many other drug plant principles, was 10,000 francs from the Paris Institute of Science.

Besides its immediate humanitarian applications, the chemical investigation of Cinchona was of far-reaching importance. When attempts were made to extract its medicinal properties, study their structure, and reproduce them in the laboratory, the cornerstone of modern drug synthesis and chemotherapy was laid. To doctors and patients, the isolation of quinine meant that now, for the first time, there was a reliable antimalarial whose dosage could be controlled. In addition, the alkaloid was much less irritating to the stomach than the whole-bark powder had been. It also became possible to determine the quinine content of different barks from various species; in the future, collectors would be able to seek out barks of proved superiority.

The new procedure indicated that the best bark came from Bolivia's *Cinchona calisaya,* the latest species to be discovered and the shortest in supply. A French botanist, Dr. H. A. Weddell, spent five years mapping the range of this tree east of Lake Titicaca, near La Paz, the "quinine capital of the world." The Indians there were particularly savage and the terrain was so difficult that his native guides and bearers deserted him, but he brought back seeds that germinated in the Jardin des Plantes in Paris. Young seedlings were sent to horticultural societies in England and Holland, and at last Europeans were able to see the source of their remarkable ague remedy. In 1849 Weddell published the first comprehensive natural history of Cinchona, *Histoire Naturelle des quinquinas,* in which he described nineteen species of the seventy now known to be native to the Andes.

This information, plus the knowledge that the tree could grow outside of South America, sparked an all-out movement to break the monopoly enjoyed by Bolivia, Peru, Colombia, and Ecuador. (These countries had ruled that only dead Cinchona bark could be exported—no seedlings, seeds, or any living plants were to be removed.) Hoping to circumvent these restrictions as well as bark transportation difficulties, an enterprising Frenchman, M. Delondre, had a quinine factory carried piece by piece high into the mountains near Cuzco, Peru. He planned to manufacture the alkaloid on an international scale. Unfortunately, he learned too late that there was no bark to be had; of the limited amount permitted to be stripped, all was consigned to a New York company.

In Java the Dutch had a colony, with a suitable climate, which they were anxious to provide with a money crop like Cinchona, if the seeds could be smuggled out of South America. Superintendent Justus Hasskarl, of the Botanical Garden in Java, started out on this secret mission in 1852, but a German newspaperman uncovered the plan. The Dutch government quickly denied it, most officially, most emphatically. Meanwhile, Hasskarl dropped out of sight. Early the next year, J. K. Müller, a "tourist" according to his passport, went sight-seeing through Cinchona territory, quietly collecting seeds as souvenirs. When he found that he could not roam freely through the province where the prized *C. calisaya* grew, he approached the governor of the area with certain proposals. These were seemingly rejected, but the official passed him on to a shady character who was willing to take the risk involved in exchanging hundreds of young plants and a bag of seeds for a bag of gold. Arriving back in Java with his prize, Müller (or, rather, Hasskarl) was made a Knight of the Netherlands Lion and a Commander of the Order of the Oaken Crown, and put in charge of the new Cinchona plantations. A year or so later, when most of the inferior seeds and sickly plants that had been foisted upon him failed, Haaskarl was relieved of his duties.

Large sums of money were then spent in clearing another site on the slopes of the Malabar Mountains, where a few of Hasskarl's surviving Cinchonas were transplanted, along with seeds obtained from a secret source by the Dutch Consul General at La Paz. By 1860 a fine stand of almost a million healthy trees was causing the Dutch to congratulate themselves, for the cultivation had been fraught with a thousand difficulties (so many, and of such complexity, that Norman Taylor devoted an entire book, *Cinchona in Java,* to the details). But the old fever-bark jinx struck again. A chemist from Holland assayed the quinine content of the *C. calisayas,* whose bark had produced so bountifully in Bolivia, and reported that scarcely a single tree in Java was producing enough quinine to justify its stripping. Some say they were not *C. calisayas* at all.

While the Dutch were building up to this letdown, the English wanted to have a cheap, convenient source of quinine of their own. They, too, had had enough of the South American monopoly and they were concerned about the death toll from malaria in India—well over a million lives a year. The Dutch offered plants and advice, but the British seem to have preferred to make their own mistakes, variations of the fiasco in Java. Clements Markham, a young East India Company clerk who master-minded the project, hired outstanding botanists to collect Cinchona, among them Richard Spruce. Although in very poor health, Spruce collected and preserved over 100,000 seeds, as well as several hundred plants of the beautiful red bark, *Cinchona succirubra*. These arrived safely in India and Ceylon, where they were planted in the 1860's. The trees prospered but their quinine content also proved disappointingly low.

Incredible as it may seem, a member of the South American Aymará Indian tribe, which is so fanatically devoted to its land that it has the reputation of giving up its children more readily than its acreage, brought about the collapse of the lucrative fever-bark trade in his own country. Manuel Incra Mamaní was hired in 1843 by Charles Ledger, an English vicuña and bark trader living on Lake Titicaca. Manuel's honesty and ability made him Ledger's most valued *cascarillero*, or bark collector; and after eighteen years of working together these two were very good friends. There was one species of tree whose seeds Ledger particularly wanted, but its exact location, somewhere in the Rio Beni region, was a well-kept Indian secret. One day in 1861, he asked Manuel to reveal in friendship what he would not have considered trading for gold. This his faithful worker refused to do. Torn by conflicting loyalties, the man left Ledger to work independently. But four years later he appeared with a gift of the seeds carefully concealed in his long hair. Then he returned alone across 800 miles of bleak Andean highlands to his people. Years later, Manuel's son told Ledger how his father had been punished for this by being tortured to death in a Bolivian jail.

The seeds had meanwhile been sent to Ledger's brother in London. The British government refused to have anything to do with them and they were literally peddled in the streets, where some were bought by a British traveler bound for India. He, however, thinking to make a better deal, exchanged them for *C. calisaya* later on. The Dutch made one of the best investments in history when they bought a pound of Ledger's seeds for around twenty dollars. This modest purchase became the foundation for their international monopoly of quinine; eventually, they controlled nine-tenths of the world's supply.

Cinchona ledgeriana, as this new species was called, yielded as much as 13 per cent quinine when mature. Other varieties had been producing only 3 to 5 per cent of the alkaloid. With great skill and perseverance, Dutch agronomists in Java conducted a series of experiments that involved plate grafting Ledger's somewhat delicate species upon the hardy roots of *C. succirubra,* the red-bark stock sent by Spruce. This combination proved the most successful, and gradually all of the other trees were destroyed to prevent natural cross-breeding.

The peak quinine-producing period does not come until fifteen to eighteen years after planting, although bark has been harvested much earlier when the demand has been great. (Russia, for instance, has experimented with a two-year crop.) Dr. Ray F. Dawson of Columbia University's Department of Botany, who has been studying the vital processes in Cinchonas for many years, said that most of the quinine occurs in the outer layers of bark where the cells are dead or dying.

As a result, the trunk is continually cutting off its richest alkaloid deposits from direct contact with the active tissues of the underlying layers. This would seem to indicate that these drugs, so important to man, are only by-products of the plant's metabolism.

At harvest time the trees are removed, roots and all, from the plantation site. The logs are cut into short lengths and the bark is beaten off with wooden mallets or bone knives; metal is not used. The bark from the above-ground parts (*C. ledgeriana*) is then dried and broken into chips or pulverized for shipment as "factory bark" to quinine producers. The root bark (*C. succirubra*), called in the trade "pharmaceutical bark," while lower in quinine, is high in other useful alkaloids such as quinidine, cinchonine, and cinchonidine. These are carefully extracted and used to make a standardized mixed alkaloid preparation known as totaquine. Because of its low cost per treatment, only $.17 as compared to $1.25 for quinine, totaquine was recommended in 1931 by the League of Nations Malaria Commission for use in underdeveloped countries. It also played a vital role during World War II.

Throughout history, malaria has been a major military problem, killing such leaders as Alexander the Great and typically striking down more troops than enemy action. The disease was rampant during the American Revolution—George Washington took the fever bark while camping in New Jersey—and it killed thousands during the Civil War. During the Spanish-American War, for every man wounded four came back ill with malaria. In World War I, Allied and Central Powers troops were immobilized in Greece and Macedonia because of the scourge. World War II was no exception, with over 600,000 United States troops malarious, especially in Africa and the South Pacific. Until midway through the war, Cinchona products were the only treatment available to the Army Medical Service. The supply situation became critical as military operations were expanded to areas endemic with malaria.

In the fateful days between December 7, 1941, and the final surrender of the American garrison on the Bataan Peninsula and Corregidor in late March, 1942, the lack of quinine assumed a dominant role. The only hope for relief was vested in one man, the late Lieutenant Colonel Arthur Fischer, an intelligence officer with the Luzon Force whose knowledge of Cinchona dated back many years. He had first gone to the Philippines in 1911 with a degree in forestry and a reserve army commission. In 1917, as Director of the Bureau of Forestry in the Islands, he knew that a local quinine source was essential to control the high incidence of malaria so that agricultural resources could be developed. The Dutch had a tight embargo on all shipments of plants and seeds from their Java plantations, but Fischer found a way to reach his objective. Through the help of the Military Governor of the Philippines, General Leonard Wood, Fischer arranged for an English captain to smuggle seeds from Java. They were delivered in two Horlick's Malted Milk jars and the captain was paid $4,000, the money coming from General Wood's discretionary fund. By 1927 Fischer had a plantation of *C. ledgeriana* flourishing in the Mindanao province; nine years later the first bark shipment reached a small totaquine factory in Manila.

The factory was seized by the Japanese early in 1942, along with all stocks of the drug. Shortly after this the Japanese Army swept through Java, cutting off 38,000 acres of Cinchonas, the Allies' last substantial source of the crude botanical. The Germans two years before had taken Amsterdam and obtained all the European reserve stocks of alkaloids. By these two strokes, over 90 per cent of the world's source of quinine was denied to the Allies. (There were some plantations in India and plantings too young to yield in Central and South America, but these countries had been importing antimalarials to meet their own needs.)

On Luzon, early in 1942, new malaria cases among the 80,000 soldiers were increasing at an alarming rate. United States Army correspondence revealed the gravity of the situation: "There are now 3,000 cases of malaria in the Luzon Force . . . 20 per cent of fighting units are not effective due to malaria and 50 per cent of some units have subclinical malaria and are considered potentially ineffective. The daily admission rate for malaria now [March 23] lies between 500 and 700 cases and in the absence of quinine this rate can be expected to increase. There is sufficient quinine in the Philippine Medical Depot to very inadequately treat 10,000 cases . . . this will be exhausted in three to four weeks. When stocks are exhausted, a mortality rate of 10 per cent in untreated cases can be expected. Those who do not succumb to the disease can be classed as non-effective from a military standpoint due to their weakened and anemic condition. Blood-building foods and drugs are not available." Radio messages were sent to Melbourne, the nearest supply base, for additional supplies, but to no avail.

Colonel Fischer, who was interviewed a few months before his death in 1962, recalled that on March 18, 1942, he wrote a letter to General Wainwright's Assistant Chief of Staff, in which he outlined his plan as follows: "At the quinine plantation at Katoan, about forty kilometers west by south of Malaybalay, Bukidnon, under the supervision of Forester Altamirano, there should be several thousand trees over three years old from which bark can be harvested and sent to Bataan by plane. This bark should run from 7 to 9 per cent alkaloid content and can be used by grinding the bark and making an infusion with boiling water as a tea. The seed of *C. ledgeriana* should be harvested and sent by plane to the United States for shipment to Brazil to start American sources."

Wainwright immediately called him in for a firsthand report, and approval of the project was quickly given. Although Fischer was ill with malaria and blood poisoning in his arm, and his weight was down from 150 to 96 pounds, he left Bataan for Mindanao to supervise the harvesting. With local help, he stripped bark, ground it up in a corn grinder, and packed it in old gasoline cans. The cargo went out, but the plane was shot down. Meanwhile, an attempt was made to extract alkaloids from the bark. A priest with a smattering of chemistry improvised a laboratory with two old bathtubs and some ether and sulfuric acid begged from a hospital, but in a few days the tragic news that Bataan had fallen was relayed to Fischer. Their efforts to save the dying men were in vain. The one thought now was to escape with the *C. ledgeriana* seeds. General MacArthur sent a B-17 Flying Fortress to rescue key Philippine personnel. It was probably the last plane to leave the area, and Fischer and the seeds were on it. (Totaquine from the Island plantations later saved thousands of lives by effectively maintaining our guerrilla action against the Japanese, who could not get to this bark to harvest it.) Fischer's seeds were flown then from Australia back to the Americas, whence the species had come by way of Java some seventy years before.

After germination in the United States Department of Agriculture laboratories at Glen Dale, Maryland, four million seedlings were sent to Latin American countries. One of the larger plantations was started in Costa Rica, where 10,000 acres were leased to grow Cinchonas. Although World War II was over before the barks were ready for harvest, one of forester Fischer's youthful dreams—to make quinine available in under-developed countries as a "good neighbor policy"—had been achieved. For his wartime services, Colonel Fischer was awarded the United States Order of Merit and the Distinguished Service Star of the Philippines.

The advent of synthetic antimalarials sharply altered the role of Cinchona in the 1940's. Nevertheless, there was a period early in the war when the United States was convinced that it would be defeated unless vast sources of natural quinine, from Cinchona or other plants, were obtainable in the Western Hemisphere. Top priority was given to a program sponsored by the Office of Scientific Research and Development in which about 14,000 compounds were screened for malaria control. While this laboratory work was going on, attention was turned toward the wild stands of fever-bark trees in Ecuador, Peru, and Colombia. Ignored for decades, these low-yielding species were now treasures beyond price.

In October, 1942, the present Director of the New York Botanical Garden, Dr. William C. Steere, and Dr. F. Raymond Fosberg, now with the United States Geological Survey, were sent to South America by the Board of Economic Warfare. In the months that followed, they combed the three ranges of the Colombian Andes for wild Cinchona species, finding that *Cinchona pubescens* was common throughout, but that it had a low alkaloid content and sometimes lacked quinine altogether. *C. officinalis,* which usually produced bark of high quality, was found only in the eastern range. It was their good luck to run into large stands of *Remijia pedunculata,* which, though not a Cinchona, produced up to 3 per cent of cinchona alkaloids. Steere also rediscovered *C. pitayensis* in the central Andes. This little-known species had been considered a botanical rarity, but it turned out to be relatively abundant in southern Colombia. Steere continued his arduous exploration into Ecuador, and during the winter of 1943–44 other competent botanists joined him in surveying the trackless Andean highlands. One of these was the late Dr. Wendell H. Camp, of the University of Connecticut, who continued to make important contributions toward the understanding of this complex genus long after the war.

The hazardous field conditions encountered recalled the trials of the early explorer-naturalists who first covered this ground. One botanist, Dr. Featherstonehaugh, died from the effects of altitude sickness; all of the men suffered acutely from the damp, penetrating cold and from malaria, dysentery, and other infections. They spent weeks on end with only the crudest form of shelter. Since their supplies often had to be carried on the backs of men, not mules, rations were usually those of their Indian guides: a handful of dried barley meal or beans, called *mata hambre,* meaning "it kills hunger." The Cinchonas were found on steep mountainsides where the annual rainfall was between 150 and 200 inches. "In the dry season, it rained only in the afternoon," Steere recalled. This made the footing so slippery that plunges of a mile or so were an ever-present danger. One of the chief problems was trying to keep the sick, discouraged cargo-bearers from skipping out and leaving them stranded with their collections on the headwaters of some unknown river. The material had to get back to civilization. Three drug companies—Penick, Merck, and Mallinckrodt—were waiting in the United States to process barks into totaquine for the government. Totaquine, the "poor man's quinine," was the soldier's salvation until the synthetic antimalarials came along.

The single factor of greatest importance in this search was the availability of prompt, accurate analyses of field samples by chemists in Cinchona Mission Laboratories in Bogotá, Quito, Lima, and La Paz. In Cinchona "booms" of previous years, analyses were made only after shipments reached Europe, if at all, causing a tremendous waste of time and money. During World War II, thanks to this technical aid, exploration was placed on a much more efficient basis.

Although basic botany was not the aim of these expeditions, the results brought to light much information new to science. Dr. Walter H. Hodge, now with the National Science Foundation, reported, for instance, that one of the "false Cinchonas," *Ladenbergia malacophylla,* contained almost 4 per cent total alkaloids of the type being sought. He, and others, found many distinctions between species, varieties, and forms of Cinchonas and other plants not previously suspected.

Because the wild Cinchonas were not meeting wartime needs—hundreds of pounds of bark were required to produce a few pounds of useful alkaloids—an emergency short-range program was undertaken in Guatemala, where millions of seedlings were planted a foot apart to be harvested at two or three years of age. At the same time, Merck Research Laboratories started testing extracts from hundreds of plants other than Cinchona for antimalarial activity on chicks and ducklings. The plant samples had been obtained from various countries by B. A. Krukoff, Merck's consulting botanist, and identified through the co-operation of the New York Botanical Garden. Eventually, one of the promising antimalarials was placed on the market—not for the treatment of that disease, but as an amoebicide.

Concurrently, Lederle Laboratories became interested in *Ch'ang Shan* roots, the ancient Chinese treatment for malaria. However, the uncertain supply of these caused attention to be shifted to the related and more readily available Easter-variety hydrangea. Dr. Benjamin M. Duggar, a retired seventy-two-year-old University of Wisconsin botany professor, plunged into an intensive five-year project that was to cost Lederle nearly $500,000. He isolated from these plants an alkaloid, febrifugine, that exhibited marked antimalarial properties, but it was never marketed because it tended to cause vomiting. Dr. Duggar went on to fame, though, as the discoverer of the broad-spectrum antibiotic Aureomycin. And the Lederle flower beds at Pearl River, New York, remained filled to overflowing with "gold-plated" hydrangeas.

In still another attempt to solve the desperate need for antimalarials, biochemist Norman Applezweig, working for the United States Army Corps of Engineers, developed a completely new method for making quinine alkaloids on location in the forest. This was an ion-exchange process requiring only water and concentrated sulfuric acid. A whole "factory" could thus be packed on a mule's back and taken to the wild Cinchona stands. But, as with Delondre, who tried to get around the problem of transporting bark across the Andes a century earlier, this plan also came to naught. The process worked and was promptly classified as secret by the government—so much so that Applezweig says that he was denied access to the material. Then it was summarily abandoned when the announcement was made that quinine had been artificially reproduced in a Harvard laboratory.

Chemists had been struggling to synthesize quinine ever since 1856, when William Henry Perkin, an eighteen-year-old English lad, had tried and failed. (As a by-product of these experiments, however, Perkin came up with aniline purple, the first artificial dye.) In 1944, two young Americans, Dr. William E. Doering of Columbia and Dr. Robert B. Woodward of Harvard, duplicated the chemical architecture of the quinine molecule, making possible the synthetic production of this antimalarial. It is no disparagement of their brilliant work to point out that it did nothing to relieve the critical World War II shortage, for the process was long, complicated, and much too expensive for large-scale reproduction. Such synthetic quinine might have cost as much as $1,000 per gram.

In the meantime, the drug atabrine, synthesized in 1928 from a yellow coal-tar dye by I. G. Farbenindustrie in Germany, was being looked at again. It had been marketed in 1932 by Winthrop Chemical Company but made little headway against the established quinine. By 1944, however, two United States producers, Winthrop and Merck, began turning out almost a billion pills a year, equivalent in therapeutic effect to the world's former production of quinine, which had been twenty million ounces a year. Ex-servicemen who had to take these little yellow pills daily will recall such side effects as nausea, diarrhea, and a yellow-tinged skin. By no means perfect, atabrine was nevertheless a lifesaver in its time.

A succession of synthetics followed atabrine. During the amphibious assault at Anzio in the marshlands near Rome, the Allies discovered that the Germans were using chloroquine for malaria. The Americans had known about this drug, but its value had not been picked up in the screening and testing programs. Chloroquine later became the drug of choice during the Korean War. Another drug, primaquine, synthesized by Dr. Robert C. Elderfield of Columbia University in 1945, attacked malaria parasites harbored within the body's tissues, but it had to be administered in controlled doses under the close supervision of a doctor. Standard military treatment became a weekly dose of chloroquine to suppress symptoms, and then, upon leaving the malarious area, fourteen consecutive days of primaquine therapy to kill the parasites that might otherwise dwell for years in the liver and other organs, causing relapses. In 1961, chlorequine and primaquine were combined in one pill to be taken once a week during exposure to the disease. Just as effective as the old method, this pill has the advantage of a coating that disguises its very bitter taste. Unfortunately, people of certain ethnic backgrounds seem to be sensitive to primaquine.

A still more recent advance was announced by the National Institute of Allergy and Infectious Diseases in 1963. Clinical trials have shown that a single injected dose of a new synthetic, CI-501, developed by Parke, Davis and Company, will protect persons exposed to experimental malaria for almost a year. Whether these results will be duplicated in field trials in malarial areas of the world remains to be seen, but the outlook is promising.

Meanwhile, the perfect antimalarial has not been found. This is a very difficult order to fill because human malaria, carried by infected female Anopheles mosquitoes, is caused by four species of the protozoan Plasmodium: *P. vivax* (most common), *P. falciparum, P. malariae,* and *P. ovale* (rare). The disease occurs in two stages: the clinical phase, when parasites invade and rupture red blood cells, producing periodic bouts of chills and fever; and the tissue stage, when parasites "hibernate" and there may be no symptoms for many years. Patients in the latter stage are, however, carriers. If they are bitten by an Anopheles mosquito or if they donate their blood, they may transmit the disease even after twenty or thirty years. The frequently repeated statement that "malaria parasites die out in three years in the human body" is not true in every case. Each of the four species of parasites has its own characteristics, as do the variant strains. Therefore, the ideal medication would destroy all varieties of the parasite in each stage and, at the same time, cause no side effects.

Out of the world-wide search to find quinine substitutes, many valuable compounds were discovered and tested, but all failed in some respect. Frequently, promising drugs proved so poisonous that the curative dose approached the toxic dose. And matters are further complicated now that, in widely separated parts of the globe, the infecting protozoans have developed new strains resistant to synthetic drugs, just as some insects have become immune to DDT and other insecticides. This rarely happens with quinine from Cinchona, although it has been employed for hundreds of years. One study found a thousand fold increase in resistance of *P. vivax* to the drug Proguanil; but only a twofold increase in resistance to quinine has been obtained. So the natural product is still useful in many cases not responding to modern therapies, or where allergic reactions or side effects require that synthetics be discontinued.

While interviewing the late Aldous Huxley in the course of doing research for this book, I learned that his brother, Sir Julian Huxley, the eminent British biologist, had been saved by quinine just a few years ago. His malaria had developed into the dreaded "blackwater fever" and modern antimalarials were not having any effect. Quinine was administered and he recovered. In fact, Aldous Huxley pointed out that in many areas of the world, quinine is still the only antimalarial, and it is preferred by some colonials, especially the French.

Cinchona alkaloids also have other medical uses. Quinidine sulfate is prescribed for attacks of irregular and rapid heartbeat, and injections of quinidine in cases of heart failure can be truly lifesaving. Quinine sulfate is used to relieve muscle cramps, and it is still favored by some physicians in combating fever in respiratory infections. It has a curare-like action helpful in certain types of headaches and joint and muscle disorders. It is also used as injection therapy for varicose veins.

It may well be true that most of the noble fever-bark trees harvested today are destined to wind up in quinine water or in fortified wines such as dubonnet and sweet vermouth. But we dare not yet drink a toast to victory over malaria. The World Health Organization has reported that it is still humanity's greatest cause of physical disability and the world's costliest disease. United States Army Surgeon General Leonard D. Heaton said that, despite the vast mosquito-eradication program begun in the early 1950's, over 255,000,000 people live in malarial areas where no eradication program has even been planned.

While tropical and subtropical regions suffer most, malaria has been reported north of the Arctic Circle and as far south as the tip of South America. It occurs in the Alps and Andes and is fairly common below sea level in the Dead Sea region. As recently as the mid-1950's, it still affected more than a million persons in the United States and killed an average of 5,000 every year. While malaria is no longer a problem in this country, it is unrealistic to "feel safe" because one lives in a disease-free area. One of the most devastating outbreaks in modern times was traced by epidemiologists to an infected mosquito that "hitched" a ride from Africa to Brazil. It has been said that one mosquito and one malaria patient can infect a community, and one community can infect a nation.

The noted malariologist Dr. Paul F. Russell, of the Rockefeller Institute, summed up the situation: "What a paradox! Man, with his streamlined science, stricken each year in millions because he fails to outwit a mosquito carrying Death in its spittle!"

Meanwhile, for 1,200 miles along the Eastern slopes of the Andes the wild Cinchonas continue to flourish. Their leaves are shining in the sun from majestic heights; their feathery flower clusters are deliciously scented. The quinaquina, once the most important drug plant in the world, is to many still the most beautiful tree.

Digitalis, From a Quaint Shropshire Garden

THE HEART IS PERHAPS THE MOST REMARKABLE organ in the human body; certainly it is the world's best pump. It functions oftener than once a second a whole life through, keeping pace with the body, responsive to the demands of exertion, fear, passion, and disease, resting only for a fraction of a second between beats that go on and on, triggered by the heart's own nerve center. Yet, like any engine, it can skip a beat, and no matter. But if it gets out of time, or lags, or starts up too slowly, it needs attention.

Digitalis, from the leaves of the foxglove, is one of the best attenders.

The foxglove of the garden has a tall stalk of beautiful bell-shaped flowers and leaves like long velvet tongues. Take too many and they become the tongues of dragons; but in the right prescription, their greenness contains a calming and strengthening heart regulator.

Digitalis stimulates the vagus center, the tenth cranial nerve that has so much important work to do: besides monitoring the beat of the heart, it controls the diaphragm, contracts the stomach, regulates the larynx, and more. In addition to working on the nerves, Digitalis tones up the heart muscle and increases its contractibility. Actually, there are ten separate and distinct actions of Digitalis in the body and some of them get into rather complex physiology. Suffice to say that Digitalis is just what the doctor ordered and he often does. It is the number-one drug for the heart.

Quite appropriately, its discovery stems from the love of a man for a pretty young woman. The background for this story is an eighteenth-century Shropshire garden straight out of an old-fashioned valentine.

In 1766, young William Withering, M.D., hung out his shingle in the small town of Stafford, England. He had just received his medical degree at Edinburgh University and was concerned about the responsibility for maintaining his family's high place in the profession: his father, two brothers, and several other relatives were also physicians.

Withering had many additional interests and accomplishments, however; he played the flute and harpsichord extremely well and even took up the bagpipe. Golf, archery, dramatic societies, all attracted his attention too. The only subject he actively disliked during his student years was botany. He once wrote his parents that the offer of a gold medal by his professor "will hardly have charm enough to banish the disagreeable ideas I have formed of the study of botany." But by 1776 he was to publish a textbook that remained a standard in the field for the next hundred years: *A Botanical Arrangement of All the Vegetables Growing in Great Britain, According to the System of the Celebrated Linnaeus: with an Easy Introduction to the Study of Botany.*

Even the least romantic of medical historians gives some credit for this change of heart to Miss Helena Cookes, a charming flower painter. Through a slight indisposition, she became one of Withering's first patients. Because she was unable to collect her own flowers during this illness, her doctor did this for her and evidently found great pleasure in roaming the woods and fields searching for new species. In order to impress her with his knowledge, Withering began to apply himself to this study for the first time—the "lovable science," as he came to call it. Long after Miss Cookes was fully recovered, he continued his daily calls. This time, it was to continue her education in a sort of home-training program. He commented: "The harpsichord, the voice, the pencil, and every exterior accomplishment were already at her command; my duty was to extend her taste for literature." Withering loved poetry, especially that concerning nature and he even had some of his own verses published anonymously. In a few years, he was to write:

> "The Foxglove's leaves, with caution given,
>   Another proof of favouring Heav'n
>   Will happily display;
>   The rapid pulse it can abate;
>   The hectic flush can moderate
>   And, blest by Him whose will is fate,
>   May give a lengthened day."

By 1772 the cozy evenings of reading together before the fireplace and strolling in the lanes had resulted in marriage for this talented twosome. Three years later the Witherings moved to Birmingham because he had not made a success of his medical practice in Stafford. For some time, though, he continued to serve the Stafford Infirmary, making the journey of sixty miles each week over miserable roads in all sorts of weather. It was on one of these trips that he learned of the foxglove as a therapy. He described the incident as follows:

"In the year 1775, my opinion was asked concerning a family receipt for the cure of the dropsy [an accumulation of fluid in the body]. I was told that it had long been kept a secret by an old woman in Shropshire, who had sometimes made cures after the more regular practitioners had failed. I was informed also that the effects produced were violent vomiting and purging; for the diuretic effects seemed to have been overlooked. [A diuretic increases the flow of urine.] This medication was composed of twenty or more different herbs; but it was not very difficult for one conversant in these subjects to perceive that the active herb could be no other than Foxglove."

The young physician did not dismiss the home remedy as useless, because he had a firm belief that "the empirical usage and experience of the populace lies within the reach of everyone who is open to information." Pasteur once said that chance favors the prepared mind. Fortunately, Withering's was there ready to grasp the significance of the old folk cure. Some accounts identify the woman as a "Mrs. Hutton" and say that he paid several golden sovereigns for the information, but he does not mention this in his own writings.

The foxglove had almost as stormy an early history as Cinchona. The plant was pictured and described by the first century A.D. physician, Dioscorides, and it became an ingredient in a number of quack salves sold in Italy in the Middle Ages. At times it served as a "chemical jury" in ordeal trials to determine guilt or innocence by its poisonous action. Potent teas made with it were used as a cheap means of intoxication by country folk, and the results reflected the true meaning of that word. Also known as throttlewort, from the tenth century on, it was in and out of favor with herbalists who recommended it for everything from colds to epilepsy. One wrote: "It will scoure and clense the brest of the thicke toughness of grosse and slimie flegme and naughtie humours." There was a persistent belief on the part of Withering's colleagues that his discovery was specific for tuberculosis, and long after his death this completely fruitless treatment continued. When Digitalis did not help their tubercular patients, many doctors abandoned it as a drug—in fact, denounced it—although Withering never claimed that it would cure that disease.

The plant genus is said to have been named Digitalis (from the Latin *digitus,* meaning finger) by Hieronymus Tragus (also known as Bock) in 1539 in Strassburg. The Bavarian physician Leonhard Fuchs also mentioned it in his Latin herbal *De Historia Stirpium* in 1542. It is a biennial that produces only a dense rosette of leaves the first year, but in the second season it can grow four feet high with many lavender flowers lined with mottled crimson. In Devonshire, the youngsters called the plant "flop-a-dock" because when they blew into the flowers and struck them with their hands, the flowers popped like balloons. Other common names were "fingerhut" in Germany, (the blossoms resemble the finger of a glove), "dead man's bells" in Scotland, and "goblin's gloves" in Wales.

Withering began extensive experimentation with all parts of the plant in 1775. His scientific approach to pharmacology and his early use of clinical trials have been favorably commented upon by physician authors ever since. Thousands of the "sick poor" were treated by him every year, and these nonpaying patients became the first to benefit from his Digitalis therapy. One of the alternative treatments for dropsy patients in those times was "tapping," in which water-logged tissues were punctured and patients were stretched out on bedsprings, to drip, drip, drip into pails below. Amazingly, this did save lives and the practice continued until our grandfathers' day.

There was no doubt in Withering's mind that teas made with various parts of the foxglove drained swollen limbs, but the results were far from uniform. For a young doctor trying to build a reputation, these experiments were perilous; his wife is said to have persuaded him not to use the drug on his private patients, who were scarce enough as it was.

Digitalis is still one of those tricky drugs that have to be carefully administered according to each individual's reaction. There certainly were mishaps in the folk use of the remedy, as Withering noted: "I found a Yorkshire tradesman incessantly vomiting, his vision indistinct, his pulse forty a minute. On enquiry, it came out that his wife had stewed a large handful of green Foxglove leaves in half a pint of water and given him the liquor which he drank in a draught, in order to cure him of an asthmatic affection. This good woman knew the medicine of her country, but not the dose of it, for her husband narrowly escaped with his life."

As he was working out the problem of dosage, Withering wrote in medical and botanical journals that *"Digitalis purpurea* merits more attention than modern practice bestows upon it." However, only a few doctors tried the drug and then only as a last resort. During these years of trial, Withering seems to have feared that these failures would cause the plant to be rejected permanently by the medical profession. His own uncertainties are underscored in his account of a consultation: "On July 25, I met Dr. Darwin at Mrs. X's house [a patient of Dr. Darwin]. I found her nearly in a state of suffocation, her pulse extremely weak and irregular, her breath very short and laborious, her arms of a leaden colour, clammy and cold. . . . Her stomach, legs and thighs were greatly swollen. She had experienced no relief from any means that had been used. . . . In this situation, I know nothing likely to avail us except Digitalis: but this I hesitated to propose . . . since an unfavorable termination would tend to discredit a medicine which promised to be of great benefit to mankind and I might be censured for a prescription which could not be countenanced by the experience of any other regular practitioner. But these considerations soon gave way to the desire of saving the life of this valuable woman and I proposed that Digitalis be tried. . . . Dr. Darwin very politely acceded. . . . The patient took five draughts and in the first twenty-four hours, made upwards of eight quarts of water. On August 1, I found the patient perfectly free from every appearance of dropsy."

The colleague who consulted Withering was Dr. Erasmus Darwin, grandfather of the great naturalist Charles Darwin, and a fellow member of the illustrious Lunar Society that met in Birmingham to discuss scientific matters whenever the moon was full. The membership included James Watt, Joseph Priestley, Josiah Wedgwood, and, whenever he could come, Benjamin Franklin, who was a patient of Withering. This friendly group of intellectuals was rocked to its foundations in 1780, when Dr. Darwin rushed into print with the first account of the use of Digitalis in medical practice, without giving Withering any credit at all. Historians say that after Darwin's eldest son died while in medical school in 1778, the bereaved father wanted to see the youth's dissertation on dropsy published. What is not so understandable is his addition, after his son's death, of nine case histories of cures with Digitalis. The first of these cases was the one just described in which Withering effected the cure—but Withering's name appeared nowhere in the manuscript.

By this time, Withering was beginning to be seriously troubled by a lung condition, bronchiectasis, that was to cost him his life in 1799 at the age of 58. He continued to drive himself not only as a physician, but also in his scientific research projects, which included the invention of a microscope and an instrument for accurately drawing perspective. Because of his contributions in chemistry, meteorology, and mineralogy, the mineral witherite was named in his honor, as was the plant genus Witheringia.

But he still did not feel that he had done sufficient research on Digitalis to merit publication. Meanwhile, the prejudices of some members of the medical profession were broken down when Principal Cawley of Brasenose College, Oxford, was cured by a layman who gave him foxglove "after some of the first physicians of the age had declared they could do no more for him." Withering noted that the dose given was at least twelve times too much—more than enough to kill him. Clearly there were wide variations in individual tolerance.

After ten years of experimentation, Withering was persuaded by friends to report his findings. Accordingly, his great medical classic *An Account of the Foxglove and Some of its Medical Uses: with Practical Remarks on Dropsy and Other Diseases* was issued in 1785. The author's modesty is reflected in the opening paragraphs: "The use of the Foxglove is getting abroad and it is better the world should derive some instruction, however imperfect, from my experience, than that the lives of men should be hazarded by its unguarded exhibition. . . . It would have been an easy task to have given select cases whose successful treatment would have spoken strongly in favor of the medicine, and perhaps been flattering to my own reputation. But Truth and Science would condemn the procedure. I have, therefore, mentioned every case in which I have prescribed the Foxglove, proper or improper, successful or otherwise."

He included observations on 163 of his own patients and a number reported by other physicians. On the basis of his experience, he advised that the best part of the plant to use was the dried powdered leaf, made up in cold water infusions rather than teas because prolonged boiling might impair the active properties. He further observed: "It has power over the motion of the heart to a degree yet unobserved in any other medicine. . . . The most frequent sign of too much Digitalis is nausea and vomiting and when occurring, they indicate the cessation of the drug."

These conclusions have withstood the test of time. Standardized tablets containing the powdered leaf are used in medicine today, though there are also preparations of crystalline digitoxin and certain other glycosides extracted from the leaf. After Withering's work, Digitalis began to appear in pharmacopoeias and there it has remained ever since.

The physicians of Withering's day could not distinguish between the dropsy of heart disease and that caused by kidney disorders; these differences were first noted by Richard Bright forty years later. And it was not until 1871 that the active principles of Digitalis became known, when the French chemist Nativelle isolated a mixture of the glycosides.

Decisive later work was done in Switzerland by Professor Arthur Stoll, who also unraveled the complicated ergot alkaloids. In his book *The Cardiac Glycosides,* published in 1937, he pointed out that Digitalis has a rival in the ancient drug squill or Mediterranean sea onion, *Urginea maritima* whose bulbs grow half immersed along the sandy shores. The Ebers Papyrus of about 1500 B.C. contains an Egyptian heart-disease prescription made up of specified proportions of: dates, bulbs of squills, amamu plant, sweet beer, and tehebu tree, to be boiled, then strained and taken for four days. Dr. Stoll wrote that squill became neglected as a result of the enthusiasm over foxglove, but it "has a value of its own and does not simply live on the failures of other heart remedies."

Lily of the valley, *Convallaria majalis,* contains convallatoxin, the most potent of all Digitalis-like drugs. (A closely related compound has been synthesized and is being tested on animals.) In addition to Strophanthus, Rauwolfia, and Cinchona derivatives, Pheasant's eye, *Adonis vernalis,* and the spectacular Night-blooming cereus, *Selenicereus grandiflorus,* also have cardioactive constituents. Even some toad poisons exhibit Digitalis-like activity; toad skins were actually prescribed thousands of years ago in China for dropsy.

One of our country's foremost authorities on medicinal plants, the late Dr. Heber W. Youngken, Sr., author of *A Textbook of Pharmacognosy* and *Pharmaceutical Botany,* explained that there are dozens of botanicals with a long history of use as heart stimulants and diuretics. In the forty years that Dr. Youngken served as a member of the Revision Committee of the United States Pharmacopoeia and the National Formulary, he saw a number of drug plants wax and wane in popularity. While he was a student, aconite from *Aconitum napellus* of the buttercup family, called by the ancients "the queen mother of poisons," was used in minute quantities to depress overactive hearts. When he was an instructor in materia medica in medical school, his chief was the same physician who attended President Benjamin Harrison during a serious heart attack. He recalled that when the President did not respond to Digitalis, fluid extract of black Indian hemp, *Apocynum cannabinum,* was tried and it saved his life. "As he recovered and lived several more years, it was obviously a good drug," Youngken said. "Other cardiotonics in those days were Christmas rose *Helleborus niger,* and hawthorn *Crataegus oxyacantha.* Like Digitalis, they acted primarily as heart stimulants and secondarily as diuretics. The strengthened heart pumped more blood through the kidneys with the result that water accumulated in the tissues was carried off. Even that pest 'quack grass' had its advocates as a diuretic. The United States Surgeon General during World War I swore by extracts made from this plant and it was in the National Formulary for a long time. Some doctors prescribed dried corn silk for the same purpose."

Youngken, noted for his morphologic and taxonomic studies of many plants, collected specimens in every state but two, and some of his most interesting shorter publications described the botanicals used by the American Indians and adopted by the colonists. A surprising number of these or their isolated chemicals are still official drugs today.

After the Revolutionary War, one of the first reuniting links between the former colonists and England was the exchanging of medicinal plants. Voyages of several months destroyed many of the living specimens, but seeds were shipped to friends by doctors who in those days were almost as much botanists as physicians. The foxglove was native to Europe, and because of its beauty it was grown as an ornamental in almost every garden. One of the first to cultivate it in the New World was Dr. Hall Jackson of Portsmouth, New Hampshire, who wrote President Ezra Stiles of Yale College in 1787: "In the last ship from London, and the last Post from Boston, I was honored with a very polite, obliging and interesting Letter from Dr. Withering; and favored, also, with a quantity of Seeds of the Foxglove by him. He writes, 'I send more than you may have occasion for, in the hope that you will distribute them into the other Provinces.' It is with much pleasure that I comply with the Doctor's humane wish, in enclosing you a small quantity of them, being fully persuaded you will find equal satisfaction in the cultivation of so useful and ornamental a vegetable."

From such beginnings, foxglove escaped cultivation and now grows freely across the United States. Until recently, most of the Digitalis leaves in commerce were gathered from wild plants in Oregon, Washington, New York, and Europe. But glycosides are very fragile constituents, and in order to insure standard potency of the end product, S. B. Penick and Company, which supplies over three-fourths of the Digitalis used in this country, began cultivating it on their Meadow Springs Farm in Oley, Pennsylvania. Here the purple foxglove, *Digitalis purpurea,* is grown as an annual from new seedlings each year, as only the first-year leaves are used. These are picked by hand in the autumn, spread on trays to dry over special ovens that control moisture content, and then packed under pressure in air-tight drums for shipment. This farm produces enough leaves each year for pharmaceutical manufacturers to make 250,000,000 pills, most of which are green like the leaves they contain. Part of the balance of the domestic demand is imported from Europe, where Grecian foxglove, *D. lanata,* is the main species used. Meer Corporation and Burroughs Wellcome supply most of this variety.*

Because Digitalis leaves vary in potency, the problem is how to gauge this potency and what to use as a reference or measuring stick. Fortunately, one glycoside from *Strophanthus gratus,* ouabain, has an action on the heart similar to that of Digitalis. Ouabain can be isolated as pure crystals, crystals that can be assayed by laboratory instruments like the spectrophotometer. So the pharmacologist can measure the potency of the green leaves against the crystals obtained from an African arrow poison. Put another way, the measure of an English garden is taken with a jungle vine.

While Digitalis still continues to be the standard drug in cardio-vascular therapy, research within the past few years has expanded its application to other diseases. Two new uses were described in 1962: Doctors at the National Institute of Neurological Diseases and Blindness used Digitalis to treat patients with glaucoma, an eye disease that may lead to blindness. Digitalis affected the main characteristic of this disorder —intense pressure within the eye—by reducing the production of fluid that fills the eyeball. The drug seems to inhibit an enzyme involved in fluid formation, cutting its production by 45 per cent. This is comparable to results obtained from a synthetic compound currently in wide use for glaucoma.

At the 1962 American Medical Association Clinical Meeting, doctors learned about the first method of treatment to slow the fatal progress of muscular dystrophy, a group of hereditary diseases marked by a progressive loss of muscular

---

* Botanical drug crops generally do not require enough acreage to attract organized agriculture. William W. Bell, Penick Vice-President, said that the total area required to grow the essential drug plants adapted to this country would not be more than a few hundred acres. While many landowners are interested in growing medicinal plants, Bell feels that the venture should never be undertaken by those unfamiliar with drug plant marketing unless they have definite contracts with reputable buyers.

strength that leaves the victim helpless. This therapy involved the Digitalis glycoside digitoxin and a steroid hormone, plus a strenuous program of exercise. It was developed and then tested for six years at the Northwestern University Medical School in Chicago. While little is known about the disease, there is some evidence that muscle cells become "leaky" and essential nutrients are rapidly lost. It appears that Digitalis makes these cell membranes less permeable, while the steroid compound helps the body to utilize available protein.

In the realm of basic science, experiments with Digitalis and several hundred other plant species being grown artificially in laboratory flasks may answer such fundamental questions as why plants produce glycosides and other substances useful to man.* Dr. Stoll suggested that the function of toxic glycosides in Digitalis might be to protect against attacks by vermin or parasites. Or, being more soluble than some other plant constituents, they may operate as transport or storage systems. Other authorities, such as Dr. Ray F. Dawson of Columbia University, have found that the production of medically active materials (alkaloids, for instance) is related to specific periods of growth. In describing his experiments in this field over the past twenty years, Dawson remarked that these substances may be holdovers from former evolutionary periods when they served a purpose vital to the plant itself, but now they may be only "botanical artifacts."

---

* In a chapter on Digitalis, only passing mention may be made of work on other medicinal plants. Most of the papers read at the 1963 annual meeting of the American Society of Pharmacognosy dealt with the biosynthesis of natural products, including ergot alkaloids, steroids, nicotine, and substances from narcotic and hallucination-producing plants. Experimental results reported in the literature refer to atropine from belladonna root cultures (West and Mika, 1957); hyoscyamine from Datura (French and Gibson, 1957); alkaloids from Vinca and cardiac glycosides from Apocynum (Babcock and Carew, 1962); and antimicrobial substances from Aspen tissue (Mathes, 1963), to name a few research projects.

No one has the answers to these questions yet, but during the past few years an increasing number of scientists in many disciplines have begun to seek them. The recent president of the American Society of Pharmacognosy, Dr. J. L. Beal of Ohio State University, worked with Professor Egil Ramstad of Purdue University on a project using radioactive mevalonic acid, an organic acid related to acetate, to show how *Digitalis lanata* builds up the glycoside, lanatoside A, in the leaves. Professor Edward Leete has done similar work on *D. purpurea* at the University of Minnesota. This method is akin to the use of fluorescent or light-producing dyes to catch a thief—the "labeled" chemicals trace the pathways of the glycosides.

One method for keeping botanical materials alive and ready for experimental use in the laboratory is plant tissue culture. (The chemical reaction going on within the plant is biosynthesis. Sometimes the terms plant tissue culture and biosynthesis are confused.) Digitalis growing in glass containers under artificial light bears no outward resemblance to the garden's stately foxglove, yet the clusters of brown and green cells being nourished by a substance that looks like jellied consommé may represent all parts of the natural plant. One goal of this research, however, is to limit production to the most scientifically interesting or economically important plant parts, thus reducing waste. It is hoped that medicinals may some day be produced in this efficient fashion for commercial harvesting, thus eliminating the expense and bother of field cultivation or jungle searching.

So far, only a few medicinal substances from higher plants have been obtained by this method and none in sufficient quantity to replace traditional sources of supply. The problems to be overcome are many and complex, but the work itself is fascinating. Consider the matter of growth control: Undifferentiated plant cells can be made to develop into specific parts such as roots through the controlled use of different nutrients and chemicals. The culture medium in which the plants are grown may be composed of measured quantities of agar, coconut milk, vitamins, minerals, and auxins in part-per-million concentrations. The auxins are growth-influencing substances like the organic compound, 2,4-D, and the fungus derived gibberellic acid. The results can border upon science fiction. (For instance, a carrot plant was produced from a single, unorganized carrot cell—not a seed. And Dr. Philip R. White, a pioneer in this field, has kept a tomato root in continuous culture for thirty years.)

Dr. E. John Staba, Chairman of the University of Nebraska's Department of Pharmacognosy, and his co-workers reported that they were able to grow organized root systems and tiny plants from undifferentiated Digitalis cells. From these Dr. Stanislaw A. Büchner of the Medical Academy in Warsaw, Poland, while at the University of Nebraska, extracted measurable quantities of cardiac glycosides for further study. Speaking of exciting research possibilities, Dr. Staba cited one that seems particularly pertinent here: by growing cell suspensions from two different plants in one flask —say, Digitalis and another plant with known medicinal properties—a unique substance, or perhaps even a new plant, might be created. To date, this has not been accomplished. But if it is, chemical compounds with extraordinary activity may be obtained.

Studies of biosynthesis, utilizing the technique of plant tissue culture, have already made important contributions in affording new insights into genetics, nutrition, metabolic processes and pathology. These findings frequently can be applied to humans, as well as to members of the vegetable kingdom. The observation of cell changes in plant tumors, for instance, advanced our understanding of the problem of malignancy. At the Rockefeller Institute in New York City, at the Boyce Thompson Institute in Yonkers, New York, and in other research centers the world over, botanicals are being utilized as delicate scientific instruments, as well as subjects for investigation in themselves.

Just where all this poking into the secrets of life may lead, no one quite knows. But these researchers, as highly specialized plant explorers, are motivated by the same sort of curiosity as that which drove Dr. Withering to experiment with the roots, leaves, and stems of foxglove, gathered in a Shropshire garden almost 200 years ago.

Curare, Life from the Amazon's Flying Death

EXPLORERS, PRIESTS, SOLDIERS, ADVENTURERS, AND writers traveling through South American rain forests have always been fascinated by curare, the generic name for the arrow poison of the region. It is also known as woorari, urari, and other variations on the Indian phrase for "he, to whom it comes, falls." No matter which term is used, it all adds up to "poison." In excessive dosage, most drugs are poisonous, but curare is one of the very few natural poisons useful enough to become a modern drug.

To obtain firsthand information for this chapter, I traveled to the fascinating old rubber-boom city of Iquitos, Peru, 2,300 miles up the Amazon. A considerable distance away, an anthropologist introduced me to a tribe of primitive Yagua Indians she was studying. They wear grass skirts and bright feathers, live in a large communal hut, and are known far and wide as experts in making blowguns. They exchange these with the Brazilian Tecunas for curare made from the moonseed liana, or vine, *Chondodendron toxicoferum*.

Proudly, a stocky Yagua with berry-juice designs on his face demonstrated his skill with the blowgun. He placed a tiny banana about fifty feet away, walked back, inserted a thin dart into the eight-foot tube, and raised it with a casualness that made it appear as light as a feather. Suddenly, in rapid succession, there was a soft "puff" from his lips and a shout from admiring tribesmen as he hit the banana exactly in the middle. Smiling broadly—the Yaguas seemed to be laughing or singing all the time—he reached into his quiver, made from a section of bamboo, and extracted another dart, a needle-sharp, foot-long sliver from the rib of a palm leaf. On the business end there was a dark brown stain: curare, so potent, so deadly, that it can kill bird or beast in a matter of minutes. Pulling a tuft of Ceiba-tree kapok from a gourd container, he twirled the cottony fluff around the butt end of his dart so that it would form an airtight plug inside the blowgun. There was a reason for everything; for instance, the little nick just back of the arrow's tip would cause it to break off inside the victim.

Dermot B. Taylor, M.D., Chairman of the Pharmacology Department at the University of California in Los Angeles, had described to me other aspects of this incredible native "know-how," which he had observed on his curare collecting trips to Peru: "These primitive experimenters can pick the best plant from eight species of Chondodendron. They know how to make a potent extract and they have devised methods of testing its potency: If a frog can jump more than eight jumps after being stuck, the brew is too weak. They also add other plants to improve adhesion of the poison to the dart. And all this without a written language!"

After I returned from Peru, I interviewed botanist B. A. Krukoff, introduced in the Strophanthus chapter. Beginning in the 1930's, when he was associated with the New York Botanical Garden, Merck Research Laboratories commissioned him to obtain authentic curare materials from the Tecunas and Javas of Brazil. With his assistant, the late Ricardo Froes, he made many expeditions into this area; but he is, perhaps, best known for his monographs on the three groups of South American plants containing paralyzing principles.

The Frank N. Meyer Medal given through the American Genetic Association to outstanding plant explorers. Pictured is the first recorded plant collecting expedition, that of Queen Hatshepsut of Egypt, who sent ships to the Land of Punt to obtain frankincense (Boswellia) trees about 1500 B.C.

[Fran]k N. Meyer, one [of] the USDA's first [pla]nt explorers, sur[vey]ing the mountain [vege]tation in Shansai, China. Death by drowning in the [Ya]ngtse River ended Explorer Meyer's career.

U.S. Department of Agriculture

William Steere with *Cinchona pubescens* specimen in the Andes, 1942.

William Steere and fellow botanists make their way over an Andean landslide, 1942.

Cinchona country, Sierra Las Golondrinas, Carchi, Ecuador.

Crossing the bridge
over Rio Pastaza
at Baños, Ecuador;
William Steere
and botanists, 1944.

While Steere and
a dozen plant collectors
slept in these
Andean huts,
a violent tropical storm
brought this tree
down in their midst,
but no one was injured.

Cinchona bark
drying in the sun.

Jivaro Indian
of Ecuador
with curare darts.

Joseph Rock
in a Hawaiian plantation
of young
chaulmoogra trees, 1924.

Dermot Taylor with vine used in preparing
curare.

It is important to keep in mind that curare may have as many as thirty ingredients and that these vary widely from region to region and tribe to tribe. So do the methods for testing the poison. Krukoff told me that in Brazil curare is bartered on this basis: If a monkey hit by a dart is only able to get from one tree to the next before he falls dead, this is "one-tree curare" and it is considered to be superior. "Two-trees curare" is less satisfactory, and "three-trees curare" is so weak that it is used to bring down live animals that the Indians wish to keep in captivity. In other words, to be struck by a poisoned arrow does not necessarily mean instant death. The results depend upon the potency.

Back in 1935 there had been some discussion about using curare as a military weapon, Krukoff recalled. "We heard from Major Dwight Eisenhower, who was in the Philippines at the time, that curare-filled bullets sealed with wax were not practical in modern warfare. However, I have often wondered why societies concerned with the prevention of cruelty to animals do not advocate such bullets for hunting deer. If potent curare were used, there would be no wounded, suffering animals, for they would die immediately."

I had heard that curare was used only for hunting in South America, never in warfare, and I asked several other explorers about this. According to one of them, "The Indians would stick a dart into an enemy just as fast as they'd see one." Another reported that some tribesmen amuse themselves with a version of Russian roulette that consists of puffing a handful of darts, one tipped with curare, at each other.

The first observers of the use of poison by South American Indians placed little value on it. These were the Spanish conquistadores, who, in their search for mythical treasures, said that they were suffering from a fever only gold could cure. Blinded by visions of El Dorado, they ignored many flourishing drug plants whose powers would some day prove invaluable in modern medicine. After the Spanish explorer Francisco de Orellana left Pizarro in 1541 and made his way down the river he named Amazonas, he wrote in his journal, "We did not escape without damage because [the Indians] killed another companion of ours . . . and in truth, the arrow did not penetrate half a finger, but, as it had poison on it, he gave up his soul to our Lord."

More than fifty years later Sir Walter Raleigh seems to have been one of the first to think in terms of potential military use and to speculate upon the possibility of an antidote for the poison. In his book *The Discoverie of the Large and Bewtiful Empire of Guiana Performed in the Year 1595,* he explained that "the true remedie" could not be extracted from the natives: ". . . there never was a Spaniard, either by gift or by torment, that could attain to the true knowledge of the cure, although they have put to invented torture I know not how many . . . these Indians know it not, no, not one among thousands; but their soothsayers and priestes do who conceal it and only teach it but from father to son." The thought of a secret weapon that could silently pick off outpost guards from a distance, or be used on the tips of swords in close combat, must have been appealing in the fifteenth and sixteenth centuries. But the development of rifles in the late 1500's caused the military to by-pass exotic substances in favor of powder and ball.

Following close on the heels of the soldiers were the priests, who found another use for curare. A Father Zea insisted upon having brought to him only live fowls, which he then killed with a poisoned arrow, claiming that the meat tasted better. "This is probably true," a pharmacologist explained to me. "When an animal is wounded, then chased, and dies in a state of fear, its secretions give the meat a gamey flavor. With curare, it would die relaxed."

Perhaps the most amazing property of curare is that small amounts can be taken by mouth with no ill effects, providing there are no open sores in the mouth or throat. (Some tribes even use it for gastric disturbances.) The poison is effective only if it enters the bloodstream; however, a mere scratch can be fatal to a small animal if a little blood is drawn. Curare kills by producing paralysis, not the rigid form that results from strychnine poisoning, but a limp relaxation of skeletal muscles. It progressively blocks off the nerve endings adjacent to the muscles, first in the extremities, then finally in the chest wall. Breathing stops because muscles of respiration cease to operate. The brain does not seem to be affected because victims remain lucid until the end.

Dr. Bernard Finch, in *Passport to Paradise,* published by the Philosophical Library in 1960, reported the following account, taken from the diary of a man struck by an arrow while searching for the "lost city of the Incas" with Colonel Rouel's French expedition in 1913: "After the initial shock had worn off, I felt a gradual weakness and tiredness of my eyes. . . . I was able to see only by separating the lids with my fingers, and even then I could not see properly as vision was blurred and the other members of the party appeared double. Gradually, I felt I could not close my mouth and my lower jaw fell open. My lips were wet and saliva poured onto my chest. I was lying in the bottom of the canoe in the hot sun, but could not raise my head or close my mouth owing to the extreme weakness of my neck muscles. I was bitten by innumerable insects and yet I found I could not brush them off my face as my arms and legs were weak and paralyzed. By now, I was unable to turn my head at all and the wound in my arm was throbbing. From my arms I felt the paralysis creeping down my chest so that it was impossible to breathe without effort." (The excerpt does not clarify whether the man died or how his reactions were recorded in the diary. Perhaps the last entry was put into the first person by an observer.)

227

Almost 200 years were to pass after Orellana's voyage of discovery down the Amazon before the first scientific experiments were made with curare in 1743, by the French mathematical geographer, Charles Marie de la Condamine, who figured prominently in the quinine story. "During my sojourn at Cayenne," he wrote, "I had the curiosity to try [to see] if the venom of the poisoned arrows, which I had preserved upwards of a year, still retained its activity. A pullet pricked in the wing with one of these same arrows seemed to faint a minute afterwards. It was shortly seized with convulsions, and, notwithstanding it was made to swallow sugar while in this state, expired."

Actually, the poison can remain potent for as long as thirty years. Sugar, salt, and sea water were believed in those days to act as antidotes, and La Condamine, in continuing his experiments, thought that he saved a third pullet by the administration of sugar, but he was mistaken. The fowl must have survived for other reasons. We still do not have a completely reliable antidote for excessive amounts of curare. Interestingly enough, a West African ordeal poison from the Calabar bean, *Physostigma venenosum,* was used to produce the first successful antagonist to the action of curare—the drug physostigmine. Further work by chemists resulted in the compound neostigmine, used most frequently in treating the serious muscular disorder, myasthenia gravis. Intravenous neostigmine is useful for moderate curare poisoning when there is no respiratory failure; but in marked poisoning, it may be dangerous.

The ritual of curare-making always has been a closely guarded secret that few white men have been permitted to watch. B. A. Krukoff believes that an early traveler, J. C. D. von Schreber, who mentioned specific plants used by Indians in Surinam in 1783, may have been the first. He called these *Toxicaria americana,* later found to be synonymous with

Strychnos guianensis. Strychnos is one of the curare constituents today. (Old World Strychnos, especially *S. nux-vomica* of India, is the source of the alkaloid strychnine, which has quite a different effect than the curare alkaloids.)

In 1800, Humboldt and Bonpland made the first accurate, detailed description of native curare brewing in Esmeralda, on the Orinoco. The following is Dr. A. R. McIntyre's translation, from his scholarly study *Curare*, published by the University of Chicago Press in 1947:

"We were fortunate enough to find an old Indian less drunk than the others who was occupied with the preparation of curare poison from the freshly collected plants. [Fresh plants are always used.] This was the local chemist. We found at his dwelling a great clay cauldron for soaking the vegetable juices, some shallow vessels for evaporation, some plantain leaves rolled into cones, serving to filter the liquid. In the cabin which was transformed into a chemical laboratory, the greatest order prevailed. The Indian was known in the mission by the name of 'maître du poison.' He had the impassive air and pedantic tone formerly found in the European pharmacist. 'I know,' said he, 'that the whites have the secret for making soap and this black powder which, if one misses, has the fault of making a loud noise that scares away the animal. Curare which we prepare is far superior to that which you make over there, beyond the seas. It is the juice of a plant which kills quietly without one knowing whence the blow came.' "

The chemical procedure which Humboldt went on to describe was essentially the same as that used today. The large vines, or lianas, were collected and the bark was scraped off and pounded. The fibrous mass of bark was then thrown into the leaf funnels and cold water was poured over this. The yellowish liquor that filtered drop by drop through the bark was poisonous, but it did not acquire its strength until it was concentrated by evaporation, in the manner of molasses. From time to time, the Indian invited the visitors to taste the liquid being heated over a fire; the degree of bitterness determined when the brew was ready. Since the concentrated juice was still not thick enough to stick to arrows, a glutinous vegetable was added to it. After boiling, curare resembled tar.

Humboldt pointed out that the vapors were not harmful, despite the legend circulating among the missionaries of that time to the effect that old women were shut up in huts and forced to make curare. If, after inhaling the fumes for two days, they were still alive, the brew was discarded as too weak. Another rumor described a tribe of Indians who secreted the poison under their fingernails so that they could kill an enemy in hand-to-hand combat merely by clawing him.

In 1812, Charles Waterton collected curare in South America and began a series of experiments in England to verify the poison's toxicity and to test all the so-called antidotes. He injected curare, which he called wourali, into animals ranging in size from a chicken to an ox. "It makes a pitying heart ache to see a poor creature in distress or pain," he wrote. "However, wourali poison destroys life's action so gently, that the victim appears to be in no pain whatever; and probably, were the truth known, it feels none, saving the momentary smart at the time the arrow enters."

Waterton found wourali fatal in all cases, with death occurring in five to twenty-five minutes. Antidotes were tested, including submersion up to the mouth in water, but none of them worked. After two asses had died, he decided to try a new technique devised by two other Englishmen, Sir Benjamin Brodie and E. N. Bancroft. He injected the poison into the shoulder of a she-ass and in ten minutes she appeared to be dead. He then cut an incision in her windpipe and began inflating her lungs with a pair of bellows. The animal revived and raised her head. But when Waterton stopped pumping, she slumped down and again lost consciousness. He immediately resumed artificial respiration and after two hours she was able to rise and walk about. Months later, after the wounds healed, she became fit and frisky. Her reward was retirement to a good stable and lush pasture.

This demonstration marked the turning point in curare's history. In most cases, life now could be rescued from the "flying death" by preventing asphyxiation, and thus its mysterious power to relax muscles might be used in medicine.

In an attempt to clarify curare's muscle-relaxing property, the great French physiologist Claude Bernard conducted a classic series of experiments on frogs in 1850. Using probes that emitted electricity produced by voltaic cells, he found that the excitability of a curarized frog's nerves and its muscles was completely unaffected by the poison, but still they did not work together properly. Curare's action, he concluded, took place at the junction between the two. Its effect was, somehow, to block the transmission of nerve impulses to the muscles. Since then, other scientists have fully confirmed the basic accuracy of Bernard's findings, and his methods are still used today in pharmacology. Modern physiologists have shown that impulses from the brain, traveling down a nerve, activate the nerve endings to produce a chemical called acetylcholine, which in turn stimulates the muscles. It is believed that curare's antagonistic action on this substance blocks the nerve impulses from reaching the muscle. Although the actual mechanism of how this takes place is still somewhat of a mystery—Dr. Taylor at U.C.L.A. is one of those seeking the answer—curare has proved to be a complete, almost perfect muscle relaxant.

Its early clinical uses, however, were extremely varied in results because there was no such thing as standardized curare. Its potency differed tremendously from batch to batch. One doctor tried three different sources before he obtained favorable results in his long treatment of a girl suffering from St. Vitus' dance. Since jungle witch doctors tossed everything from snake venom to poisonous ants into curare pots, no wonder physicians used it only as a last resort.

In 1858, Dr. M. Vella, an Italian, tried curare on three patients with traumatic tetanus, or lockjaw. This often fatal disease—nine out of ten untreated persons die—causes very painful muscular contractions. Dr. Vella dissolved crude curare in water and applied the solution directly to the wounds. Pain was reduced and spasms were temporarily stopped, so he continued the treatment for fifteen days. One of the patients, a soldier struck in the heel by a rifle ball at the Battle of Magenta, left the hospital at the end of that time, cured.

As the years went by, curare was employed in easing the last stages of the always fatal rabies. It was cited as useful in many disorders, such as strychnine poisoning, convulsions, epilepsy, infantile paralysis, nervous tics, and many forms of spastic paralysis, to name just a few. But the outcome was always uncertain. Despite the fact that scientists and travelers had amassed an amazing amount of detail concerning curare, there was no clear idea of which plants went into which brews; they were just a hodgepodge of herbs.

As early as 1820, chemists at the Botanical Institute in Bogotá attempted to isolate the active ingredients in the arrow poison, and they did manage to extract a bitter principle which they differentiated from strychnine. More than 100 years later, there was a growing feeling of urgency about this research because the increasing use of firearms had gradually caused the art of poison-making to decline. Raw materials were so scarce that Dr. Harold King in England first isolated d-tubocurarine, the chief paralyzing alkaloid, from an old, dried museum specimen of unknown botanical derivation. This was in 1935 and it constituted a milestone, chemically speaking, in the development of the drug.

In 1938, an American writer, Richard C. Gill, drew attention to curare as never before. Layman though he was, Gill has been widely credited with making important scientific contributions. One curare brochure distributed to doctors stated that "Gill . . . an explorer and naturalist, assisted in making available in the United States a single, identified plant species, *Chondodendron tomentosum,* which is the basis for a purified curarizing extract . . ."

This climbing liana with heart-shaped leaves and grape-like clusters of elongated purple fruits is called *ampihuasca* by the Chazuta Indians of Peru's San Martin Valley. The plant was first collected and described by Ruiz and Pavon in 1798. It is not a member of the nux vomica family to which Strychnos belongs, Loganiaceae; it is a moonseed or Menispermaceae. These two families supply the potent curarizing effects in Amazon arrow poisons, although, as noted earlier, other plants are added to make the substance sticky or to confer some "magical" powers. The long and difficult taxonomic studies required to classify and describe these plants were not done by Gill, the writer-explorer, but by professional botanists—Krukoff, H. Moldenke and the late J. Monachino, of the New York Botanical Garden; and A. C. Smith, now Assistant Secretary of the Smithsonian Institution, who has explored extensively in the curare regions of the Amazon.

Because almost everyone interviewed in connection with this chapter reacted strongly to the mention of Gill's name, insisting that he either ought to be given "due credit" or, on the other hand, "exposed for the adventurer that he was," his history is briefly reviewed here.

In the late 1920's, Gill and his wife, Ruth, left Lima, Peru, where he had represented an American company, and settled in the beautiful Rio Pastaza Valley in Ecuador. Here they hewed from the jungle a coffee and castor-bean plantation, also designated by some who visited it as "a sort of dude ranch."

The Gills were amateur ethnologists and the Indians honored their interest by making Gill a *brujo* or witch doctor. About four years later, Gill sustained an apparently minor injury in a fall from a horse. However, in a few months his body became numb, first on one side, then on the other; he returned to the United States and was hospitalized in Washington, D.C.

While undergoing treatment for spastic paralysis, he was advised that his chief hope for a cure lay in exercises that would be both painful and prolonged. "The only drug that might help you," the doctors told him, "is that arrow poison, curare. But in its present crude state, it is too dangerously unpredictable to use in a case like yours." The doctors agreed that if properly identified plants could be obtained and a standardized form of curare scientifically produced from them, not only Gill but thousands of other patients could be relieved of suffering and spasticity. These words convinced the bedridden writer that he had found his true mission in life at last. He was confident that his past contacts with the Indians would enable him to ferret out their secret recipes and processes—after all, was he not an honorary *brujo*?

With truly superhuman effort and his wife's constant care, he performed his painful, muscle-strengthening exercises for four years. Finally, he was able to travel. With financial help from friends like C. H. S. Merrill, Gill returned to Ecuador in 1938 and set up a base camp close to an Indian village about twenty days' travel by dugout from his hacienda. There he bartered bolts of cloth, mirrors, fish hooks, and beads for permission to photograph the curare ritual. This complete photographic record was an important contribution in itself and most difficult to achieve because the Indians considered his camera "white man's magic" designed to counteract their own.

Later that year, Gill brought to the United States some thirty pounds of curare, plus many sacks of medicinal plants. Unfortunately, several things happened to mar this story of vision and courage. Drug manufacturers refused to work with his material in the beginning because they were too busy with other projects. Gill seems to have been bitterly disappointed and those who knew him then say that he became difficult to deal with, secretive, and insistent that there was no chance of ever synthesizing the natural product. He claimed that he, and he alone, was able to supply raw materials for the drug. Eventually he set up his own curare business in California. His dramatic version of the story, appearing in magazines and later in his book *White Water and Black Magic,* published in 1940, was widely accepted as the only side of the picture.

Did his contributions further science in any way? Richard Gill died in 1958 at the age of fifty-seven, so we have only his writings and the recollections of those who worked with him. I went to Iquitos to interview a man who knew him very well, Mr. Jim Horning, an American engineer who first went to South America in 1910 and stayed on to explore for abandoned Spanish gold mines in Ecuador, Peru, and Colombia. Here are some of his comments from a taped interview:

"We called Gill 'Depilatory Dick' because he always insisted that a plant the Indians called *arelina blanca* was used by them to keep their faces free of beards. The fact that some races are less hairy than others escaped him, as did the common practice of plucking out whiskers with shell tweezers. He tried to interest drug manufacturers in this, as well as in plants he thought controlled fertility. He also insisted that the native women had such beautiful hair because of secret plant preparations. Again, he closed his mind to the fact that they do not dye, bleach, burn, or otherwise torture their hair. Well, nothing much came of all this. Frankly, I have been long exposed to so-called fabulous native remedies and I feel that most of them have to be taken with a grain of salt and lot of boiling water. It's frequently the boiling water that does the trick."

"What about curare?" I asked.

"I was in on the curare thing from the beginning," Horning replied. "In fact, in the mid-1930's, I did some library research for Gill, who was then in Ecuador, and on the basis of what I found out, I got in touch with Merck on Gill's behalf. Later, I was one of the original members of the much-publicized Gill-Merrill expedition organized to search for curare plants. Gill was a very tall, handsome fellow with powers of persuasion to beat anyone I've ever met. He talked a lot of people into supporting his various projects and when they didn't pay off, he found himself with enemies. I don't say he was dishonest—he believed in what he was doing. He just wasn't practical. The expedition began to fall apart, so I went back to my work in the Andes."

"Do you think the adventures in Gill's book were mostly fictional?" I asked.

"It has been some time since I read the book, but I recall that a number of incidents seemed treated with poetic license. However, Gill's life was so incredible that a court reporter's transcript of the facts would appear utterly unbelievable."

Because Horning had left the expedition before the curare plants were collected, he could not clarify botanical matters. But through anthropologist Marjorie Smith, who is doing an acculturation study of the curare-using Yaguas near Iquitos, I met a woman who had the facts in hand. She is Señora Clara Rosa de Klug, widow of the German botanical collector Guillermo G. Klug, a man highly praised by Schultes for his meticulous work. A collector of note in her own right, Señora de Klug specializes in butterflies, which she supplies to leading museums. Some of the rare species (for example, *Agriae Klugii*) bear her name.

Señora de Klug's dark eyes flashed when I mentioned curare and I soon learned why she was so emotionally involved. While still a teenager, she left a sheltered life in Lima to marry Dr. Klug and go with him into the wilds of the

Amazon headwaters where they made their collections. One field trip that she remembers well took place in April, 1935, when the Klugs were the first to observe the Chazuta Indians use a certain plant as the main ingredient of their curare.

"My husband," she told me proudly, "was the first to send to North America the species used to make curare for modern medicine—*Chondodendron tomentosum*. Others have made this claim from time to time, but he was the first and I can prove it." Among her souvenirs was documentation of the fact that the plant had been identified by Krukoff at the New York Botanical Garden and that Dr. Klug had sent many, many curare specimens to the United States. Commercial supplies still come chiefly from Chazuta territory.

When I asked Krukoff about this he said, "Without that specimen collected by Klug, we would not know that the main ingredient of Chazuta curare is *C. tomentosum*. Much later, Richard Gill brought various useful botanical specimens and curare samples to Merck Research Laboratories. Among these we also identified *C. tomentosum*."

As for that other company's brochure citing Gill, upon further investigation of old records, researchers there reported that their first important experiments had, indeed, been made possible by the forgotten German collector Klug; Gill actually had supplied them with "trade" curare from unidentified sources. Nevertheless, Gill deserves much credit for going into the jungles, despite his affliction, and coming out with botanicals of whatever kind first or not because curare plants are reached only after dangerous rapids and rock-strewn shallows are braved via canoes or rafts. The gigantic bush ropes of Strychnos are sometimes as thick as a man's body. Chondodendron, on the other hand, is a medium-sized liana with very characteristic flat stems. These are twisted in strands around enormous trees which, even when uprooted by tropical storms, continue to be held erect by these natural cables. Collectors must make their identification from bark and wood alone because flowers and fruits are high in the tangled forest canopy. Then as many as fifteen or twenty trees may have to be cut down in order to free the vines.

As one company's directive to field men implied, it is not easy to obtain help with this heavy labor. The following suggestions were based upon a log kept by collector Frederick H. Vogel: "There is not enough available labor to exploit *C. tomentosum*. In order to obtain any help at all, one must deal with the *patrones,* never directly with the workers. Indians do not chew coca leaves in this region of Peru, but they have been just as effectively debauched with cheap, fiery *cachaca* liquor until they will not work without it. All their hard earned money goes for *cachaca,* the chief item of trade. The few absolute necessities of life are bought on credit from the *patrone's* company store and allegedly worked off by discounted labor. None of the poor Indians can read, write or figure, so the *patrone* shopkeeper has a CPA's dream with his books. The labor force varies from day to day, time or method meaning little, either to the *patrone* boss or his men. One's attention to all details must be constant and several bottles of *cachaca* must always be ready at hand to flag up their lagging spirits."

After the vines are chopped down, they are usually cut into one-foot lengths and taken to a location where the extraction process continues in the manner described earlier. Since curare is often exchanged in a barter trade, regular supplies cannot be routinely "shipped out" on a production-line basis, and because of the difficult terrain, the purchaser carries them out as best he can. E. R. Squibb collectors are advised to allow one and one-half days by truck from Pucallpa to Tingo Maria in eastern Peru—if the roads are good between the larger villages. But they are warned that the same trip can also take as long as forty-five days.

The thick, black, crude curare is packed into tin receptacles and this is the way it arrives at the drug companies for further refinement. Considerable confusion about the various kinds of curare was cleared up in the 1880's by Rudolph Boehm, who found that the containers used at that time were fairly indicative of the different ingredients. On this basis, he divided curare into three types: tubocurare was packed in hollow bamboo canes; calabash curare took its name from hollowed-out gourds; and pot or jar curare traveled in clay vessels. (If this tradition were still followed, modern commercial supplies would be called kerosene-can curare.)

The true botanical and chemical picture is infinitely more complicated, and any drastic condensation of the extensive literature on this subject can't help being inadequate. But of the three types, tubocurare is the only one in which moonseeds —various species of Chondodendron, that is—are the main ingredients. Dr. King in England worked extensively on these in the 1930's, as did Squibb chemists Dr. J. D. Dutcher and Dr. O. Wintersteiner, who isolated d-tubocurarine in 1943 from fresh plants collected by Klug. This alkaloid is the basis for most of the curare preparations used in medicine today.

Calabash curare, the most potent type, has *Strychnos toxifera* as its main ingredient. The most important botanical contributions were made in the 1840's, by the brothers Robert and Richard Schomburgk. Dr. King obtained the first pure alkaloid, diaboline, and Nobel Laureate Paul Karrer at the University of Zurich has isolated forty-eight new alkaloids. One of these, toxiferine, has been synthesized by him and is used in Europe as a muscle relaxant which is said to have fewer side effects than other curare preparations.

Pot curare is largely based upon *Strychnos castelnaeana,* the plant La Condamine experimented with in 1745. Oddly enough, it has been little investigated since then.

Authorities emphasize that there is still much to be discovered about curare. There are a number of research projects under way, such as the three-year study at the University of Oregon supported by the National Institute of Neurological Diseases and Blindness. This is an investigation of the ways in which small amounts of curare cause paralysis.

While the botanical and chemical work was being accomplished, pharmacologists were busy devising means of improving the drug. Squibb's Horace A. Holaday perfected a unique biological assay method much more precise than the old frog test. Called the "head-drop potency test," it consisted of injecting curare of unknown strength into a rabbit's ear. The amount necessary to paralyze the neck muscles and cause the head to drop down was set at one unit; thus doctors were given a drug with predictable action.

Doctors A. R. McIntyre and A. E. Bennett, of the University of Nebraska, were pioneers in the broad clinical use of this new controlled preparation. Among the first patients treated were those suffering from spastic paralysis, Richard Gill's affliction; after injections of curare, their rigid muscles relaxed and re-education of their paralyzed limbs was greatly simplified. Curare has been used on a host of other paralyses and spastic disorders such as multiple sclerosis, hereditary St. Vitus's dance, and Parkinson's disease.

It should be noted that curare, in itself, is not considered a curative. Its value lies in its ability to relax muscles by breaking the neuro-muscular junction. When used in association with other drugs, its role is that of a powerful teammate.

Its strength was next directed toward reducing the incidence of broken bones in shock treatment for mental disease. Almost 50 per cent of such patients were suffering compressive fractures of the spine, and occasionally arms and legs were broken and skulls were fractured. Dr. Bennett injected his patients with curare solution about two minutes before shock treatments were given. The results were astonishing: in a group of 122 patients, there was not a single fracture or dislocation, and curare did not interfere in any way with the effectiveness of the therapy.

In the meantime, curare was solving problems in abdominal surgery by relaxing muscles so that a lower level of general anesthesia could be used, thus cutting down on risks and postoperative nausea and vomiting. Curare is especially helpful in operations involving older persons or those having heart conditions. It is now teamed with various anesthetic agents and used routinely in thousands of cases where tense muscles must be relaxed—tonsillectomies, rectal surgery, difficult deliveries, eye surgery—and the reduction of fractures.

Since curare was first standardized in 1943, there has been only one fatality attributed directly to its use, and it is believed that even this victim could have been saved by prompt administration of artificial respiration, which should always be available whenever curare is used. Although a completely effective antidote for extreme overdosage has yet to be found, there are some useful chemical antagonists to its action, which actually is of very short duration. Until the perfect antidote is readily available, however, travelers ought to resist the temptation to bring back curare souvenirs from the Yaguas and other Amazon employers of the "flying death."

All in all, during the few years that curare has been used in modern medicine, the jungle's deadliest killer probably has *saved* far more human lives than it ever has taken.

Chaulmoogra, King Rama's Oil for Leprosy

OIL FROM THE SEEDS OF TREES IN SOUTHEASTERN Asia and India has stood the test of time in the treatment of leprosy for thousands of years. Countless herbs and chemicals have been tried in desperate attempts to control the ravages of this scourge, which unjustly bears the greatest social stigma. But until the last decade, chaulmoogra oil enjoyed wider use and more favorable reports than any other therapy.

Dr. R. C. Cochrane, the noted leprologist, who edited the 1959 book *Leprosy in Theory and Practice,* stated: "When one reviews the long history of leprosy, one outstanding drug which has been in the forefront is chaulmoogra oil. This remedy held pride of place . . . and was the basis for all specific therapy until the sulfones [chemical compounds related to sulfa drugs] were introduced. . . ." Even today chaulmoogra oil is the only treatment in much of the vast underdeveloped areas of the world, and some of its advocates, such as the British physician Sir Leonard Rogers, have found combined sulfone-chaulmoogra therapy is more effective than either drug used alone.

According to the 1963 United States Public Health Service estimate, there are 15,000,000 leprosy victims in the world, 80 per cent of them in Africa and Asia. Authorities believe that the disease was brought to North America by the men who sailed with Columbus, and later by slaves imported from West Africa. There may be as many as 5,000 cases in the United States at the present time.

The symptoms of leprosy appear so gradually that they are seldom noticed immediately: discolored patches on the skin; nodules on the face, arms and legs; and loss of skin sensitivity, which the patient may first become aware of only after receiving a severe burn or cut without feeling any pain. It is little wonder that the ancients found leprosy so baffling. Diagnosis still presents its problems and even the most modern drugs have many limitations. Chiefly used are the sulfones, introduced in the 1940's; but anti-tuberculosis drugs, steroid hormones, and such antibiotics as streptomycin are also helpful in healing lesions. If the patient is diagnosed and treated early, the outlook is favorable, but it often takes three to five years of therapy before the disease is arrested.

The cause of leprosy was not known until 1874, when the Norwegian physician Gerhard Armauer Hansen discovered that the bacillus *Mycobacterium leprae* was always associated with the condition. Ever since, many doctors and patients have preferred to call the affliction Hansen's disease. This bacillus closely resembles that which causes tuberculosis and for this reason the two diseases have much in common. In fact, some authorities believe that the cure for both may someday be found in one drug.

Leprosy, a chronic illness with incubation periods of five years or more, is thought to be contracted through the skin and mucous membranes. The destruction of hands, feet, and other extremities is a secondary effect of nerve damage, rather than an erosion of the tissues by the bacillus. Children are much more susceptible than adults. Among Caucasians leprosy strikes almost three men to every woman, among Orientals the ratio is about ten to one, and among Negroes it is about even. Although the victims have been treated as outcasts from most societies, the disease is now known to be one of the least contagious of all so-called communicable diseases. Only about five per cent of all persons having long and intimate contact with a case in the same household eventually develop the malady.

The first leprosy victim I ever saw was the boy who carried my luggage and took care of my room in a jungle frontier town on the Río Ucayali in Peru. I was told by a physician that there is quite a lot of leprosy in South America and later, in Iquitos on the Amazon, I saw a so-called "Biblical-type leper" wearing a loincloth and swathed in filthy rags. (Many authorities doubt that the "unclean" people described in the Bible had true leprosy and in any case, they denounce the unwarranted association with sin.) This pathetic man ran aimlessly through the open air meat market where smoked monkeys dangled on hooks, their human looking hands raised in supplication; the skinned heads of various beasts, eyes intact, stared blankly; and blood and entrails mixed with mud underfoot. Above circled the sanitation department, black vultures. It was a nightmare scene that Franz Kafka might have invented and to top it all, when the leprosy sufferer picked up small children and kissed them on the mouth, the crowd roared with senseless mirth. I had heard that there is sometimes an overwhelming drive for affection in advanced stages of leprosy, as in some tuberculosis cases—surely this is one of the cruelest tricks of nature.

Although chaulmoogra seeds were recommended for leprosy in the oldest Chinese and Indian writings, the Western world did not begin to make use of the botanical until 1853, when Dr. F. J. Mouat of the Indian Medical Service introduced the folk cure into medical practice. Perhaps he had heard the East Indian legend about King Rama of Benares, who developed leprosy and fled to the jungle, where he lived on herbs and berries. His diet included the seeds of the *ḳalaw* tree and soon his symptoms subsided. Eventually he was cured. One day while strolling along a forest trail, he heard the roar of a tiger and the screams of a terrified young woman in a nearby cave. He rushed in and rescued Piya, a once-lovely princess now disfigured by the scourge that takes no notice of class or caste. Somehow, she had not eaten of the *ḳalaw* fruits, so King Rama collected these for her and tenderly restored her health. They were married and, so the romantic story goes, raised sixteen sets of twins and lived happily ever after.

Recent studies of ancient texts on Ayur-Vedic (Hindu) medicine have unearthed this prescription used a thousand years or more before the Christian era: "Chaulmoogra oil is very efficacious in leprosy. It is given in doses of ten to twenty drops after meals and it is also used externally on the affected parts. The treatment is to be continued for at least three months." Compare this with a regimen employed at the United States National Leprosarium at Carville, Louisiana, as recently as the late 1940's: "Treatment is usually begun with gelatin capsules containing five drops of chaulmoogra oil taken daily after meals. The dosage is increased until the patient's tolerance is reached. Chaulmoogra is frequently used locally in ointments or liniments."

The basic difference seems to be the addition of gelatin capsules. (The oil was also injected intramuscularly, a painful procedure.) Because the Carville patients were confined under medical supervision, their treatment was continued for the long periods of time required. It is quite likely that freely roaming leprosy cases down through the ages abandoned the disagreeable, slow-acting remedy too soon. This might account for the spread of the disease despite a known remedy.

Chaulmoogra played an important part in the development of the scientific, humane treatment of Hansen's disease in the United States. In 1766 the Spanish governor Ulloa established the Louisiana colony's first lazaretto (leprosarium) below New Orleans. After it was destroyed by a hurricane, the leprosy patients were simply ostracized. Finally, in 1878, a municipal "pesthouse," where patients could live but where they received little care, was established on the outskirts of town. (A Dr. Beard gave them sporadic doses of strychnine, potassium chlorate, and "normal horse serum.") So great was the public dread of the disease that the authorities decided to move the patients farther from the city, and they were transported at night in an old coal barge eighty miles north to Indian Camp Plantation, near Carville, and housed in deserted slave cabins. With the introduction of chaulmoogra oil in 1901 by Dr. Ralph Hopkins of Tulane Medical School, the Louisiana project gained widespread recognition, and in 1921 the federal government began to operate it as a national leprosarium.

Scientific interest in chaulmoogra reached a peak after 1904, when Dr. Frederick B. Power of the Wellcome Research Laboratories in London isolated the fatty acid constituents and prepared a refined oil that substantially reduced the toxic side effects. Then from Hawaii came the report that extraordinary results had been achieved in treating leprosy with intramuscular injections of this refined oil. In one year alone, nearly 200 patients were discharged as cured from the Kalihi Receiving Station in Honolulu. Further experimentation proved that the oil effectively checked the growth of the leprosy bacillus; no other drug showing similar action in laboratory cultures was also suitable for treating the afflicted.

Unfortunately, supplies were insufficient to meet the estimated yearly requirements of 300,000 gallons. There was an additional problem. Some Western scientists thought that the true remedy could be obtained only from the seeds of the giant evergreen *Taraktogenos kurzii,* growing in remote places in India and Burma. However, the word *kalaw,* the Burmese name for the tree, was applied to more than one species, and the seeds of these various species were so similar that only botanists could tell the difference. Native collectors indiscriminately mixed the seeds together and sold them to drug dealers in the bazaars of Rangoon, Calcutta, and other cities. Scientists were at a loss as to how to cope with this; not one of them had seen *T. kurzii* growing in the wild state and they had no idea of its range. As with Cinchona for quinine, properly identified seeds were needed so that plantation crops might provide a convenient, reliable source for the vital drug.

This situation aroused the interest of the noted explorer and horticulturist Dr. David Fairchild, Chief of the Plant Introduction Section, United States Department of Agriculture, from 1903 to 1928. (The importance of seeking non-native plants was recognized as early as 1827 by President John Quincy Adams, who instructed our foreign consuls to send back useful botanicals. But it was Dr. Fairchild who founded what is today the New Crops Research Branch, which employs ninety explorers in the quest for plants of value in agriculture, industry, and medicine.)

When Dr. Fairchild became concerned about tracing *T. kurzii* to its haunts, he got in touch with Dr. Joseph F. Rock, then teaching botany and Chinese at the University of Hawaii. In November, 1920, Rock agreed to undertake the chaulmoogra search for the USDA. From previous trips to the Orient for the Hawaiian Sugar Planters Experiment Station, he knew that beautiful trees (*Hydnocarpus anthelmintica*) used as ornamentals around the temples in Bangkok, Siam (now Thailand), yielded an oil closely resembling chaulmoogra. He decided that it would be a good idea to collect their seeds so that they also might be scientifically appraised for their value.

In an article for the March, 1922, *National Geographic,* Rock described some of the highlights of his particular drug plant expedition. He first sailed to Singapore, then went by rail to Bangkok, a distance of just over 1,000 miles that took five days: the train didn't run at night and passengers were obliged to stay in "indifferent rest-houses." The scenery en route was magnificent, causing Rock to exclaim, "Nature writes its story with a mighty hand, and orchids and graceful vines on the wayside are the commas and exclamation points of a harmonious composition."

In Bangkok no one could tell him where to find the decorative trees growing wild, so he pushed on 400 miles north to Chiengmai. After many days of fruitless searching, he picked up a clue that the two species he wanted were in southeastern Siam, which meant backtracking through Bangkok. He was finally lucky enough to find a Siamese forest ranger who was able to guide him to a stand of the ornamental variety, and he collected the seeds to send back to Hawaii.

But it was now apparent that for "true chaulmoogra" he would have to return to Chiengmai and penetrate more deeply into the interior and even across the mountains into Burma. For the next stage of his journey he chartered a houseboat for a ten-day trip down the Meh Ping River. "Rapid after rapid was negotiated, forty-one in all, requiring two days. The first large one was Keng Soi and the second Omlu, where the river made two wide curves, forming the letter 'S.' To my mind, this was the most dangerous of all. After passing the whirlpools we stopped and I went back, followed by my crew, to a few natives who had been fishing along this rapid. Instead of buying fresh fish, my men bought the oldest and rottenest they could find. This made further residence on my boat next to impossible, and I energetically demanded the removal of the offensive fish. They were eaten post haste."

At the village of Raheng, their destination, the hardest part of the journey still lay ahead. By various modes of transportation, including ponyback and bullock cart, Rock crossed the mountains into Burma. Near Moulmein he was shown a grove of thousands of *kalaws*. Although they turned out to be *H.*

castanea, related to the chaulmoogra producer, but not quite "it," Rock still collected and shipped a supply of the seeds. They had never been examined chemically, and he thought they might have the same constituents.

In Rangoon, the Forestry Service suggested he try the Upper Chindwin District of North Burma. Some 500 miles away at the end of the railroad line, he unloaded his gear in the village of Monywa near the border of Assam. "What a dreadful place! Dust, dust, dust, several feet deep, and the bullock carts conveying my luggage from the railway station to the *Shillong,* a trim stern-wheeler, were hardly visible in the alkaline clouds stirred up by clumsy feet. Kalaw seed is here sold in the bazaars, but I was told that it came down 'from the north'! The bazaar is a living entomological collection. . . ." He did not tarry long, and relieved to be on a clean boat again, he journeyed up the Chindwin River a distance of 150 miles or so. The boat ran aground many times because it was between rainy seasons and the water was very low. To free it from sand bars, the third-class passengers were ordered off and obliged to make their way as best they could along the banks until deeper water was reached.

At the village of Mawlaik, Rock learned that the elusive trees were at least another hundred miles away, over the mountains. Before setting out this time, he asked for a letter in Burmese addressed to the *tagees,* or headmen, of the villages he would be passing through to help him hire a crew of workers. Then it was up the Chindwin River again, by dugout canoe. After traveling a day in thick fog, he met a *tagee* who, after seeing the "magic letter," turned around, returned to his village and reappeared with a string of coolies in tow. They were mostly women, many with naked children strapped to their backs, and their rate of pay was one anna (about two cents) a mile. After a two-day march overland, they reached a village where at long last there were genuine chaulmoogra trees. But as luck would have it, they were not bearing fruit. The headman explained that their crop had been poor but that a village further on, Kyotka, had had a good crop the year before and there was a chance there would be another good one this year.

It was a chance Rock was willing to take and he was rewarded four or five miles outside Kyotka by the sight of whole hillsides covered with *T. kurzii,* bearing mature fruit. After setting up camp in the village, he took thirty-six coolies "determined to come back loaded with Chaulmoogra seeds." They worked furiously picking the fruit, which was the size of an orange, and stripping out the numerous seeds embedded in the pulp. To keep the seeds from losing their moisture and thus their germinating power, they were then packed in powdered charcoal and wrapped in oiled paper for the long trip back to Hawaii. After a successful day's work, the group returned to the village, noticing tiger tracks on the way but not thinking much about it. Rock planned to spend the night and leave the following morning, but as he wrote, "I had reckoned without the tiger."

Two of his coolies owned a rice field outside the village in the jungle, and that night their wives and children were sleeping in a small hut on the edge of the field to keep watch over the harvested rice while the men stayed in the village. At six in the morning, as Rock was ready to leave, the headman came to him saying that one of the children from the rice field, a five-year-old boy, had stumbled into the village, crying that a tiger had killed his mother. "Great excitement ran through the village. The temple drums were beaten and the gongs sounded an alarm. All the male villagers armed themselves with spears and knives and, marching ahead of them, I went to the scene of the tragedy." It was a gory sight. The tiger had entered the small hut where three women and two children were sleeping, killing two of the women and badly mauling the third. The little girl had disappeared and a trail of blood led into the jungle.

Rock had a litter built and the surviving woman was taken back to the village, where he dressed her wounds. He then worked with the whole village all afternoon making a drop-door trap. For bait, the body of one of the women was used, separated from the main trap by a fence of bamboo stakes. "For safety the village priest invited me to spend the night in the little wooden temple at the feet of Buddha. To sleep was unthinkable. It began to rain, the thunder rolled, and wierd lightning effects added height to the somber monarchs of the forest. Crash followed crash . . . the trampling and trumpeting of elephants, wild cries, and shouts of confusion." He did not discover until the next morning what all the commotion was about. The rampaging elephants had come into the village, demolished the huts, and devoured the harvested rice. Rock observed that "the sky still wept for this tragedy."

He was told that the villagers waited for him at the site of the trap. There he found the man-eater had been caught, and was about to be killed by spears. When the men opened the trap, they discovered that the tiger had gotten into the section where the bait was and had left only a few remains of the woman's body. These were buried nearby, and with the carcass of the tiger suspended between two poles, all returned to the village. Rock wrote, "I left Kyotka that afternoon, in spite of the rain and the advanced hour of the day. The forest looked still more somber and weird. The trip back was not a pleasant one, for we had with us the injured woman whom we were taking to Mawlaik [where the nearest hospital was] . . . she died the day after our arrival."

It was a sad finish to an otherwise successful mission. The dearly paid for chaulmoogra seeds were shipped, and Rock continued on to Calcutta and Assam, searching for other botanical specimens. In Hawaii the USDA had set aside 100 acres for a chaulmoogra plantation. At the end of 1921, thousands of seedlings from the three species Rock had collected were flourishing. It takes eight years for the plants to mature, and by 1930 a supply of the fatty-acid constituents of chaulmoogra oil was available for therapy at the Hawaiian leprosarium on Molokai and at Carville in Louisiana. Rock's early hunch that related species, even those used as ornamentals, might have similar application in medicine, paid off. Today an Indian tree, *Hydnocarpus wightiana* of the same family (Flacourtia), is used as well.

After continuing to explore for the USDA until the mid-1920's, Rock then led four expeditions to China and Tibet for the National Geographic Society and others. His field work, which covered a quarter of a century, gave us the blight-resistant chestnuts and over 700 species of rhododendrons, to name just a few of his many contributions. In December, 1962, Dr. Joseph Rock died in Honolulu at the age of seventy-nine.

Just a few weeks later, the United States Public Health Service announced that Charles C. Shepard, M.D., had cultivated human leprosy bacteria outside of the human body for the first time in history. His work, continuing at the Communicable Disease Center in Atlanta, Georgia, meant that antileprosy drugs at last might be tested in the laboratory under biologically controlled conditions. The fact that only slight progress has been made in the conquest of leprosy has often been attributed to the impossibility of infecting animals for research purposes. Dr. Shepard and his associates are concentrating upon testing synthetic drugs that have been used in tuberculosis control; vaccines to prevent this disease, such as BCG, are also being investigated for their effect upon the growth of local leprosy lesions. (So far, no one has succeeded in producing systemic leprosy in animals or in human volunteers by infection.)

Early in January, 1963, the late Dr. James A. Doull, medical director of the American Leprosy Foundation and one of the originators of the World Health Organization, told me: "Since the 1940's there has been a trend toward the abandonment of chaulmoogra in certain centers considered more advanced than others. Measurement of its value as a therapeutic agent could only be made by carefully controlled studies. Such studies have not been made."

Many authorities seem to have condemned chaulmoogra without giving it a fair trial. Professional men, in criticizing the age-old folk remedy, have stated, "We don't know how or why chaulmoogra works, so we are at a loss to improve it." Perhaps a concerted effort to fathom these mysteries of the drug's action might reveal some of the secrets of leprosy in the process.

Colonel Sir Ram Nath Chopra, "the father of pharmacology in India," has explained that past observations of patients given the oil from native bazaars have not really been reliable indicators of the drug's value. In the 1958 edition of *Indigenous Drugs of India,* he wrote: "The oil sold in bazaars is usually rancid and devoid of therapeutic properties, as it is expressed from old seeds. . . . Much of the discrepancy in results obtained can probably be accounted for by the badly adulterated oil. . . . Even now when large supplies are available, there is a great temptation for the retail dealers [in some countries of origin] to mix cheaper oils with it. . . . Whenever there is any doubt as to the nature of the oil, it is always better to test its purity."

Despite these drawbacks, Dr. Chopra concluded his analysis of the various modern methods of employing the botanical's derivatives by stating, "It is evident that chaulmoogra oil is really effective in the treatment of leprosy."

How strange it is that the long search for a cure for this scourge now is focused on the right hind foot pads of selected white mice in an Atlanta laboratory! This is where the baffling bacillus has chosen to grow. *M. leprae* prefer a temperature of 68°F., and the feet of the mice are cool. (Right hind feet are chosen only for the sake of being systematic.) In speaking of the promising research results so far, Shepard said, "They seem to offer a gateway to the prevention and cure of an ancient and dreaded enemy of mankind."

Meanwhile, King Rama's oil continues to be the only treatment available to vast numbers of leprosy sufferers throughout the world.

It Started with Sarsaparilla

MILLIONS OF PEOPLE THROUGHOUT THE WORLD TO-
day are taking fertility-regulating pills, drugs originally designed to overcome sterility and still employed by many for
that purpose. Few users realize that their destiny as parents
literally has its roots in a tropical vine with heart-shaped
leaves and tiny flowers—a wild yam called Dioscorea. Diosgenin, the miraculous substance produced by the storage organs of these plants, is the starting material for the synthesis
of the complex steroids that physicians prescribe, under several trade names, for family planning.

The consequences of this use alone are so far-reaching
that Dioscorea may well be the most important drug-yielding
plant ever discovered. In addition, cortical hormones derived
from yams provide relief from arthritis, rheumatism, asthma,
extensive burns, and serious eye and skin infections. The grave
course of many metabolic diseases is altered by hormones.
Tissue-producing male hormones rebuild bodies wasted by
illness or stunted by abnormal growth. Female hormones
ease menopausal symptoms and overcome disabling conditions that formerly required major surgery. A variety of hormones are also showing results in our two major threats to
health—mental illness and heart disease.

Such incredible therapeutic results as children for the long-childless and the arrest of certain forms of cancer make one wish for fresher, more descriptive terms than "wonder drug" or "medical milestone." The desire to see the plant and learn more about its development led to a personal investigation of the Dioscorea story. My research ended in the remote San Juan Evangelista area in the state of Veracruz, Mexico, the heart of the yam country. It began with an interview in the mid-Manhattan office of a consulting biochemist whose clients are drug manufacturers in the United States and abroad.

Norman Applezweig is the author of the comprehensive reference book *Steroid Chemistry,* published in 1962, which has an invaluable 5,000-item bibliography. For this reason, and because of his world-wide contacts, Applezweig was asked: "What percentage of steroid hormone products used today comes from yam starting materials?"

His answer: "I should estimate about 70 to 75 per cent, with the balance derived from animal sources. Other plants, such as soybeans and the Agaves that produce sisal, contribute a small amount to the total."

In recalling the early days of the hormone industry, dating only from the 1930's, he cited Professor Russell E. Marker as a key figure. At one point, Applezweig stared reflectively at the primitive Mexican figurine that sets the motif in his office and said: "The Mexican government should strike a medal for Marker because of what the $30,000,000-a-year yam industry has meant to that country alone. This becomes $120,000,000 in finished products and it is growing all the time. As for the rest of the world, we owe to him, more than to any other man, our ready and low-cost supply of steroid hormones. Without his contributions, we probably would not have synthetic hormones as we know them today."

Before an attempt was made to interview Russell Marker in Mexico City, this much was learned about his background

An illustration
om the sixteenth century
tec *Badianus Manuscript,*
showing a plant
now thought to be either
Dioscorea or Smilax,
used to treat
the skin disease, scabies.
(Third plant on right.)

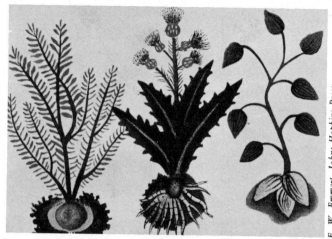

Walter Hodge
examining two large,
"elephant foot" species
of tropical yams,
in South Africa.

H. Scott Gentry
with one of his
diffcult-to-preserve
flowering specimens—
the top of an Agave
collected in west Texas.

Norman Applezweig, who worked with Russell Marker on the Mexican yams.

Norman Applezweig Associates

Syntex, S.A.

Don Cox (left) and Agronomist Luis conferring on yam cultivation problems.

A Mexican yam and derivatives.

Cinnamon zeylanicum or cream bark from Hunkitt and Sonolland's Plantae Javanicae Rariore (1838). This species was placed in its broad sense with the genus Cinnamonum, but still and apparently included the C. zeylinicum or Cinnamomum.

This drawing of the Cinchona tree was sampled by the plant were drawn by San Miguel de Carlisteban, a Spanish government official in New Granada (Colombia) to Jan Josef Delestino Mutis, who, in turn sent them to Linnaeus. In 1764, Linnaeus supplemented his classification of Cinchona. (China Jemmillia Aroma, The Cinchona of Rubiola, 1955)

Left: This facsimile illustration shows clearly, in the handwriting of Linnaeus, the original isonllma of the genus Cinchona and also the species, officinalis. (From Wellcome Historical Medical Museum)

Right: A drawing of C. officinalis (Curtis Bot. Mag. v. 80, 1863) Linnaeus first described this species in the Genera Plantarum of 1742, but the definitive description did not appear until the 12th edition of the Systema Naturae of 1767, after Linnaeus had received sketches and notices from Mutis. Thus the species identified as C. officinalis is, in fact, quite different from that described in 1742 from La Condamine's drawing.

Don José Celestino Mutis (1732–1808), Spanish physician and naturalist was one of the foremost disciples of Linnaeus. Attracted by the many fields of study in South America, he went to New Granada (Colombia) in 1760 as physician to the Viceroy. He devoted most of his life to botany, his greatest interest being in Cinchona. For 18 years Mutis carried on a correspondence with Linnaeus furnishing him with many specimens of plants, including Cinchona, which the Swedish naturalist described and named. This genus was named by Linnaeus in 1742 and described with stems in their Plantae Genuinellidas (1883) and it is from one of the plant which Mutis named in honor of Linnaeus (Linnaea borealis Plant, and that which Linnaeus named in honor of Luis Mutis.)

Linnaeus (1707–1778) based his classification of the Cinchona tree on the "fever bark" tree by La Condamine published in the Histoire de L'Académie Royale des Sciences in 1738. The illustration reproduced here is the annotated page of Linnaeus' own copy of his Materia Medica of 1749 in which he supplemented the taxonomic description of the new genus with pharmaceutical particulars.

Cinchona pubescens illustrated here is from Loja in the Andes, the first Cinchona bark used by Linnaeus not obtained.

This is the beautiful red bark tree whose roots yield nearly the same constituents as the other species in this genus. Cinchona bark is comparable to India and Ceylon where they were first planted in the late 1800's. The twigs are covered and covered the landscape, but their quinine content proved disappointingly low. (Photograph from Wellcome Historical Medical Museum)

and accomplishments. He was born in Hagerstown, Maryland, in 1902. By the time he was sixteen he had made up his mind to be a scientist, and was reading every technical book he could find. He was graduated from the University of Maryland in 1923 with a degree in organic chemistry, and after a two-year fellowship he worked for three years in the laboratory of an oil company. But Marker was restless. Dating from college days was a fascination with the vast and complex molecular universe of organic matter. One group of compounds in particular held a magnetic attraction—the steroids, which are so complex that years of painstaking work often are required just to isolate and identify them.

Steroids, a generic term that includes the sterols (which occur in both plants and animals), cortical hormones, sex hormones, bile acids, and other compounds, are composed of molecules with a nucleus of seventeen carbon atoms arranged in four rings. For the purpose of our story it is important to know the positions of these carbon atoms; notice the number eleven position in ring C, for it will play a vital role. As pictured, these rings are "naked." Actually, they have additional carbon, oxygen, hydrogen, or other atoms in side chains attached at exposed points and between the rings. Look again at the eleven

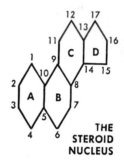

THE
STEROID
NUCLEUS

position. Cortisone and other hormones from the adrenal cortex (the outer layer of the adrenal gland) have an oxygen atom there, but getting an oxygen at this position in the molecule proved to be one of the most difficult problems known to chemists.

In order to synthesize hormones from laboratory chemicals —or build them from plant starting materials—it was necessary to find a chemical reaction for each step that placed the right atom in the right spot. This field of chemistry was virtually untouched in the mid-1920's, when Marker first became interested in it, although some physicians as early as 1902 had begun to study the effects of hormones produced by the body and to wonder about the possibility of using these chemical messengers as drugs.

In 1928, Marker joined the Rockefeller Institute to do basic research in organic chemistry. For the first time he had an opportunity to put his ideas to work. But according to Applezweig, he began his career there in a most unusual way. Dr. P. A. Levene at the Institute recognized Marker's exceptional gifts and wanted to hire him, but there was no money in the budget for an additional person. Dr. Levene solved the problem by telling Marker that, while there was no job opening, there was a chemical reagent allotment; Marker's salary for the following six years came from this small fund. In spite of this lack of status, Marker lived up to his early promise. In Levene's laboratory he produced hundreds of complex compounds which no one else could make at that time. He had the remarkable ability to shut himself up in a laboratory for forty-eight hours and come out with pure crystals, not in milligram quantities but by the kilogram. However, six years later, as a result of a disagreement and in spite of his previous excellent work, Marker one day suddenly left the Institute, never to return.

He next became a professor of organic chemistry at Pennsylvania State College, where, on a research grant from Parke, Davis & Company, he published the amazing total of 147 scientific papers on sterols between 1935–1943. He also took out some seventy-five patents, assigned to Parke, Davis. During this period he was particularly interested in the hormones secreted by the sex organs of the body. Others had isolated estrone, the female hormone, and androsterone and testosterone, two male hormones, in 1929 and 1931 respectively.

Progesterone, the "pregnancy hormone," was also known by this time. In fact, one out of three pregnancies was said to end in miscarriage because of insufficient progesterone. But production of these hormones was then based entirely on costly, multi-step extractions from animal glands and excretions. Grams were produced when hundreds of pounds were needed. Because foreign cartels—legal in Europe—controlled manufacturing processes through their patents, progesterone cost more than $200 per gram in this country.

Marker became convinced that vegetable sterols were the answer to this bottleneck, and he began an exhaustive search to prove his belief. Through his scientific study, he knew that sterols were found most frequently in the botanical order Liliales, to which the onion, asparagus, and lily families belong, as well as the yam of the Dioscorea genus and the desert-grown Yucca and Agave. Yucca looks like branched sausages; Agave has long, spear-shaped leaves. Marker was particularly interested in saponin compounds extracted from these. Saponins produce foam in water and act as a poison by destroying red blood cells. Navajo Indians use the fleshy Yucca leaves as soap and shampoo; the natives of the Andes collect Quillaja bark from the "soap tree" to wash woolens; and a number of primitive tribes employ saponin-bearing plants as fish poisons (the fish are not poisonous when eaten).

Marker knew that saponins could be chemically "tailored" to resemble animal hormones by removing the sugar part of the molecule and isolating a series of compounds called sapogenins. These plant sapogenins were to become the starting materials for manufacturing the sex and cortical hormones we use today. His first paper on vegetable sterols was published in the *Journal of the American Chemical Society* in 1939, under the title "Isolation of Sarsasapogenin from Mexican Sarsaparilla Root."

Interestingly enough, sarsaparilla from the genus Smilax

was one of the medicinal plants described in 1568 by Nicholas Monardes, a physician of Seville, in his *Joyfull Newes out of the New-Found Worlde*. It became a standard syphilis remedy among pirate surgeons and was popular in many folk cultures for rheumatism and other ills. In the mid-1800's sarsaparilla was something of a national phenomenon in the United States. Touted as a spring tonic, it was said to "eliminate poison from the blood and purify the system of all leftover infelicities of winter." A favored ingredient of "lost manhood" cures, it was the male counterpart of today's patent-medicine pitch: "Are You Only Half a Woman? Get Rid of That Tired Feeling!" Swiss anthropologist Alfred Metraux found Amazon Indians using sarsaparilla to cure general debility and he said that it invigorated the entire system.

Our ancestors were on the right track, but the steps between teas and tonics from crude roots and standardized doses of pure hormones were many and complex. These raw materials provided compounds that could be converted to hormones by intricate chemical steps; the home-brewed remedies did not contain hormones as we know them.

For Professor Marker and his associates at Penn State, sarsaparilla was only the beginning. Hundreds of plants from all over the world were analyzed and dozens of sapogenins not previously known were isolated and identified. Many of these were obtained from botanicals growing in southeastern United States, like Helonias and Trillium, which had a history as country cures. Some had been used by the American Indians to prevent premature birth and were ingredients in popular "female complaint" nostrums. One of these pictured on its label an Indian maiden kneeling beside the plant and saying, "Take and Be Healed—The Great Spirit Planted It." (Recent studies by Drs. C. L. Butler and C. H. Costello have proved that estrogenic and uterine-stimulating action does, in fact, exist in certain plants used in producing such over-the-counter staples as Lydia Pinkham's famous tonic.)

During his summer vacations, Russell Marker went on his own botanical explorations throughout the Southwest and down into Mexico, searching for an abundant plant with a high enough yield of sapogenin to start commercial production. He decided that Dioscorea was the most likely source. There were over 600 species growing throughout the world, mostly in the tropics. For his purposes, those found in Mexico and Central America proved to be superior. Named after the Greek physician Dioscorides, Dioscoreas are the true yams, not botanically related to sweet potatoes, or Ipomoeas. Although both are vines with tuberous roots, they belong to the two different classes dividing higher plants of this type: yams to the Monocotyledoneae; sweet potatoes to the Dicotyledoneae.

Edible yams have been cultivated for thousands of years, and wild-growing, poisonous varieties have been used in native remedies for snake bites, scurvy, rheumatism, skin diseases, and a score of other afflictions. In times of famine, yams containing saponins are specially treated with heat before being prepared as food; otherwise they would produce hemolysis, in which red blood cells dissolve in the plasma, causing blotching and bruising of the skin and possibly death.

One of the earliest European botanists to travel in America, Leonard Plukenet, made the first scientific identification of a Dioscorea in 1705. In the 1800's, "dioscorein," a popular product derived from a dried solid extract of the yam root, was marketed by W. S. Merrell. The 1836 edition of *Howard's Botanic Medicine* stated: "An infusion of the root, *Dioscorea villosa,* also known as China Root or Yam Root, is a valuable remedy in bilious colic. An ounce of the powdered root must be boiled in a pint of water and half of it given as a dose. Dr. Miller of Neville, Ohio, values the tincture highly as an expectorant, as a diaphoretic [perspiration stimulant], and in large doses as an emetic [to produce vomiting]. We have no doubt of its value in these complaints and think it highly probable that further investigations will disclose usefulness in other diseases."

This prediction came true, but only after a time span of about 100 years. In 1940 Professor Marker published his first paper on the sapogenin diosgenin, which had been discovered in 1937 by Ueno and Ohta Tsukamoto in a native Japanese species, *Dioscorea tokoro*. In this article and others soon to follow, he described how to synthesize—from diosgenin —the pregnancy hormone progesterone in five steps and the male hormone testosterone in eight steps. He also gave directions for shortened routes to other hormones. These papers are classics in scientific literature because they led to the solution of the world-wide steroid hormone shortage.

Marker immediately wanted to start processing yams on a commercial scale in Mexico, but he lacked the necessary capital. So he turned to major pharmaceutical companies for help, no doubt thinking that they would jump at the chance to underwrite this project, in view of his recent discoveries. But his plan was rejected as utterly unworkable.

By now he had published half a hundred scientific papers on plant sterols. He *knew* that his ideas for mass production were practical. Within his grasp was the source material for relieving the sufferings of millions. But still no one would listen. His frustration must have been monumental. The drug companies pointed out that Mexico was a rough country with inadequate transportation and poor industrial facilities. Digging isolated wild plants and hauling tons of unwieldy tubers out of jungles and across mountains was surely doing things the hard way, not to mention the labor problem. No, it was just too farfetched for serious consideration by American businessmen. They were impressed with the professor's scientific accomplishments, but accepting his commercial judgment was another matter.

Manufacturers were making some progress on the total

synthesis of hormones with man-made chemicals. Also, soybeans, grown by the millions of bushels in the United States, looked promising as a starting material. And production methods used on animal glands and bile were gradually improving. All of these were sound arguments; fortunately they did not discourage the scientist.

Marker left the Penn State faculty in the middle of the 1942 term. After advising his wife and children of the need for an indefinite separation, he set out for Mexico City, very much a man alone with his convictions. He rented an abandoned pottery shop there and set up a makeshift laboratory. Then he took off for the hills with an old botany book, a spade, a machete, and a supply of burlap bags. He would dig up the yams himself, if need be. Knowing only a smattering of Spanish and no Indian languages, he nevertheless managed to find out from herb vendors where the *cabezo de negro* grew. The storage organ of this plant, which he named *Dioscorea mexicana,* grows partly above ground and resembles a cross between a lump of coal and a pineapple. The fibrous inside, producing diosgenin, is like the flesh of a firm juicy apple.

Just seven weeks after leaving the States, Marker had secured permission from the Mexican government to collect Dioscorea; he had organized laborers in a widespread rootdigging project; and he had set up three drying stations under the supervision of Mexicans he had trained to get the raw materials to him in proper condition for processing.

In less than two months, he was back in his little Mexico City laboratory working on the yams that arrived in reasonably steady deliveries. Norman Applezweig said that about this time Marker became convinced that his laboratory notes on his methods were being copied, and he began to carry them around with him at all times. However, he still continued to publish his findings in scientific journals.

Desperate for quick results in order to secure financial backing, he remained in the lab around the clock, sleeping on a cot and eating tinned rations. His first goal was to produce the pregnancy hormone progesterone. Success involved more than scientific knowledge alone, as an extremely delicate technique was required to move an atom from one position in the four-ring steroid molecule to another position, and to split off unwanted side chains. Nevertheless, in fifteen days Marker produced twenty-five grams, or about an ounce of progesterone. An investment broker put him in touch with some mining speculators, who took one look at the small pile of crystals worth over fifty times their weight in gold, had them evaluated at a city hospital, and then plunged $50,000 into the enterprise. Four more yam-collecting stations were set up in Oaxaca and Chiapas. After a month of feverish activity, Marker had two kilograms, almost four-and-a-half pounds, of progesterone in his makeshift laboratory.

There are several versions of what happened next. One story is told that during the late summer of 1943 the quiet and unassuming former professor set out to sell his progesterone, which he carried in two jars wrapped in newspapers, one under each arm. After some initial difficulty, he succeeded in obtaining an interview with Dr. Frederick Lehmann, who, with Dr. Emeric Somlo, owned Laboratorios Hormona. In 1932, these two Europeans had established one of the most successful drug houses in Latin America. Marker knew that they bought synthetic hormones whenever they could, in order to fortify their extracts from animal products.

Once inside Lehmann's office, Marker asked how much Hormona would pay for progesterone. Perhaps $80 a gram, was the reply. He unwrapped one precious kilo, casually saying that he had made it himself. Lehmann was speechless: the annual production of the whole world was not very many kilograms! Then the second package was unwrapped. Two kilograms, or 2,000 grams, of progesterone were normally worth about $160,000, but no one had ever had the opportunity to buy that much at one time. Lehmann immediately telephoned Somlo, who was in New York on business, and they decided to try to strike a bargain on the price, after first making sure that this really was progesterone. Because the two kilos substantially altered market values, Hormona ended up paying considerably less than $160,000.

Later, Somlo and Lehmann agreed to seize this unique opportunity to establish a company that would be basic in hormone raw materials, so they offered Marker 40 per cent of the stock in the venture, while they retained 60 per cent. Marker agreed to this and the new firm, Syntex, Sociedad Anonima (i.e. anonymous society or corporation, usually abbreviated to S.A.) was incorporated on January 21, 1944. During the remainder of the year, Marker turned out ten more kilos of progesterone, which declined steadily in price because he had, in one stroke, cracked the international monopoly.

A year later Marker left Syntex without divulging certain details of his progesterone procedures. Somlo and Lehmann finally found a replacement in Dr. George Rosenkranz, a young Hungarian who had received his steroid chemistry training under the Swiss Nobel Laureates L. Ruzica and T. Reichstein. Rosenkranz proved adaptable, to say the least, for instead of Ph.D. colleagues and well-educated technicians, he now had to manage a laboratory with one college graduate and several charming, but giggly, *señorita*-assistants who had not finished high school. Nevertheless, by working night and day he was able to make progesterone from yam starting materials in about two months. He then produced the male hormone testosterone and using testosterone, he synthesized the female hormone estrone by a series of complicated procedures. This caused one of his lab workers to exclaim: "This chemistry is *magnifica*—Adam goes into the test tube and Eve comes out!" Rosenkranz remained in charge of the Syntex research program until 1954, then moved on to become president and, eventually, chairman of the board.

Meanwhile, what of Russell Marker? After leaving Syntex, he was involved with the founding of a number of businesses and he eventually became a drug-company consultant, while continuing to live in Mexico. Ironically, the American companies that had called his plan to establish a Mexican hormone industry "impractical" were now leading customers of the firm he made possible. But no doubt it was gratifying to him to know that he was responsible for bringing progesterone within reach of those who had need of it; a gram now sold for less than fifty cents instead of $200 or more. *Fortune Magazine* hailed the jungle-root chemical industry pioneered by Marker as "The most remarkable technological contribution ever to come from south of the border."

Marker did not rest on his past achievements in the manufacturing of sex hormones, however. From the time he was at Syntex, and probably long before, he had been convinced that adrenal cortex hormones such as Compound E—later called cortisone—could be made from plant starting materials. (It is worth noting that 80 per cent of all steroid hormones used today are cortical.) Compound E had been isolated from beef adrenals in 1935 by three independent groups: Kendall at the Mayo Foundation, Wintersteiner and Pfiffner of Columbia University, and Reichstein in Switzerland. Its structure is so complex that it has been described as a chemist's nightmare—and a stockholder's too, because many millions of research dollars have been poured into its study. Among other attributes, Compound E had oxygen at that all-important eleven position in ring C of the steroid molecule.

In 1944, Dr. Lewis Sarett, a twenty-seven-year-old Merck chemist, prepared a few milligrams of Compound E in a complicated and costly thirty-seven-step process, using cattle bile as a starting material. Bile acids have oxygen at position twelve, next door to number eleven, but it was still described as "a whale of a trick to seal up twelve and move to eleven." Besides, thousands of slaughtered cattle were required to make enough Compound E to treat one patient, and treatment is usually continuous with this type of medication.

Among the hundreds of plant sterols he had studied himself, Marker had not found one with oxygen at eleven. But of the thousands of plant sterols in existence, he was convinced that there must be one suitable for conversion to Compound E. In addition to long hours over the test tubes, he embarked on another far-flung field search for a plant precursor of the adrenal cortical hormone. His explorations took him to the Isthmus of Tehuantepec near the Guatemalan border, where the temperature may register 110° to 120°. There he fell ill of swamp fever and dysentery. An almost extinct Indian tribe took him in and nursed him with their herbal treatments.

While Russell Marker was deliriously tossing and turning on a reed mat in a primitive hut, chemists all over the world were engaged in a desperate attempt to make Compound E. As an example of the kind of effort being expended, the Worcester Foundation for Experimental Biology devised a scheme for producing 50,000 grams of cortical hormones a month by setting up each day 1,000 fresh beef adrenals in an ingenious glassware apparatus that kept the glands alive by pumping blood, oxygen, and penicillin into them. Oxygenating at eleven was easy when the living gland did the job, but the procedure was far too costly. In another project, the Upjohn Company produced fifty grams of hydrocortisone, similar to cortisone, from the adrenal glands of 2,200,000 hogs. The cost was $800 per gram. And so it went. . . .

Meanwhile, Merck had sent some of Dr. Sarett's precious Compound E to Dr. Phillip S. Hench, chief rheumatologist at the Mayo Clinic, for testing on his patients. On September

21, 1948, Dr. Hench injected 100 milligrams of Compound E into a twenty-nine-year-old woman who had been bedridden for four and a half years with progressively crippling rheumatoid arthritis. This is Hench's matter-of-fact description of what happened: "The patient was admitted to the Clinic July 26, 1948. Many joints were stiff, swollen, tender and painful on motion. . . . On September 20, the patient's joints were worse than they had ever been. On September 21, she could hardly get out of bed. On that day we began daily intragluteal injection of 100 mg. of Compound E. . . . On September 24, painful morning stiffness was entirely gone. By September 27, articular [joint] as well as muscular stiffness had almost completely disappeared and tenderness and pain on motion, and even swellings, were markedly lessened. The next day she shopped downtown for three hours, feeling tired thereafter, but not sore or stiff."

These results were obtained seven years after Hench had jotted a note in 1941, "Try Compound E in rheumatoid arthritis." This hunch was based on the observation that arthritis in women almost invariably subsided during pregnancy, suggesting that extra hormone output might be responsible. In April, 1949, the Mayo Clinic doctors reported their success in treating fourteen severe cases of arthritis with Compound E. The response to this news was overwhelming. Doctors, hospitals, and drug companies were swamped with pleas for the new wonder drug. Some laymen, believing vitamin E was involved, cleared the shelves of this item. To avoid confusion, the name cortisone was then given to Compound E.

Because Merck, the leading producer of cortisone, was turning out only enough to treat ten patients for a year, medical spokesmen issued the disheartening statement that it might be a decade or more before this drug would be available to the general public. This touched off the world-wide search for a low-cost source in the plant kingdom, including the quest for the lost Strophanthus—the only known plant with oxygen at the number eleven position. While the United States Department of Agriculture and drug companies had botanical explorers scattered in the field, chemists at home were busy trying to make cortisone synthetically.

But in August, 1949, it was Russell Marker who once again startled his colleagues by announcing in the *Journal of the American Chemical Society* that he had isolated from yams a substance he called botogenin, which had oxygen at number twelve. "Botogenin gives a desirable starting material for the synthesis of cortisone," he concluded. His discovery was hailed in the *New York Times,* the *Chemurgic Digest,* and countless other publications here and abroad.

However, botogenin was never developed commercially because Upjohn researchers had learned that bacteria could accomplish what chemistry could not. Fermentation chemistry up to that time had been a relatively simple science, useful in manufacturing beer, wine, citric acid, and other products. Now scientists began to realize that bacteria and molds are highly effective and cheap chemical laborers. Drs. Herbert C. Murray and Durey H. Peterson led the Upjohn team in putting these organisms to work chewing off atoms and attending to the chemical tailoring operations necessary to change one steroid into another. Through the aid of two newly discovered techniques, filter-paper chromatography and infra-red spectroscopy, the brew from the culture plates could be quickly tested for advanced steroids. Several cultures—including one from soil collected on the Upjohn-Penick expedition to Africa—proved ideal in converting progesterone into cortisone and other eleven-oxygenated hormones.

These research results were published in April, 1952. Covered by a fifty-four-page patent issued to Upjohn, this work opened the door for low-cost production of hundreds of advanced cortical steroids. Today over 70 per cent of the prescriptions written for cortical hormones start with Russell Marker's Mexican yams. Roughly, for every sixty-six pounds of dry root, one pound of diosgenin is extracted, and after numerous laboratory procedures about two ounces of cortisone are obtained. Thus the bottleneck has been solved.

According to Norman Applezweig, who was working with Marker in Mexico in 1949, this is how another of his important contributions came about: Marker had a painful, arthritic finger and one day an herb dealer advised him, "My people have a plant that is very good for your kind of trouble."

When the finely chopped root was brought to him, he should have known better, but he brewed some tea as he was instructed to do and drank it. The next day he was covered with bruises: his blood had hemolyzed because of the saponin.

When Applezweig saw him he exclaimed, "What happened to you? You look as if you've been hit by a truck!"

Despite his condition, Marker stayed in his laboratory in order to complete an analysis of the plant. It was found to contain three to four times more diosgenin than the *cabezo de negro,* which had been the mainstay of the yam industry up until that time. This new botanical also had other advantages: it was available in greater quantities and it matured much faster—an important point because mature roots contain much more diosgenin than immature ones. Applezweig brought pressed leaf samples to the New York Botanical Garden, where the identification of *Dioscorea composita* was made. The plant had been known only as "barbasco," a misleading term applied to many other Latin American plants, mostly fish poisons derived from roots. Applezweig said, "I spent almost a year examining various barbascos before concluding that our sample had nothing in common with the others." Since then this species has been the chief commercial source of steroidal starting materials.

Fortunately, Russell Marker recovered from the effects of

saponin poisoning. However, he sought seclusion and nothing is known about his later activities; no new scientific papers have been added to his 1949 total of 164. He was not available for interviews in Mexico City. But the yams he made famous —surely they were accessible. I boarded a DC-3 loaded with cargo and a few Mexican families bound for the port city of Veracruz. From there I hoped to see the fabulous botanicals growing in the wilds and to follow their processing into the finished drugs that help so many millions of patients.

Taming the Wild Mexican Yams

THE MOST INTERESTING WAY TO ENTER THE STATE of Veracruz, heart of the wild yam country, is through Veracruz harbor, where Hernando Cortez landed his 500 men in 1519 and immediately scuttled his ships so no one could escape. They made a seven weeks' march inland and began their destruction of the Aztec empire of Montezuma II. On August 13, 1521, the Spaniards were victorious and Mexico was never the same again.

The country continues to change, of course, and in the past decade the $30,000,000-a-year yam industry has played an important part in this change. Of all botanicals used in the preparation of drugs, the yam seems to be one of the most "nationalized" at the present time. While there is no embargo of the type once imposed upon Rauwolfia, the yams used in medicine are still almost exclusively Mexican. They are collected and transported under governmental controls.

The plants themselves resist losing their identity as Mexican yams. Cinchona trees, for instance, were more productive when cultivated in Java than in the South American countries of their origin. But for a dozen years the yams have frustrated the skilled horticulturists who are trying to turn them into a profitable crop for American farmers. Dr. J. R. Haun, in charge of this project at the New Crops Research Branch, USDA, Beltsville, Maryland, advised me in March, 1963:

"We have not solved all the problems concerned with the domestic production of Dioscorea. However, we do not feel that it is impossible to solve them. Dioscorea species will grow extremely well in the delta south of New Orleans and in the area around Belle Glade, Florida. We are now distributing 30,000 plants to test locations for field trials, having developed a propagating method that is 95 to 100 per cent effective. This involves juvenile shoots and the use of mist and chemical sprays; under favorable conditions, two years are required for a seedling to become a mature plant. Our chief limiting factor at present is the lack of a propagation method that will be feasible commercially. Our aims in developing a domestic source are based upon the possibility that greatly increased usage of steroidal drugs in the future will outrun the wild sources currently available."

Whether or not the Mexican wild sources will be depleted is an extremely touchy question. However, at least seven firms* are collecting and processing yams and they continue to make considerable investments in new buildings and equipment in Mexico, obviously expecting to continue operations for years to come. Government and industry spokesmen who wish to remain anonymous have made the following observations: "Based on current needs, there is probably a sixty-year supply of yams in Mexico—but world use of the finished products is increasing at a phenomenal rate. We would be extremely short-sighted if we did not make alternate plans. . . ." "There isn't a company involved in this that isn't exploring other possibilities. I know of one firm that is using some stigmasterol from soybeans. Another is rumored to be using *mostly* stigmasterol now, in unlabelled containers. . . ." "Wild

---

* These chapters describe typical yam collecting and processing operations used throughout the industry.

Mexican Dioscorea will remain our best source because field cultivation in the States is impractical. It takes years for diosgenin to build up; meanwhile the plants are occupying valuable land. Labor costs here are prohibitive, too. . . ." "There is always the chance that the Mexican government will slap an embargo on this product; there have been embargoes on botanicals in India and in Egypt and it can happen here. Glaxo, an English firm, is obtaining corticosteroids from the African *Agave sisalana.* We are continuing our evaluations of the Agave and Yucca as possible sources."

With all this controversial background buzzing around in my mind, the first thing I wanted to do when I arrived in Veracruz was to get my bearings before going into the jungle interior where the yams are collected—and perhaps absorb a little of the atmosphere of Mexico. One of the best places to do this is the ancient Spanish fortress of San Juan de Ulua, overlooking the busy docks of Veracruz. The great coral blocks forming the sea wall have withstood 400 years of pounding surf and from them one can observe both the old and the new Mexico in a sweeping glance.

In the harbor, ships from all over the world take on cargoes. But turn around and enter the fortress by a crumbling drawbridge and it is easy to imagine the cries of prisoners— native patriots or notorious bandits—manacled inside the windowless cells. Water still drips from stalactites in the dungeons, although the chains have long since rusted away. This haunted spot is now modernized as a coast guard station in the new Mexico—and yet a good many of the young guardsmen have the classic profiles of Aztec warriors.

Before the Aztecs there had been the rise and fall of Mayan, Mixtec, Zapotec, Toltec, and other civilizations, all the way back to the Asian migrants who wandered down from the Bering Straits around 15,000 B.C. Then as now the Veracruz area was a crossroads. The yams seem to grow chiefly along the paths of these migrating civilizations in the land cradling the Bay of Campeche, but there is no indication that they ever were cultivated for medicinal use.

When I visited a block-square market place in the city of Veracruz, the profusion of beautiful flowers and the herb vendors reminded me of another facet of the early cultures. In one of the stalls, a wizened old woman was dispensing drug plants, probably the same types of dried, fragrant, greenery used a thousand years ago. However, she added a modern touch by tearing off *Reader's Digest* pages and deftly fashioning them into small cornucopias to hold her "prescriptions."

Cortez praised the Mexicans' knowledge of medicinal plants and the fabulous botanical gardens established by Montezuma I. His letters to Charles V of Spain attracted the first European botanical explorer to Mexico, the king's physician, Francisco Hernandez. Dr. Hernandez found the Aztec materia medica extremely advanced; the systematic study of drug plants in precisely designed botanical gardens did not begin to get under way in Europe until the sixteenth century. Some authorities feel that the Europeans were inspired by the Mexicans. Almost all Aztec records were destroyed, but we do have one manuscript written by an Aztec doctor, Martinus de la Cruz, and translated into Latin by another, Juannes Badianus, in 1552. This herbal, known as *The Badianus Manuscript,* is America's earliest medical book. In 1940 an English version was prepared by Emily Walcott Emmart, with 118 plates reproducing the stylized botanical drawings. Plants of the genus Dioscorea are mentioned twice: *Chipahuacxihuitl,* or the "graceful plant," on Plate 8, was used as a poultice for boils. A Plate 10 plant, possibly Dioscorea or Smilax, was a treatment for scabies, a skin disease.

Dr. Bernice G. Schubert, a curator of Harvard's Arnold Arboretum, told me that Plates 9 and 17 also bear some resemblance to Dioscorea. Dr. Schubert is an authority on the taxonomy of this genus. She is also one of the very few women botanists in the United States to have gone into the field to explore for drug plants; while she was with the USDA, she searched for yams and other cortisone starting materials in Mexico, Cuba, Costa Rica, and Puerto Rico. She is a soft-spoken, feminine person, but one of the male botanists who was with her group paid her this tribute: "While we were traveling by horseback in very rugged territory, Dr. Schubert became seriously ill, but she remained in the field until the project was completed. Then she helped put together the first compilation of the 3,000 plants known to contain alkaloids, a valuable reference co-authored by the USDA's Dr. J. J. Willaman.

It was Dr. Schubert who suggested that if I wanted to know more about the experimental cultivation of Dioscorea in Mexico, I ought to interview Don K. Cox. "He has mapped the ranges of the wild commercial species," she said. "And through his intensive studies over the past decade, he probably knows more about their habits than anyone. He has been directing the scientific work at the Syntex *Campo Experimental,* or plantation, in San Juan Evangelista, Veracruz."

For this interview, I flew southeast from Veracruz about 160 miles to Minatitlán in the Isthmus of Tehuantepec, where Mexico narrows to less than 200 miles. It was beastly hot and I couldn't help thinking of Russell Marker, who came down with a raging fever while exploring the area. Possibly he had malaria, because I noticed men in yellow United Nations jeeps, called "canaries," spraying the swamps with DDT.

Don Cox—baptized simply "Don"—turned out to be a pleasant-looking Yul Brynner type. However, old friends say that he was shaving his head with an electric razor long before Brynner became an international personality. He was born in California forty years ago, but he prefers to live in Mexico with his family. While we had a snack of the very tiny shrimp caught in the Bay of Campeche ten miles away, he explained that his specialty was forest ecology, the study of plants in relation to their environment. Duke University's Professor W. Dwight Billings inspired his choice of career. After his postgraduate work at Duke, Cox spent several years doing research for the United States Forest Service. Then, in 1952, he came to Mexico because Syntex needed a field botanist.

"No university in Mexico grants a degree in botany," he said. "But there are some excellent botanists here, such as Professor Eizi Matuda, who named fifty-four Dioscorea species."

After Upjohn in 1952 discovered the fermentation process for turning yam starting materials into cortical hormones, there was a tremendous increase in the demand for the plants. Syntex became a prime supplier for Upjohn, and later for Johnson & Johnson and other companies making finished ethical drugs. They wanted to be sure that they could fulfill these contracts. At the same time, they were in agreement with the Mexican government regarding conservation measures for this vital natural resource.

"So they established one of the largest botanical research programs of any firm in the steroid field," Cox said. "Only Schering of Germany has a similar project in Guatemala. Those of us engaged in this research—Schering and the USDA included—exchange information on very good terms. I even correspond with the Russians. Just today I received a letter from Professor A. J. Kupzow, a Moscow geneticist who wishes to exchange Dioscorea seeds and information. Also, anything we develop in the way of improved agricultural methods will probably help the farmers."

The Mexican government rules that forestry produce, including yams, may not be collected or shipped without an official permit. Permits have not been granted in the case of every request. Because of the high export tax on raw materials, the crude botanicals are first turned into intermediates, meaning anything beyond the extracted diosgenin. Although Syntex pioneered in this field, Searle, General Mills, American Schering, a company operated by the Mexican government, and others are now processing yams. Eli Lilly is closely associated with the Syntex operation in that it contributes half of the research budget. Some of this money supports the botanical research done by Cox and his group, which has consisted, at times, of forty-five workers. One of his first assignments was to determine the geographical distribution and abundance of the yams. At that time two species were known to contain diosgenin, Marker's *D. mexicana* and *D. composita,* but Cox says, "We have now increased this list to eleven. In all, there are sixty-seven Dioscorea species in Mexico alone."

In the course of interviewing Cox over a period of a week or so, I was to hear him say more than once, "The importance of working with properly identified material cannot be overemphasized!" I learned that a couple of errors had slowed up the work on yams. An early collector had put together specimens of two different species in one collection—unfortunately, this was the collection that the English scientist William B. Hemsley studied in 1884 when he established the species *D. composita!* The second mix-up had been described to me by several botanists. This is how Cox put it: "Botogenin was originally isolated from what was identified as *D. mexicana.* Subsequent work showed that the botanical identification was erroneous, as botogenin exists only in *D. spiculiflora* and its variety *chiapasana.*"

As soon as he was hired by Syntex in 1952, Cox returned to the United States to review the exploratory work done by the USDA, whose quest for cortisone starting materials began in 1949 when Dr. John T. Baldwin, Jr., was sent to Africa for Strophanthus. After Baldwin's return, Dr. Walter H. Hodge continued to make extensive collections in South Africa and elsewhere. Botanist H. Scott Gentry, described by Cox as "one of the world's top-ranking field botanists," probably chalked up the most mileage in this search, during his explorations in southwestern United States, Africa, and Asia. In an interview at the New Crops Research Branch in Beltsville, Maryland, Gentry had told me that the USDA exploratory program had stretched over a dozen years and involved the analysis of about 7,000 plants, under the direction of Dr. D. S. Correll.

When I saw Gentry, before I went to Mexico, he was mounting Agave specimens on herbarium sheets—no easy task, because these are succulents with thick, juicy, leaves that sometimes reach ten feet in length. This is the genus that contains the maguey, or century plant, *A. americana,* and sisal-fiber-producing species. The Agaves not only are a modern source of steroids, but also are used in a variety of ingenious ways by primitives: the tender shoots are eaten as a cooked vegetable or raw in salads; the fleshy part of the broadest leaves is scraped off, leaving a strong flat piece of "paper," which the Aztecs used for their picture writings or codices; the thorn on the tip of the leaf can be pulled off in such a way that a yard-long strand of very tough "thread" is attached to this "needle," all ready for sewing; ropes are made from the plant; and the fermented juices have been used since prehistoric times to produce the beverages mescal, pulque, and tequila. A few years ago studies at the Hygienic Institute in Mexico City found Agave products to be rich in yeasts and vitamins.

Also before going to Mexico, I had heard Dr. Monroe E. Wall, who, with Dr. J. J. Willaman, supervised the chemical work on the USDA plants, tell the American Society of Pharmacognosy: "I feel that we have studied a good cross section of the plant kingdom and it is unlikely that better steroidal starting materials will be found in any of the 175,000 higher plants than those in the genus Dioscorea. Species of the Agave and Yucca are also rich in steroidal sapogenins but do not have the crop potential of the Dioscorea. However, I intend to keep working on this and recommend that others do too."

Dioscorea exploration is complicated by the fact that many of the species have leaves that resemble each other at first glance. Also, one can't tell from the above-ground foliage how large or how old the root is—a disadvantage in commercial collection because the mature roots contain by far the most diosgenin. Botanical identification is difficult because flowering plants are seldom found. However, as Cox and I were driving from Minatitlán to the experimental station at San Juan, he did spot a *Dioscorea composita* that proved to have very tiny, firm, fleshy, green flowers hardly distinguishable from the stem. The leaves were heart-shaped and the vine resembled a Philodendron. Although it was the rainy season and the ground was soft, the yam was not easy to dig. It was brown and weighed about four pounds, the average size collected. The flesh inside was moist, fibrous, and faintly rose colored.

"Botanically, this potato-like part is referred to as a rhizome," he explained. "It is an underground stem rather than a root. Iris is another plant with a rhizome. Commercially, we also use *D. floribunda* that grows south of here in tropical oak woods. Its flesh is bright yellow inside and the shape resembles a brown hand with twisted fingers."

A number of authorities have spoken enthusiastically about the commercial possibilities of *D. spiculiflora,* which Wall, in 1955, found to contain two new chemical entities. He named these gentrogenin and correllogenin after Gentry and Correll, his USDA colleagues. This yam has special promise so far as cortisone is concerned.

By the time we arrived in San Juan Evangelista it was late afternoon. The last twenty miles had been rough riding in the truck, over a cow path rather than a road. As we entered the village, with its plaster houses painted in hot pinks and electric blues, the first sight to greet us was a parade. A band was playing and colorfully dressed people were marching and singing. "Don't let this reception go to your head," Cox said with a smile. "You are the first *gringa* to be seen here in the eleven years I've been around, but this isn't in your honor—it's just another holiday. But believe me, they take their holidays seriously."

A short drive out of the village brought us to the Syntex plantation which reminded me of the tidy farms run by state universities; there was even a Class A weather station, but there were also tropical overtones of the Garden of Eden. The whitewashed concrete block buildings housing the staff, laboratories, and machine shops were surrounded with beautiful ornamental shrubs, trees, and flowers. Dozens of species of Dioscoreas on trellises shaded the doorways and windows. All this was clearly designed by a botanist whose interest in nature went far beyond pure science. There was a transient menagerie of snakes, parrots, monkeys, armadillos, a kinkajou, red deer, and other creatures from the surrounding area.

At dinner, I asked Cox why he had his revolver on the table beside his plate and he said that lately there had been an invasion of unwelcome animals—a couple of rats. They had begun to run back and forth on the primavera wood supports that held up the palm-thatched roof. This was annoying, especially to a scientist running an immaculate research center, but the day before, the situation reached the impossible stage. "I had asked the cook to prepare a mole sauce for you; this takes two days and it is not made from moles, but from chocolate, chilies, and a dozen other things all simmered until the flavors blend. Last night she placed a large bowl of this before me and plop! one of the rats fell into it. So she had to start all over again. If all goes well, we'll have it tomorrow." We did and it was delicious. Octopus and roast armadillo also appeared on the menu.

That evening a fiesta was held, with all the plantation workers and their families turning out. A wooden platform was brought in so that the stomping which accompanies the regional dances would have a satisfactory thump. These steps are executed in a strangely deadpan manner with no movement of the arms or body, and the participants keep going until one is certain they will drop from exhaustion. Mexicans in their late seventies danced every single dance with gusto. Never have I been among people who seemed to enjoy life more. From the village of San Juan I could hear the music every night until the roosters and burros greeted the dawn with their unnerving medley.

At the fiesta, I asked Dr. Carlos Avila Perez, the physician in charge of the nearby government hospital, about local folk medicine. "The Popoloca and other Indian tribes outside of the village use many plants as curatives," he said. "First they consult the *curanderos,* or healers, who treat them with herbs and donkeys' milk. If this doesn't work, they decide that there is a supernatural force operating and they turn to a witch doctor, or *brujo.* He makes his diagnosis by building a fire, and in its smoke he claims to 'see' the shape of the diseased organ. He takes his machete and chops at the smoke symbol and this is supposed to effect a cure. If the ailment is psychosomatic, as about half of all disorders are estimated to be, then it will do the job. The *brujos* build their reputations on these successful cases." (A recent study at the University of Texas advised M.D.'s to go along with these beliefs as much as possible—even to the extent of prescribing donkey milk to be taken with antibiotics to treat tuberculosis. The idea is to keep the patient under medical supervision at any cost.)

Dr. Avila Perez mentioned that marijuana leaves were soaked in alcohol and used as poultices for rheumatism. In a neighboring region babies are born in hammocks which have achiote seeds spread underneath them, and achiote is also used for skin rashes and measles, much as we use calamine lotion. The tribes that wandered down from the Bering Straits had a long walk—probably to Tierra del Fuego—and they seem to have taken their "drugstores" right along with them. I had noted Peruvian Indians using achiote in the same way and they also used species of Dioscorea as medicinals.

When I asked Don Cox if he ever relied upon folk remedies as leads for new pharmaceuticals, he said: "I never have and I doubt that I ever will. The natives treat on a hit-or-miss basis with no real diagnosis. For example, of the hundreds of medicinal plants supposedly good for diabetes, I don't know of a single one used by a reputable physician. Folk remedies do have biological action, but the results are unpredictable. For instance, we had a sad case here not long ago which proves this point." He then told about a botanical extract that the native women slip into their husbands' food if they think the husband has been carrying on too much. The next time he takes an alcoholic drink, he becomes violently ill—exactly the same principle as that of Antabuse, the drug used in the modern treatment of alcoholics. However, in the instance cited the dose was too potent and the man suffered permanent heart and nerve damage.

"He will never be the same again, either mentally or physically," the physician observed.

The next day, I toured the experimental station which Cox had designed with such scientific precision. All of the plantings were watered every day by a complicated but unobtrusive irrigation system. The beds holding delicate seedlings were shaded from the broiling sun by Saran mesh. Beyond these were open fields of Dioscoreas under cultivation. Some fifty species in all were growing on the plantation, but none were destined to go to market to become finished drugs. The main objectives were to develop practical methods for commercial cultivation and to determine exactly which genetic characteristics and growing conditions produced the highest yield of saponins.

"Even after ten years, there is still much to be discovered,"

Cox said. "I have estimated that it will take at least another decade to complete the genetic studies required."

Cuttings of the yams are kept in relatively sterile sand-beds that have been fumigated. They root quite easily. Then they are set out in propagation beds that have an overhead irrigation system—a mist spray under fifty pounds of pressure. In the past six years, 20,000 individual plants have been propagated. Two beds were filled with plants grown from seed. "We feel that eventually the only practical way to grow Dioscorea commercially will be from seed; there can be up to 10,000 seeds on a single plant, by the way," Cox said. "Weeds and nematodes—microscopic worms—are a serious problem, so we are running pesticide and herbicide studies. It is thought that these two problems, plus depleted soil fertility, caused the decline of the Mayan civilization a thousand years ago."

I asked Cox if he had any idea why plants produced saponins. He replied that in his opinion they are by-products of some unknown metabolic process and of no apparent use to the plants themselves. His work in the Syntex Mexico City laboratory indicated that the saponins are stored in the cytoplasm that lines the cells and not in the juices. "We found that liquid squeezed from yams during processing contains none of this active material; it remains in the dry part."

During my stay at the experimental farm, I learned more of the details about the early search for Mexican Dioscoreas. In his six years of field exploration, Cox surveyed jungle swamps and Sierra foothills, for the yam grows in altitudes up to 4,200 feet. It requires fifty inches of rainfall a year, but it "likes" as much as 100 inches, he found. And it must have a definite dry season. He was usually in the field for several months at a time. On one occasion he had almost given up hope of finding a cleared space to pitch his tent for the night. "The vegetation was so thick you could stick a crutch in the ground and it would sprout," was his description of the area.

He finally found an abandoned house where the weeds had not quite taken over, and had just fallen asleep when he was awakened by what seemed to be a band of shouting men. It was the entire male population of the village he had just passed through, and they were brandishing clubs, machetes, and ancient firearms that looked like small cannon, but were actually .44's from about 1900. They were accompanied by vicious, snarling dogs.

Cox had his .38 Walther handy, but knew that if he pulled it he would be dead in a matter of seconds. The men seemed to want to haul him off to jail because they had decided that he was planning "to take over the whole countryside." Fearing that if they locked him up every bit of his equipment would vanish, he did some fast talking. They finally agreed to let him go—but go he must, and immediately.

"If there is one basic need in this line of work," he observed, "it is knowing the language of the people. I have been accused of being a Communist spy and everything else, including, to put it politely, a sissy. Men have kept me under surveillance for days as I went about the job of collecting plant specimens. I know perfectly well that they thought I was crazy—how else to explain a grown man's spending all his time looking at flowers, like Ferdinand the Bull."

On another occasion, Cox spent four days chopping his way into the Honduras interior, inhabited only by the little-known Mosquito Indians. He was rewarded by a collection of a new species of Dioscorea. But he had an experience that caused him to stop staying at local inns. Before going into the jungle he stayed overnight in a small hotel on the coast. "These places are always noisy and it seemed that the shooting, shouting, and so forth was worse than ever. The next morning when I opened my door, I stumbled over two bodies —the quarreling couple of the night before. And before I could start on my collection trip, I had to do something about their orphaned child, who was sitting there crying. It just seems simpler now to take all the necessary camping provisions, be self-sufficient, and get some sleep."

In 1954 Cox went to Africa to do a two-month survey and brought back a number of Dioscorea species to serve as breeding stock. There was also a period when he explored for Rauwolfia and other plants for Pfizer. But for the past eleven years most of his attention has been concentrated upon the Mexican yams. After the preliminary exploration to determine the extent of the distribution (which generally followed the line of similar rainfall), he began systematically to break up the various regions in order to estimate the quantities available. Dioscoreas are usually found in tropical savannahs (parklands) and are generally more abundant in abandoned fields or second-growth vegetation. They are not commonly found in deep forests. Few drug plants have been subjected to population studies; possibly Cox's survey, which extended down to Panama, was one of the most extensive.

How does one go about counting the countless number of wild-growing plants over such a vast area?

"You don't ask the natives," Cox said. "They have a mixture of hometown pride and greediness that can be very misleading. If what you are looking for seems to have any monetary value, they will naturally say that they have the 'most' and the 'best.' Sometimes they actually do have an abundant supply —for *their* needs. For instance, they could have enough peyote to keep the whole village potted for a year, but this still might not be sufficient for starting a laboratory analysis."

Cox, in his population study, sought out back-roads or trails and, by walking or driving slowly, simply counted the number of plants seen within a certain area with a hand counter—of the sort used by museum guards. In another method used, a line transect was made by counting the plants that touched a line laid out on the ground. With this data, it was possible to convert to tons of root per square kilometer. These methods produced surprisingly accurate results.

"Using the quadrat method, we grid a region on cardinal compass points," he explained. "In each corner of a square kilometer, we mark off a smaller square of 400 meters, called a quadrant. By counting all the plants in the quadrants, we can convert this sample into the total for the entire area. To do this for the whole of Mexico would take about twenty-five years, and by then everything would have changed. But once the density is established for any given region, similar regions can be estimated."

Dr. Arturo Gomez Pompa, who is in charge of the Mexican government's commission to study the results of Dioscorea collection, had told me that the Mexican folk use of the plant —as an antirheumatic, expectorant, or diuretic—was not causing concern about depletion of supplies. However, the increasing use of hormones in treating cancer, heart disease, and a host of other ills, as well as the worldwide use in fertility control, did cause some anxiety three years ago when the commission was organized. "Although actual exploitation is very large, so far we have found conditions satisfactory," he said. "Last year permits were given for gathering 66,000 fresh tons. Although I have seen one Dioscorea rhizome weighing over 300 pounds, they average about 4.5 pounds per plant—so this means that around 30,000,000 plants were collected in only one year. Because the collection rate is definitely increasing, we are continuing to work with the hormone industries to maintain this natural resource at the proper level."

He said that the main states for collection are Veracruz, Oaxaca, Tabasco, and Chiapas, and, to a lesser degree, Puebla. Cox later pointed out that in virtually no place is there continuous year-after-year exploitation of the plant. "Our studies have determined that even with constant digging in one area, there is no danger of extinction," he said. "And in intermittent harvesting, the most common, by far, there is an actual increase in the number of plants, although their average size is decreased."

But how could digging up plants increase their number? He explained it this way: "When the yams are in the forest as part of the ground flora, they have to compete with all the other vegetation. But when that land is chopped and burned, the common agricultural method, the rival plants are killed off but the yams with their underground stems survive. In fact, some species can even be thrown into a bonfire and still sprout. And there is reason to believe that when the yams are under a burning field, the increase in soil temperature caused by the fire above, acting on the large amount of moisture in the yams, actually stimulates sprouting. This leads to what is called an aspect dominance: the only thing left in a chopped and burned-out field is the Dioscorea vine. The field is normally planted with corn or beans, and the simple cultivation implements that are dragged through the soil break up the yam roots and scatter them. These pieces sprout and form new plants as do ordinary potatoes when their 'eyes' are cut out for replanting. Apparently the same thing happens when the yams themselves are harvested. Bits of broken-off root remain in the ground to form several new plants.

"The single ecological factor most responsible for the present abundance of Dioscorea is, therefore, Man," Cox said. "When cultivated fields of corn or beans are finally abandoned as no longer fertile enough for food crops, the yam takes over, and where only two or three plants existed a few years before there now may be forty or fifty. By disturbing the natural environment, man has created an ideal situation for this plant's growth. The corn in the fields shades the young yams, helps to conserve moisture, and provides a support for the twining vine. Under adverse conditions, the roots may stay dormant for years."

After a week at the experimental farm, Don Cox drove me to the Syntex Laboratories in Mexico City. By the time I completed this trip, I had seen firsthand the processing steps required to convert the "wet roots" collected in the surrounding countryside into finished pharmaceuticals. Some twenty or more chemical conversions were necessary.

Our first stop was in the nearby town of Acayucan, where Syntex has a typical yam collecting station. The natives dig the yams and bring them in to the storage sheds, sometimes on their backs. They are bought at the rate of about $1.10 per hundred pounds; this much can be collected in less than a day. The average wage for laborers in the area is about seventy-five cents a day, so yam collecting is somewhat more profitable, by their standards. The yams are washed and chopped up, then put into shallow concrete fermentation tanks that look like wading pools. Bacteria in the air go to work on this "chowder" and release the diosgenin content. Then this lumpy stew is dried in the sun or in drying drums, bagged, and sent on to the processing plant in Orizaba.

In traveling west toward Orizaba, we left the coastal grasslands and entered thorn forests of Acacia and Mimosa. Then broadleaf evergreen stands took over, with mangoes, coconuts, papayas, and bananas. A few miles further there were sugar-cane, coffee, cocoa-bean, and tobacco plantations. Up on some of these hills Dioscoreas were gathered. Cox said, "There are such extreme variations in the Mexican flora that in one area it is possible to walk through five different plant communities. The country is very mountainous, with only 20 per cent of the land suitable for cultivation." Ahead we could see the extinct volcano, Mt. Orizaba, at 19,000 feet the highest in Mexico. ("Mexico" is thought by some to have come from a word meaning The Land of People Buried Under Lava.)

At the Orizaba factory, the diosgenin extracted from the dried crude roots looked like mounds of soggy graham crackers. It was from this unlikely material that Searle's director of research, Dr. Albert L. Raymond, had said as many as 10,-000,000 chemicals could be made. In 1950 sales of diosgenin were zero. By 1965 the world-wide market for its fertility-controlling end products alone could easily jump to $100,-000,000 per year, according to Dr. Albert Bowers, Syntex director of research in Mexico.

In the Mexico City plant, Dr. Bowers pointed out the equipment that turns diosgenin into a white crystalline substance with the chemical name 16-dehydropregnenolene; it was a huge autoclave, or steam sterilizer, that uses chemical reagents to "chop off the side chains." A new, simplified method of synthesis that reduces processing costs while doubling yields was developed under Bowers' direction and recently reported in *Chemical and Engineering News*. It is now possible to produce these complex hormones (chemically known as 19-nor steroids) in sufficient quantity for even more exhaustive biological testing and clinical evaluation.

Syntex is one of the few companies that, while supplying bulk botanical materials to the pharmaceutical industry, also develops and markets finished specialty drugs under its own label. With the establishment of Syntex Laboratories in the United States in 1960, and the transferral of substantial numbers of research personnel to California headquarters in 1962, the corporate image is being "Americanized." Spokesmen for the firm point out that while their greatest volume of business still comes from supplying yam starting materials, last year's profits were largely derived from the sale of their own packaged drugs—and future emphasis will be placed upon the latter.*

This northern migration into United States drug-company territory has caused the historically controversial Syntex oper-

---

* The plantation at San Juan Evangelista and some of the Syntex processing plants are now being operated by Schering, A. G. (Germany).

ation to become even more so. However, authorities seem to agree that the emphasis placed upon basic research at Syntex, particularly the contributions of Dr. Carl Djerassi and the brilliant young scientists who have come from all over the world to work with him, is extraordinary. Professor Djerassi of Stanford University is a member of the Syntex board of directors and he is also in charge of the scientific work at the new Syntex Institute for Molecular Biology in Palo Alto, California. The author of more than 350 publications, he won the American Chemical Society Award in Pure Chemistry in 1958 when only thirty-four years old. At that time, Harvard's Robert B. Woodward said, "Djerassi's volume of work is probably without parallel for one of his age."

In furthering its research objectives, Syntex ships for experimental purposes a greater variety and volume of steroids than almost any other laboratory in the world. For example, it has specially prepared forty compounds, six being observed in patients, for the National Cancer Institute's drug-screening program. Dr. Jonathan L. Hartwell of the Institute told me early in my investigation that Syntex has been in the forefront in developing not only the chemical intermediates from yams, but also the synthetic steroids. "Of the more than 100 chemical compounds that the National Cancer Institute has in clinical trial," he said, "more than half are steroids."

One of these, an improved male hormone called Masteron, was developed by Bowers' group in Mexico City. According to many reports in the medical literature, this hormone is just as effective in treating breast cancer (deemed beyond help from surgery or radiation) as testosterone, but it has the advantage of causing little or none of the masculinizing side effects found with the older drug.

After leaving Mexico City I talked with Dr. Albert Segaloff, of the Alton Ochsner Medical Foundation in New Orleans. Since 1955 he has been chairman of the National Cancer

Institute's nationwide breast-cancer drug-screening program. This form of cancer is the most prevalent of any type of neoplastic disease in *either* sex. If diagnosed and treated early it is 90 per cent curable, but for far-advanced cases there was formerly little hope. In the program co-ordinated by Dr. Segaloff, forty-nine leading research hospitals, such as the Mayo Clinic, Sloan-Kettering, and Johns Hopkins, have been finding that thousands of patients are helped with these new hormonal substances.

Cancer is just one field in which steroids from yams offer great promise. Another application in particular seems to bring the search for plant precursors of cortisone full circle. Remember the 1941 note jotted down at the Mayo Clinic by Dr. Hench, who noticed that arthritis almost invariably subsides during pregnancy? Doctors are now administering the antifertility drugs, which millions of women take to control ovulation, in *special dosages* to female arthritic patients. These individualized prescriptions produce a state of "false pregnancy," during which arthritis symptoms are reduced in women responding to this therapy.

Few of these patients and their physicians realize that a member of the plant kingdom provides this blessed relief. Nor could they guess that for a dozen years millions of dollars and the efforts of many scientists have been expended by the government and the drug industry in seeking the wild Dioscoreas and attempting to tame them. Wild or tame, they undoubtedly will continue to serve us well for years to come.

3

Frontiers of Research

INTRODUCTION

IN THE WORDS OF A LEADING RESEARCHER, "WE are going back to nature because, good as the test tube is, it hasn't abolished man's greatest killers and cripplers—cancer, cardiovascular diseases, and mental illness." The first three chapters in this last section of the book explore some of the heartening botanical breakthroughs in these vital areas. Parts 1 and 2, in focusing on the men and their methods and on the biographies of individual botanicals (actually, overlapping and impossible to separate), described some of the physical hazards and technical problems of drug plant search and research. These were largely resolved in success stories.

In Part 3, there will be success stories, too; in fact, there is nothing in GREEN MEDICINE to equal the impact of the rediscovery of Rauwolfia's value. But from this point on, we shall see that scientists are beset by many problems that are extremely difficult to pin down and to solve. Researchers, themselves, are torn by moral, ethical, and even legal conflicts. The mental disease field, for example, might well be diagnosed as "highly disturbed, with multiple personalities, obsessions, compulsions, and other syndromes." As this is written, almost every major magazine is featuring the sensational aspects of hallucination-producing drug plant experiments at leading universities. These topical "news pegs" illustrate the intensity of the controversy over "internal freedom," or the right to explore mind and mood-changing materials—but these much-publicized incidents are not the whole story, by any means, as I have discovered in my four-year investigation of the subject. Here we shall consider the background leading up to the employment of these drugs, and through the words of the internationally-respected scientists who actually introduced them to medicine—learn why they have been considered potentially important tools in the understanding and treatment of mental illness.

The second frontier explored in this section is a virtually untapped geographical area—the sea. Fishing for pharmaceuticals is a challenging endeavor that is just beginning to be reported in papers presented at scientific congresses, and yet it is an occupation as old as man himself. In their preliminary studies, marine pharmacologists indicate that while the world's most fabulous medicine chest—the locker of Davy Jones—is largely unopened, it may hold the answers to many pressing medical problems.

The third frontier, and concluding chapter of this book, is concerned with a global concept, basic to everything previously described: the vegetable kingdom belongs to us all. We should continue to evaluate the native knowledge of medicinal plants still employed by peoples living close to nature, but, as plant hunters like Doctors Halstead, Schultes, and others have emphasized, we must not simply invade primitive cultures and take what we want—we also have an ethical responsibility to give. The final chapter will describe a few of the many pioneering efforts to assist developing nations in making the most of their own drug resources. We should keep in mind Dr. George M. Hocking's observation:

"Among 80 per cent of the world's peoples, crude drugs still constitute the basis of prevailing medical practice." While space limitations prevent the comprehensive treatment that the subject deserves, we shall, at least, acknowledge the fact that brilliant scientists in countries other than the United States are transforming botanicals into useful medicinals that equal, and, in some cases, surpass our own contributions.

Around the globe, the words of the famous physiologist, Dr. Anton J. Carlson, are brought to life: "Real research takes everything that the ablest of us can deliver. It is not a union schedule of 40 hours a week, but a sweating proposition of 18 hours a day!"

The successes and the failures found in these pages are the results of just that kind of effort—effort that lengthens the working day of the scientist and the useful years of humanity.

Periwinkles and Other Plants
with Promise in Cancer

DURING THE LAST MONTHS OF HIS ILLNESS, SECRE-
tary of State John Foster Dulles received about 600 unsolicited
letters offering suggestions for cancer treatment and mentioning fifty-seven plants by name. Dr. Hartwell, of the National
Cancer Institute, published an analysis of these in *Cancer
Chemotherapy Reports,* May, 1960, in which he pointed out
that a number of the folk therapies dating back to ancient
Egypt, Greece, and Rome, have modern scientific approval.

To cite two examples: Pathologists have found that mum-
mified bodies show evidence of cancer, and according to the
Egyptian Ebers Papyrus of 1500 B.C., yeast was used in treating the disease. In the early 1950's folic acid, a yeast derivative, was introduced to the medical profession as a "modern"
anticancer therapy. Dioscorides, the physician who traveled
with Nero's army, wrote about the use of autumn crocus in
cancer. Today a product related to colchicine, an alkaloid
from this plant, is used by doctors to treat chronic granulo-
cytic leukemia. Colchicine itself is a specific for gout.

"The belief in popular herbal medicine is just as widespread as ever," Hartwell told me. "And there actually is
evidence of antitumor activity when extracts from such historical folk remedies as garlic and bloodroot are administered
to cancerous experimental animals."

When the Cancer Chemotherapy National Service Center (CCNSC) was established in 1955 within the National Cancer Institute at Bethesda, Maryland, a scientific mass screening system for anticancer compounds of every description was organized. Nine drug companies and 175 research centers in this country and abroad are now under contract to conduct various phases of this program. Hartwell is in charge of the Natural Products Section, Drug Development Branch, and a good share of his work is with plant explorers of the United States Department of Agriculture. The search for plants to be screened for cancer is currently the largest drug plant project of the USDA. Duplicate samples of every plant they collect, whether for potential food crops, industrial oils, or whatever, are sent to the CCNSC. In addition, Hartwell asks for specific plants based on tips gleaned from ancient writings or from folklore clues such as those contained in the Dulles correspondence.

After the botanical specimens are obtained, they are processed into extracts and screened for anticancer action in cooperating laboratories. The active ingredients are then isolated from the most promising extracts, and if these pure compounds pass toxicity and pharmacological tests, they may then be given to patients under controlled conditions.

A vital aspect of the vast screening network coordinated by the CCNSC is the tabulation of information from all these institutions and from individual scientists and physicians. Formerly there was a tremendous amount of duplication of effort, but this has been reduced considerably in the past few years. Attendance at international conferences also helps Cancer Institute specialists to keep abreast of research in other countries, including those behind the Iron Curtain; since 1959 the Russians have been co-operating with us on cancer projects.

As an example of the kind of information these researchers have at their fingertips, I learned that mistletoe is being investigated for cancer. The Russians, Germans, and Swiss have products on the market that were evaluated, along with fresh extracts of various mistletoe species, at the Roswell Park Memorial Institute in Buffalo, New York. They found that the fresh pressed juice of the *Viscum album* species yielded the most active material, causing more than 50 per cent tumor inhibition in mice. The tumor inhibitory effect was comparable to that of chemical agents now generally employed in cancer therapy. The use of mistletoe against cancer dates back to antiquity; it was recommended by Plinius the Elder.

Although it seems incredible that the sacred plant of the Druids, mistletoe, is utilized, even stranger botanical extracts are being investigated. Hartwell has been in touch with a medical missionary who has spent many years among the Jivaro head-hunters of Ecuador. The missionary is convinced that substances contained in the thirty plants that go into their *tsantsa* brew for shrinking heads have the same action on tumors. In addition to his own observations, he has case reports from hospitals in South America where cancer patients showed evidence of improvement after receiving injections or applications of material extracted from the potion.

A few years ago, top government scientists might have shied away from such weird-sounding therapies, lest their scientific reputations suffer. But doctors like Jonathan Hartwell are open-minded. He devoted five years of his own life to the pharmacological investigation of a Penobscot Indian cancer remedy that had been in disrepute as a quack "cure." Today an extract of this plant, podophyllin, from American mandrake or May apple, *Podophyllum peltatum,* is the preferred treatment for certain warts, and some cancer specialists use it for other skin growths. Incidentally, this is not the ancient mandrake, Mandragora, used as a sedative. (In 1963 Sandoz Ltd., in Basel, announced an anticancer agent, SPI-SPG, which is obtained from species of Podophyllum by

partial synthesis. It is available only in Switzerland and requires a prescription. While the first active substances isolated
from this botanical were highly toxic, this new drug has no
serious side effects when administered under careful medical
supervision. Clinical experience with a large number of patients over the past few years showed that it inhibited the
growth of certain solid, malignant tumors and, in the most
favorable cases, led to a clinical disappearance of the tumors
during the period of observation. The best results have been
obtained in tumors of the upper digestive tract and in breast
cancer that has spread to the lungs.)

The CCNSC plant program in the United States began
four years ago with the evaluation of 600 botanicals collected
by the USDA in their search for cortisone sources. Since
then, over 14,000 plant extracts have been tested. The upsurge
of interest in just the past year or two is reflected in the fact
that, of this total, 5,400 plant extracts were screened in 1962
alone. At least that many were evaluated in 1963.

Co-operating institutions have undertaken broad studies
of the floras in their areas. At the University of Arizona, Dean
Willis R. Brewer, of the College of Pharmacy, and Professor
Mary E. Caldwell are directing the collection and extraction
of plants growing in the deserts and mountains of southwestern United States and northern Mexico. When I visited
their laboratories, I asked how they managed to get enough
botanicals to study from the barren-looking terrain. Dr. Caldwell said, "We have reaped a surprising number of promising
plants from our three-year harvest of this rocky, arid soil.
When you start to collect every plant that grows, you find
an amazing variety of vegetation."

At Loma Linda University in California, chairman of the
pharmacology department Mervyn G. Hardinge, M.D., and
his staff, supported by National Cancer Institute grants, are
collecting, extracting, and testing that state's rich flora for

anticancer agents. Hardinge, an authority on vegetarian diet, is also investigating the role that food may play in the development and growth of cancer.

As I visited cancer research centers I heard many comments like the following: "We have always been interested in flowering plants, but until the success with Vinca alkaloids from periwinkles came along, we couldn't persuade the 'powers-that-be' here to support such research. . . . Yes, Vinca started a trend away from the concentration upon antibiotics from molds. As recently as 1959, 75 per cent of this type of cancer research involved the screening of fermentation products; the balance was largely concentrated on synthetics."

The John L. Smith Memorial for Cancer Research in Maywood, New Jersey, operated by Pfizer, the world's largest producer of antibiotics, has been one of the most active screeners of these microorganisms for CCNSC. Here, as many as 500 soil samples a week have been examined for anticancer possibilities; a spoonful of soil may contain as many as 40,-000,000 organisms. In this program 7,000 new broths were fermented a year, but only 1 or 2 per cent had any activity worthy of note, and most of these were duplicates. Therefore, Dr. K. V. Rao, who isolates the active principles, said that he has definitely become more interested in the higher (flowering) plants. He now has a number of trained botanists in this country, Chile, and India sending him about 300 specimens a year.

The basis for this increased botanical research was summed up by Hartwell when he observed, "Plants provide a fertile source of compounds with novel structures that are needed in cancer chemotherapy but which are difficult for the chemist to synthesize." At the University of Wisconsin, which screens plants for other American research centers as well as some in India, Costa Rica, and Peru, Professor S. Morris Kupchan provided an illustration: "We have reported anticancer activity in an extract from Aristolochia, a plant used for cancer since Graeco-Roman times. Aristolochic acid possesses a novel structure and this is the first time that a compound of this type has shown antitumor activity. Even if it is not useful in human cancers, it may provide a lead for chemical modification that might eventually yield a useful drug." (Colchicine, synthesized by Stanford University's Professor Eugene van Tamelen, one of our country's leading natural product chemists, is a case in point.)

There are also authorities who believe that drug plants in their natural state offer more promise than synthetics. This is a controversial area, but Dr. Alfred Taylor, the physiologist who pioneered botanical screening for cancer at the University of Texas at a time when all the emphasis was on synthetics, was willing to speak for the record: "In our twenty years of cancer research," he said, "we have never had as much success with chemicals invented by man as we are now having with plant extracts. There is not a single chemical agent that will completely inhibit the growth of, or destroy, tumor tissue without causing undue disturbance to nontumor tissues. In plants we have more compounds than chemists can ever hope to synthesize. And, as a rule—not in all cases, mind you—but as a rule, the naturally occurring compounds are less likely to be poisonous than the synthetic because they are developed in association with life."

Back in 1942, Taylor devised a method for cheaply and quickly testing toxicity simultaneously with anticancer effects. He injected test compounds into the yolk sacs of fertile eggs that were previously infected with cancer cells. By this method, it became possible to check the effect of a compound against cancer growth and, at the same time, the growth of noncancer tissue—the chick embryo. The toxic effect of the compound on the embryo was an additional factor. The answers were available within twenty-four to forty-eight hours.

Taylor and his colleagues started out with poisonous plants, thinking that these might kill off cancer the quickest; but they soon found that some of the most innocuous extracts, such as those from muskmelon and cucumber, had just as good or better anticancer properties when tested on chick embryos and mice. (This does not mean that humans with cancer can cure themselves with such a diet.) Since then Taylor's group has tested thousands of whole-plant extracts for the USDA and CCNSC. Taylor places great importance on careful processing methods, because anticancer properties can be destroyed by heat, harsh chemicals, or even a few days of standing at refrigerator temperatures. At present, he is exploring the effect of special diets as a form of cancer prevention in animals with inherited susceptibility to the disease.

We need to pursue every promising lead because cancer is not one disease, but a family of a hundred or more related disorders having many similarities and many differences. Basically, there are solid tumors, mainly divided into sarcomas and carcinomas, and there are leukemias, diseases of the blood-forming organs characterized by a marked increase in the number of white blood cells and enlargement of lymphoid tissue of the spleen, lymphatic glands, and bone marrow. As we know, there are many conflicting theories about the causes of cancer; but at least there is general agreement on what the disease is—cell growth gone haywire. Scientists refer to cancer as neoplastic disease, from the Greek *neos plastikos,* meaning new-formed. All treatment is directed toward inhibiting this new, abnormal tissue formation, while leaving the rest of the body unharmed.

Many natural and synthetic drugs have shown remarkable anticancer action, but either they are too toxic for continued use or their effects are short-lived because resistance is built up. Dr. Frank L. Horsfall, Jr., president of the Sloan-Kettering Institute for Cancer Research, which screens more compounds than any other single laboratory except the National Cancer Institute, said: "Over the years we have tested 22,500 chemical compounds and about 56,000 materials of natural origin. We have found some 480 synthetics and 640 biological materials to be active against cancers of various types in animals. Results indicate that no single substance effective against all types of cancer is likely to be found from present chemical approaches. For example, cancers spontaneously arising, or chemically induced, or transplanted in the same host species may all show quite different responses to the same substance. However, at present doctors do have more than twenty-five extensively tested agents for the chemotherapy of cancer in man."

Cancer is not the leading cause of death in the Western world; diseases of the heart and circulatory system claim far more victims. But more money is being spent on cancer research, perhaps because it is such an insidious killer, occurring in almost every tissue of the body and striking at any age. About half a million new cases of cancer will be diagnosed in the United States within the next year, but the outlook for these patients is increasingly optimistic: the current survival rate is one in three, and more than 1,200,000 Americans now living have been pronounced cured of cancer by their doctors.

The story of the botanical Vinca, its discovery and development into drugs now available to physicians,* dramatizes many of the problems involved in turning folklore plants into lifesaving pharmaceuticals. But most importantly, it underscores the vital ingredient in all of this research: *hope.*

For nine months a forty-nine-year-old machinist suffered from Hodgkin's disease, a form of cancer that attacks the lymph glands, spleen, and liver. None of the treatments tried

---

* Velban (vinblastine sulfate, Lilly), and Oncovin (vincristine sulfate, Lilly.)

had altered the course of his illness. He now had a ten-inch tumor pressing against his windpipe, causing constant pain that could not be suppressed with drugs. He had lost fifty pounds and could neither walk nor lie flat in bed. On March 2, 1960, he received his first injection of vinblastine. (First isolated as VLB in 1958 from leaves of the ornamental periwinkle shrub, *Vinca rosea*, by Dr. C. T. Beer, working under Dr. R. L. Noble at the University of Western Ontario.) Within four days this patient was comfortable; a week later he was walking; and in less than two weeks the tumor had begun to shrink noticeably, according to doctors treating him at the Marion County General Hospital in Indianapolis. Four months later, the tumor was gone; the man had gained twenty pounds and was back at work. Eventually he regained all the weight lost, and biweekly injections kept him free of cancer for two-and-a-half years.

Then, as often happens, the disease grew resistant to the medication and the machinist's symptoms began to reappear. By this time, Dr. Gordon H. Svoboda, the Eli Lilly phytochemist responsible for turning the VLB alkaloid into the pharmaceutical vinblastine, had isolated twenty-three new alkaloids from Vinca, in addition to six already known. One of the Svoboda discoveries, vincristine, was given to this patient, and although it is a close chemical relative of VLB it has strikingly different biological effects. Most noteworthy is the fact that resistance to the first alkaloid does not seem to carry over to the second; more than a year after the start of vincristine therapy, the machinist remains free of cancer.

The highlighting of this one case history is not intended to indicate a cancer cure, for the word "cure" may not be applied until a cancer patient has been without evidence of the disease for at least five years after confirmed diagnosis and completion of treatment. Vinca alkaloids may not help all of this country's 15,000 victims of Hodgkin's disease, nor are they the only accepted method of treatment. In fact, for quite a few years the focus in cancer therapy has been on synthetic drugs, radiation, and surgery.

The attending physician is, of course, the person to determine what is best for an individual case. But in the life-or-death situation posed by terminal cancer, distraught families sometimes try to obtain the latest medication, even if it is still undergoing preliminary testing. Since a new drug cannot legally be dispensed by other than the testers until it has passed all of the Federal requirements, such quests by patients' relatives often end in bitter disappointment. In medical reporting, the possibility of raising false hope is constantly weighed against the preservation of a free flow of science news, which often causes cancer patients and their families to take heart and stimulates the support of further research.

Last year newspapers carried the story of a little girl in Dallas who had acute leukemia. She was receiving vincristine, then still experimental. The article mentioned that a six-weeks' supply of the drug—one gram in this case—was extracted from two tons of crushed Vinca leaves. (It had been given to the doctors free of charge by the manufacturer, but it cost them several thousand dollars to produce a gram.) When the superintendent of a California highway crew read this, he ordered his men to pull up all of the Vinca growing along the embankments and send it to a cancer researcher "for processing." This was not the right variety of Vinca, and when it arrived it was not in proper condition to turn into an injectable drug anyway. The well-meaning Californians were undoubtedly very disheartened by this news. The plant collected was *Vinca minor,* a creeper with shiny dark-green leaves and lilac-blue flowers commonly used as a ground cover around foundation plantings and in bare spots of lawn. It is sometimes called "running myrtle." So far it has proved to be devoid of activity in cancer tests.

306

Dr. Norman R. Farnsworth, a young pharmacognosy professor at the University of Pittsburgh's School of Pharmacy, has made an exhaustive study of the botanically confusing periwinkles, to which all the Vincas belong. He published a definitive monograph in *Lloydia,* September, 1961, covering the botanical, pharmacological, and folk-medicine history of these species. And he has also supervised the experimental planting of several thousand Vinca plants at Chancellor Litchfield's Tumble Run Farms in Coudersport, Pennsylvania. This is a pilot study designed to supply basic scientific information rather than raw materials for mass-produced drugs. Because the discovery of anticancer action in Vinca stemmed directly from its use as a native remedy, Farnsworth's research is particularly interesting.

The species that produces the cancer drug now on the market is *"Catharanthus roseus* G. Don (*Vinca rosea* L., *Lochnera rosea* Reichb.)." It requires a past president of the American Society of Pharmacognosy like Farnsworth to explain how pretty ornamentals, listed in nursery catalogues as Little Pinkie, Twinkles, Purity, and Bright Eyes, ever came to be saddled with this burdensome name. Briefly, the Swedish botanist Linnaeus called it *Vinca rosea* in 1735, hence the "L." following that name; in 1828 Reichenbach added Lochnera; but G. Don established the genus as Catharanthus in 1838. Here we shall continue to refer to the anticancer plant simply as *Vinca rosea.* Unlike the ground-cover variety, it is a woody tropical shrub that quickly grows to heights of one or two feet. In this country, it is cultivated in pots or hedges for its beauty. As the horticultural names indicate, some flowers are white and some are pink; there are crimson ones, too. All may have red "eyes" in the center of the blossom.

The periwinkle group belongs to the alkaloid-rich dogbane family, which has given us a number of useful drugs, including Rauwolfia. Farnsworth described many old folk-medicine uses for all of the periwinkles—for dysentery, menstrual disorders, toothache, and so forth—but in a very thorough search he did not find *Vinca rosea* cited as a cancer cure. However, it has been employed in the Philippines, South Africa, India, Australia, and elsewhere as a tea for diabetics. In fact, infusions of the leaves have been sold as a patent remedy for many years in England and South Africa.

The trail that led to the discovery of VLB began in the Collip Medical Research Laboratory in London, Ontario. Dr. Noble, an endocrinologist, gave me this background: "The plant *Vinca rosea* was first drawn to my attention from a practical point of view in the summer of 1949. A patient told my brother, a physician, about the use of the leaves for diabetes by Jamaicans. We got in touch with a doctor in Jamaica who sent us a small supply of leaves. By August 9, 1949, we wrote this doctor that we had tested the leaves on four rabbits and had not found any effect on their blood sugar. This project did not become a major one until Dr. Beer, a biochemist, joined our staff in 1954–55; Dr. J. H. Cutts, a pharmacologist, became part of the group in 1956."

After finding that the animals did not respond to oral feedings, the researchers decided to inject an extract made from the leaves. The blood sugar was not reduced this time either. But within a few days after the first injection many of the animals died of an overwhelming infection that was traced to Pseudomonas bacteria, commonly found where animals are housed. At this point the project might well have been abandoned, but these scientists were not so easily discouraged. Further bacteriological studies showed that there was no such organism in the extract itself. After a considerable amount of detective work, the investigators concluded that the animals had lost their natural resistance to infection because something in the drug plant had depleted their supply of protective white blood cells or had damaged their bone marrow. While there was a rapidly falling white-blood-cell count, they noted that other factors in the blood were not altered nor were vital organs harmed. This selective action—the reduction of white blood cells—suggested that the substance might be useful as an anticancer drug, and eventually the material was tried on animals having transplanted tumors, with good results.

The first publication of this work appeared in 1955 in the *33rd Annual Report of the British Empire Cancer Campaign*. By 1958, Beer had isolated a crystalline alkaloid from a number of active substances and called it vincaleukoblastine. Noble said, "This name was not chosen from the local Indian dialect, as one might suppose, and it was soon mercifully shortened to VLB." By this time it had been determined that the roots, stems, and leaves of Vinca all contained active material, but the seeds did not. The leaves, which could be most easily extracted, produced the highest proportion of pharmacological activity. Staff members went to Jamaica to collect wild plants for comparison with those cultivated in Ontario, and the tropical species proved superior.

The Canadians presented their findings at a symposium held in 1958 at the New York Academy of Sciences, which later published their paper, titled "Role of Chance Observations in Chemotherapy: Vinca Rosea" in Volume 76 December 1958 of its *Annals*. It contained the statement "results of our research . . . should not be considered in terms of a new chemotherapeutic agent. . . ." Farnsworth called this "one of the classic understatements of all time." The scientists spoke only of "potential" value, although they had observed VLB's antitumor action on several types of cancer in animals. In the introduction to the paper, a significant point was well made: "The cancer worker in the smaller institution or academic department must view with awe the vast chemotherapeutic screening projects in the United States; at the same time, he must consider what contribution he is in a position to make. Perhaps the role of chance observation is neglected in his consideration of ways of searching for new agents. Although somewhat irregular in comparison with the systematic prediction, synthesis, and screening of an entirely new series of compounds, chance observations may well be worthy of greater consideration than they have received."

Noble, who presented the paper, stated that cancer was far from his mind when he began the work on the "diabetes remedy." He has been paid this tribute by Hartwell: "This illustrates the case of a man looking for one thing and finding another, not from dumb luck, but because he was a scientist. The blood counts would not have been necessary for the anti-diabetic work alone. But a well-trained researcher will do more work than necessary for the particular study at hand and will be alert to other effects and their implications."

In one of the odd research coincidences that can lead to bad feelings and even lawsuits—but in this case had a constructive conclusion—the Canadians met Dr. Irving S. Johnson of Eli Lilly at the New York meeting and learned that Dr. Svoboda had been working along exactly the same lines in Indianapolis. Neither group was aware of the other's Vinca project until this conference. To their credit, from that point on they pooled their knowledge so that the best possible drugs might be produced for cancer patients.

The Lilly research on *V. rosea* began in 1954, when Svoboda made a nine-months' survey of Far Eastern plants for his company's botanical screening program, which, by the way, is not subsidized by government funds. He was not interested in obtaining substances to treat any particular disease. As he explained to me, "We hoped that out of, say, 1,800 plants tested, we might get just one to pay off in a useful drug. That would be par for the course." He remembered that during World War II diabetics in the Philippines used a native Vinca (*sitsirika*) when supplies of insulin were cut off, so he added this to the 440 botanicals earmarked for testing.

In 1956, the Meer Corporation in New York, a leading supplier of botanicals, was asked by Lilly to obtain properly identified samples of Vinca, all varieties, wherever they might be found. Dr. William Meer recalled that they contacted botanical collectors in Madagascar, Australia, South Africa, South America, the West Indies, Europe, India, and even the United States, where the plant can grow naturally in the Deep South. All parts of the plant were gathered because at that time they didn't know exactly where the active principles might be found. (Both the Canadians and Farnsworth were also working on this but had not yet published their findings.)

"In most cases," Dr. Meer said, "it took from 60 to 120 days to receive these samples and then our work was just beginning, for the identification and authentication of periwinkles was not easy because of considerable confusion in the botanical literature." As he told his colleagues at the American Society of Pharmacognosy's 1962 meeting, the commercial cultivation and collection of *Vinca rosea* posed many unique and interesting problems. The harvesting of the life-giving leaves is but the last step in a long, exhaustive research program, involving speculative expenditures of time and money in such things as setting up a cultivation project abroad. While the drug was still in the experimental stages with no definite commercial application, Meer contracted with farmers in the hill country of eastern India to buy all the Vinca they could grow. These fields have been supplying most of the leaves used in making anticancer compounds since 1959, with a little additional material collected in the West Indies. The foreign supply is plentiful, although it was briefly threatened by the Chinese communist border invasion. To establish a domestic source, Meer is considering a cultivation program in the southern United States. Fortunately, the second strippings of the leaves yield just as much of the needed alkaloids as the first year's harvest, so the Vinca crop does not have to be replanted annually. It is good to know that there is a sufficient supply of this vital raw material at the present time.

By December, 1957, Svoboda had submitted an extract of the whole Vinca plant to the Lilly screening program. Mice infected with P-1534 leukemia showed a 60 to 80 per cent prolongation of life when treated with this substance. "Without the use of this particular form of leukemia as a screening device," Svoboda pointed out, "the anticancer activity of Vinca alkaloids would have gone unnoticed. Dr. Johnson had set up a unique system here for annually screening up to 7,000 compounds for antitumor effects. So far, it has predicted the subsequent action in cancer patients with 86 per cent accuracy. It is the only mouse-tumor system that detects and indicates the extent of activity in all Vinca alkaloids; the most widely used tumor system in other laboratories shows only weak action, or none, for these compounds."

Svoboda and his associates reviewed their Vinca research in the *Journal of Pharmaceutical Sciences,* August, 1962. This statement was included: "With the exception of leurosine, all of these alkaloids may significantly prolong the life of P-1534 animals, even when treatment is delayed until the animals are in near terminal states. In addition, in the case of leurocristine [generic name is vincristine] and leurosidine [a new alkaloid], very preliminary studies suggest that if such animals survive, they may become resistant to additional challenges with the same tumor. 'Curing' of strain specific tumors in highly inbred strains of laboratory animals is in itself rare, but resistance to subsequent challenges of the same tumor is almost unique." These investigators were careful to point out that they did not know whether this cancer immunity could be carried over to humans—after all, even P-1534 "super-mice" aren't men. But it is certainly an exciting research lead. As Dr. Edward G. Feldmann, the journal's editor, commented:

"In the case of cancer, we are faced with a foe which appears to be exceedingly more complex than any previously encountered. . . . We should be truly heartened, therefore, with the hardwon gains which this article serves to typify. . . . Yesterday's despair has been turned into today's hope."

Gordon Svoboda is the president of the American Society of Pharmacognosy. His colleagues in the ASP, representing a cross section of natural-products specialists in other drug companies and in government and academic life the world over, have explained that while the anticancer action of the alkaloids he isolated is dramatic news, of equal significance is the fact that in doing so he developed techniques of great value to science. Even if the substances were inactive, his unique method for obtaining them is an outstanding contribution.

This becomes readily understandable when one learns that the yield of vincristine is the lowest of any medicinally important alkaloid isolated on a commercial basis to date. Its presence in the dry plant constitutes 0.00025 per cent of the whole amount. For comparison, belladonna alkaloids are a thousand times more concentrated. Besides the difficulty of identifying such minute amounts of materials, to have isolated more than forty-three different alkaloids (at the last count) from a single plant with a total alkaloid content of only 0.7 per cent is in itself unparalleled in the history of botanical investigation. For this work, Svoboda won the American Pharmaceutical Association's 1963 Research Achievement Award in Natural Products. In a continuing search for alkaloids, Dr. Svoboda and his co-workers recently isolated twenty-four alkaloids, eleven of them new, from the roots of an African species of Vinca. Some of these substances have produced unusually high prolongations of life in mice infected with P-1534 leukemia.

Dr. James G. Armstrong, of Lilly's Clinical Research Department, continues to direct the evaluation of Vinca alkaloids, which are exhaustively tested before release. By now, more than

200 physicians in many countries have observed its effects in patients who had forty-seven different forms of malignancy.

Their medical-journal reports contain X-ray and other laboratory data to document the conclusions. The patients described had, in most cases, become resistant to other drugs, including those for pain relief; many were moribund, or dying, at the time of the first injection. There was often widespread involvement of bones and vital organs. That some of these people on maintenance doses are now free of symptoms and leading normal lives surely proves that the word hopeless has no place in the discussion of cancer today.

Some of the most encouraging news came from the 1962 American Association for Cancer Research meeting, where eleven papers described how Vinca compounds attacked the disease in all parts of the body. Vincristine showed particularly promising results in the treatment of acute lymphocytic leukemia in children. These are the heartbreaking "early-Christmas" cases we read about so often during the autumn months, the just-diagnosed youngsters who are not expected to live to hang up their stockings on December 25. The average life span in untreated patients has been said to be about four months from the onset of this form of leukemia.

Doctors at the National Cancer Institute, one of six research centers studying vincristine, reported a conservative complete remission rate of 54 per cent in a group of children with advanced leukemia not responding to any other treatment. By the fifth month of vincristine, 60 per cent of this group were still alive, while another control group receiving different therapy had only 10 per cent surviving (*Pediatrics,* November, 1962).*

---

*After this chapter was set in type, the first comprehensive summary of current knowledge of Vinca alkaloids appeared in the scientific literature. Authors I. S. Johnson, J. G. Armstrong, M. Gorman, and J. P. Burnett cited 91 references on the chemistry, pharmacology, pos-

The introduction of vincristine therapy for childhood leukemias was hailed by the American Medical Association as one of three outstanding advances in drug progress for 1963. While not every patient benefits, continuing research by the Lilly scientists, the Canadian pioneers, and others, has improved dosage schedules so that increasingly better results are achieved, as well as wider application.

The fact that Vinca alkaloids are chemically unique has had a far-reaching effect upon basic research. The drug's mode of action in the cancer patient's body is still unknown, but several highly technical theories have been proposed, involving glutamic acid metabolism and the inhibition of cell energy. Human cancer tissue, exposed to Vinca alkaloids, is being intensively studied for cell changes by biologist Dorothy G. Walker and Jane C. Wright, M.D., at New York's Bellevue Hospital, and by others elsewhere.

Another type of investigation involving tissue culture, this time with the plant itself, is being conducted by Dr. David P. Carew at the University of Iowa, College of Pharmacy. The *Vinca rosea* he has painstakingly cultivated in laboratory flasks has produced alkaloids—exactly how and why remains to be seen. Are they identical with those obtained from naturally grown plants? Will they have the same anticancer action?

As Dr. Alfred Taylor once pointed out: "The plant kingdom has forms as diverse as oaks and fungi; variety in form is paralleled by variety in biochemistry. We have scarcely begun to explore its potential. Whole areas are practically untouched. What do we know of the active constituents of seeds, for instance? Virtually nothing!"

Vinca extracts are the only derivatives from higher plants

---

sible mechanisms of action, and experimental and clinical activity of these new anticancer agents. (*Cancer Research,* Vol. 23, No. 8, pp. 1390–1427.) The reports continue to be ever more heartening.

now in clinical trials in the National Cancer Institute's botanical screening program, but Dr. Hartwell says that others are expected to reach this stage shortly. The success with Vinca definitely started a trend. In the minds of countless researchers, there is no question but that many other plants hold promise in the treatment and understanding of cancer.

Rauwolfia, the Park Avenue Snakeroot

A SUDANESE PSYCHIATRIST FOR THE WORLD HEALTH Organization, Dr. Tigani El Mahi, recently advised his colleagues: "Always stay on good terms with the local witch doctor. I've learned a lot from medicine men." Dr. T. A. Lambo, a British-trained Nigerian psychiatrist, prescribes rituals, dances, even sacrifices for his anxiety-ridden patients as his adaptation of modern psychiatry. Western mental health experts have given wide recognition to his community system of treatment for the tensions engendered by the rapid changes in African life.*

Dr. Raymond Prince, a psychiatrist from McGill University in Canada, has been spending a good share of his time in recent years in Nigeria's western bush country, studying the methods of witch doctors in treating mental illness. His project is underwritten by a grant from the Society for the Investigation of Human Ecology. Dr. Prince found that the emotionally-disturbed Nigerian and the tense executive of the Western Hemisphere have illnesses that often follow the same course and require the same cure.

---

* Wolf Sachs, M.D., former president of the South African Psychoanalytic Society, published an interesting account of his psychoanalysis of a native African medicine man, *Black Hamlet* (Little Brown, 1947).

When the businessman can no longer cope, his doctor will employ talk and tranquilizers. When the native seeks relief, his doctor, whose mudhut office is identified by a white flag, ushers him inside and asks him to lie down on a grass mat instead of a leather couch; except for this superficial difference in decor, procedures are remarkably similar. The African patient may be given a draught of a mysterious yellow liquid —a small dose as a tranquilizer, a larger one to produce deep sleep. Sometimes a cake of black soap is prescribed with the suggestion that it will "wash away the evil spirits."

Prince observed that mentally ill natives may have to return to their witch doctors for several years of "talking things over," plus medication, before their troubles clear up. If the patient is wealthy, he pays a high fee, usually in domestic animals; otherwise he works off the debt by tilling the doctor's fields. It is the steep cost of witch doctoring that causes some patients to switch to Prince's free clinic. Because of his research project, he welcomes this opportunity to compare his techniques with those of the native practitioners.

Witch doctors apparently take a more kindly attitude toward "patient snatching" than their Park Avenue counterparts might. One native specialist not only permitted the Canadian to observe his methods of therapy, but also gave him a sample of the magical liquid. "When this was later analyzed in London," Prince reported, "it was found chemically to resemble reserpine, a tranquilizing drug known to us only since 1952. The natives drink this herb tea after boiling the roots of Rauwolfia trees that grow near their villages. They have probably been doing this for centuries, as well as using other equally effective plant remedies which we know nothing about. I feel that these might be just as valuable in Western medicine, so I plan to search for these other drugs and also investigate a question pertinent to Western society: How much does the cure depend upon the magic of 'talk,' and how much upon the use of physiologically active drugs?"

Rauwolfia has not only been used for hundreds of years in Africa, it has also been a folk remedy in India for at least thirty centuries. There it is called *sarpagandha* in Sanskirt, referring to its use as an antidote for snake bite; *chandra* in Hindi, meaning "moon" and alluding to its calming effect upon lunacy; and snakeroot or serpentwood in English, possibly because of its snakelike roots. It is sold at village fairs as *pagal-ke-dawa,* the insanity herb. Snakeroot has long been chewed by meditating Indian holy men; the late Mohandas K. Gandhi regularly drank a tea prepared from the plant. And it also has soothed countless generations of fretful babies.

First mentioned in the *Charka Samhita,* a medical treatise dating from around 1000 B.C., snakeroot was introduced to Europe by Garcia de Orta in his 1563 A.D. book on Hindu medicine *Colloquios dos simples e drogas e cousas medicinaes de India.* In 1755, Georg Eberhardt Rumpf, a physician who called himself the Pliny of India, gave the following description of snakeroot in his book *Herbarium Amboinense*:

"Men seem to have learned the powers of this plant from the so-called mongoose or weasel. This little animal, before attacking a snake, fortifies itself by eating the leaves; or, if injured in combat with a snake, seeks out this herb, eats the leaves, rolls itself around three or four times, then rests a little as if drugged, but soon afterwards regains its strength and rushes forward to re-attack. It is used for the following diseases: The natives of Bengal and Malabar say that the root ground in water produces a decoction that is an outstanding antidote against any poison that causes the body to swell and grow blue. . . . Freshly pounded roots and leaves may be placed under the toe-nails. . . . When the stalks are broken, a milky juice exudes. This is instilled in the eyes to remove the white spots or opacities. In Batavia, the plant is used thus: The root is cut into small pieces and swallowed; this is of value in cases of anxiety and of pain in the stomach. When finely ground up and drunk in water, the root is also of value in fever and vomiting, likewise for headache if the head is washed with a decoction. It is said to cure the bite of most poisonous snakes, even the Cobra *capella*."

The claims made for the plant as a universal panacea were so extravagant that Western scientists refused to consider it seriously for hundreds of years.

The genus Rauwolfia belongs to the Apocynaceae, or dogbane family, which supplies such drug plants as Strophanthus and Vinca. In 1703, the French botanist Charles Plumier named it in honor of a sixteenth-century German physician-explorer, Leonhard Rauwolf. This was rather strange, because Rauwolf, traveling in the Middle East where the genus does not occur, never brought back any samples of the plant himself. *The International Code of Botanical Nomenclature* uses the spelling of Swedish botanist Linnaeus, Rau*v*olfia, but the common spelling, even in scientific publications, is with a "w."

The plant is found growing naturally throughout the tropics, with the exception of Australia, where it was only recently introduced; and it is interesting to note that widely separated primitive people have used it in an identical fashion. Almost universally it has been acclaimed as an antidote for snake bite and poisoning, and in the treatment of maniacal forms of insanity. Another popular use is as a purgative and emetic. In Liberia it is employed in treating eye and skin diseases; the same use is made of it in Mexico, where pieces of the bark are also placed on painful teeth. Both Africans and South American natives find it good for reducing fevers.

All parts of the plant have been used, internally, externally, to cure, and sometimes to kill. Rauwolfia in large doses may lead to temporary paralysis or death, after first causing burning sensations in the stomach, vomiting, thirst, then a weak but quickened, irregular pulse, and finally convulsions and coldness of the extremities.

The fact that folk usage, however well-intentioned, is not

always wise, is illustrated by an anthropologist's recent report from South America. Missionaries were nursing a young Indian woman back to health in their home after a nearly fatal case of pneumonia. Because this is a "white man's disease," like tuberculosis and the common cold, the Indians did not have a specific remedy for it. But they wanted to give the woman something, so they smuggled in to her a very strong brew made from Rauwolfia. The patient was so weak from the disease and her prolonged stay in bed that it killed her.

So it has always been with native remedies—a matter of trial and error. When the successes outnumber the casualties with any degree of regularity, a cure is proclaimed and the potion is passed on to the next generation. Nevertheless, mankind has survived almost a million years of this "doctoring."

Dr. Robert de Ropp, a biochemist, made an interesting observation along these lines in his book *Drugs and the Mind*: "It is curious that a remedy so ancient [as Rauwolfia] . . . should have been ignored by Western researchers until the year 1947. This situation results in part, at least, from the rather contemptuous attitude which certain chemists and pharmacologists in the West have developed toward both folk remedies and drugs of plant origin. . . . They further fell into the error of supposing that because they had learned the trick of synthesizing certain substances, they were better chemists than Mother Nature who, besides creating compounds too numerous to mention, also synthesized the aforesaid chemists and pharmacologists. Needless to say, the more enlightened members of these professions have avoided so crude an error, realizing that the humblest bacterium can synthesize, in the course of its brief existence, more organic compounds than can all the world's chemists combined."

The modern story of Rauwolfia began in the late 1920's when Indian scientific researchers started reviewing the indigenous botanical drugs long used by native practitioners and physicians. Their subcontinent has many different climates, soils, and latitudes, producing an especially rich and varied flora. Kashmir in the north resembles Switzerland, and the Malabar Coast has stretches reminiscent of the South Seas. Between lies the Sind desert, much like the Sahara. In the jungles of Assam, some of the heaviest rains in the world occur—an annual mean of 428 inches and up to 905 inches in one record year, as much as 41 inches in a single day. It is not surprising that even now more than half the drugs prescribed by Indian doctors come from the lush vegetation in this environment.

In *Rig-Veda,* which Colonel Sir Ram Nath Chopra says is probably the oldest repository of human knowledge, written between 4500 and 1600 B.C., the medicinal use of plants is clearly mentioned. In *Ayur-Veda,* from a much later period, definite properties of drugs and their uses were listed. In *Sushruta Samhita,* dating not later than 1000 B.C., a comprehensive account of drug therapy is given. Some 2,000 remedies, derived mostly from vegetable sources, are described in the *Charka Samhita,* of about the same period, with references to the active principles and toxicology of many drugs. Later, during the Buddhist period, medicinal plants were cultivated by experts. Contacts with Greece, Rome, Arabia, and Persia contributed much to the enrichment of India's materia medica.

But all this knowledge was scattered and little scientific work was done until the early part of this century, when authentic information on the botanical identification, habitat, and conditions of harvesting, as well as the medicinal value of these plants, began to be collected. This research, still going on today, is complicated because of the different Indian systems of medicine: Hindu Ayur-Vedic herbal prescriptions are used by one-fifth of the world's population; the Moslems employ the Unani system; and there is also the Tibbi.

Many research centers are involved in this monumental task spearheaded by Dr. Chopra, who explained in the July, 1962, Jammu Regional Research Laboratory *Bulletin* some of the early difficulties encountered: "The medical profession, at that time mainly composed of physicians imported by an alien government from abroad, and those they trained, considered these [Indian] systems unscientific and the drugs used by them generally not effective. In fact, a lot of ridicule was cast by them on the study of indigenous drugs and their investigation was considered a waste of time and money. For these reasons, financial resources for such work were very meagre. Fortunately, the Indian Council of Medical Research started giving grants and, with the establishment of the Indian Council of Agricultural Research and the Council of Scientific and Industrial Research, work on medicinal plants flourished. During the course of nearly half a century, much has been achieved, but only the fringes of this vast reservoir of human knowledge have been touched."

One of the native drugs studied was Rauwolfia. In 1931, Dr. Salimuzzaman Siddiqui and Dr. Rafat Hussain, two skilled Delhi chemists who had been trying for some time to separate Rauwolfia into its components, reported: "We have isolated from dry powdered root, five crystalline substances which appear to be new. Clinical observations are in progress."

Later, they found that administration of these materials brought highly favorable results in cases of acute insomnia accompanied by fits of insanity. For the first time, the ancient snakeroot cures were shown to have an element of truth in them. The extracts were alkaloids of two groups: the ajmaline type (named in honor of Hakim Ajmal Khan, founder of the Ayur-Vedic, Unani, and Tibbi College, where the investigations were made) contained ajmaline, ajmalinine, and ajmalicine, which were white crystals with a weakly basic chemical reaction. The serpentine group, yellow and strongly basic, included serpentine and serpentinine. In the years to follow, these alkaloids became the basis for thousands of research projects in many countries.

About this time, two physicians, Dr. Gananath Sen and Dr. Kartick Chandra Bose, announced that Rauwolfia produced not only sedation, but also a drop in blood pressure. They wrote: "Such symptoms as headache, a sense of heat, and insomnia disappear quickly and the blood pressure is reduced in a matter of weeks from, say, 200 to 160." They urged medical men all over the world to try it and see for themselves if it were not "a drug of rare merit."

Outside of India, there was virtually no interest. But Dr. Chopra in Calcutta began to direct studies of far-reaching importance. During the 1940's, an estimated one million Indian patients were receiving Rauwolfia for high blood pressure each year. Tremendous quantities of the drug were also prescribed for mental cases. Indian medical journals contained many enthusiastic accounts of these clinical trials, but the Western world placed more faith in synthetics, derived solely from chemicals. Wonder drugs like the sulfas and the barbiturates were to us "*the* drugs of the future."

Then, in 1949, Dr. Rustom Jal Vakil, a physician, described his scientifically controlled research at the King Edward Memorial Hospital in Bombay. He had studied the reactions in fifty victims of high blood pressure, after first giving them standard sedatives, then Rauwolfia, and finally no medicine at all. He found that ordinary sedatives brought blood pressure down only a few points. Rauwolfia, after four weeks, lowered the reading by twenty points. Without medication, it climbed to the pre-trial level. Patients in this study had been receiving Rauwolfia for five years or more without suffering any ill effects of a serious, disabling, or permanent nature. "Judging from the results," Dr. Vakil concluded,

"Rauwolfia has a definite place in the treatment of cases of high blood pressure.

This report appeared, not in an Indian journal, but in the *British Heart Journal,* where it was read with great interest by Dr. Robert W. Wilkins, director of the Hypertension Clinic at Massachusetts Memorial Hospitals. Dr. Wilkins recently recalled, "This account intrigued me because Dr. Vakil seemed to know what he was doing. He wrote with honesty. He was obviously a scientist who wasn't trying to sell anything to anybody. I decided to try to obtain some Rauwolfia tablets to see if they would help some of my patients who were not responding to other medication satisfactorily."

E. R. Squibb & Sons* obtained from India the whole-root Rauwolfia tablets for Wilkins, who became the first American physician willing to accept the fact that there might be some merit in snakeroot after all. After observing fifty patients for eight months, he presented a preliminary report to the New England Cardiovascular Society early in 1952. He and his associates had found Rauwolfia to be a slow-acting drug, taking anywhere from three days to several weeks to show effect. It worked best on relatively young patients with high blood pressure, emotional problems, and anxiety. For those not helped by Rauwolfia alone, he added small amounts of a more powerful blood-pressure-reducing drug, an extract of green hellebore, *Veratrum viride,* which has its own interesting history as an American Indian potion used to test the stamina of young Indian braves.**

---

* Later, in 1953, Squibb was the first company in the United States to market a chemically and biologically standardized product of whole root *R. serpentina,* called Raudixin.

** Professor S. M. Kupchan, an authority on the chemistry of Veratrum species (known in America as Indian poke and itch-weed), said they were used for sorcery in the Middle Ages and in folk medicine as local counter-irritants in neuralgia, as cardiac tonics, as emetics, and to treat fevers. Subsequent careful pharmacological investigation of purified

Wilkins found that the results were good. Patients felt better and there were no signs of addiction or serious complications. One young businessman was convinced that the treatment had saved him from a nervous breakdown. His blood pressure had soared over the 200 mark, when it should have been around 130 to 140. He couldn't sleep, his heart pounded, and he felt as if the top of his head were going to blow off. Three Rauwolfia tablets a day for four weeks brought his reading down to 175 and he said, "I haven't felt so well in years!" After two months of treatment, his blood pressure leveled off at 140, where it remained with the help of small daily doses.

Some idea of the importance of these findings may be gained from a few statistics: high blood pressure, or hypertension, is one of the more serious factors in diseases of the heart and circulatory system, which are, by far, the leading cause of death in the United States. Forty-four out of every hundred persons die as a result of cardiovascular disorders. Hypertension impairs the function of the kidneys, overburdens the heart, and usually is involved in apoplectic strokes. Even youngsters can be hypertensive. By the age of thirty, almost three per cent of us are hypertensive, suffering from such symptoms as blurred vision, headache, dizziness, and nosebleed. By age fifty, ten per cent have high blood pressure,

---

alkaloids proved these were useful in treating toxemias of pregnancy and certain other conditions involving high blood pressure. Neisler Laboratories Research Director, Dr. C. J. Cavalitto, pointed out that while Veratrum drugs form a modest percentage of the total used for these conditions, they have maintained continued acceptance, not showing the dramatic rise and fall of use that some synthetics have experienced during the past decade. Pitman-Moore is another company whose research resulted in improved medications; some of their products are derived from the European variety, *V. album*. Riker Laboratories was virtually founded on two botanicals, Veratrum and Rauwolfia. Riker's M. W. Klohs and F. Keller, and other scientists, continue to explore the possibilities in this extremely interesting drug plant.

and the percentage increases steadily with age. Before Rauwolfia, many compounds were used for this condition, but they caused nausea, vomiting, and other complications, or they put people to sleep.

In summary, Wilkins told his colleagues: "We have confirmed the clinical reports from India on the mildly hypotensive [blood-pressure-lowering] effects of this drug. It has a type of sedative action we have not observed before. Unlike barbiturates or other standard sedatives, it does not produce grogginess, stupor, or lack of co-ordination. The patients appear to be relaxed, quiet, and tranquil."

When physicians commented that heart patients on Rauwolfia "act as if they haven't a worry in the world," psychiatrists took notice. Dr. Sigmund Freud once stated that behind every psychoanalyst stands the man with the syringe, foreshadowing the era of chemical treatment of mental ills. In 1952, however, few Western physicians had any inkling of the potential in "that old Hindu cure for lunacy."

By 1953, medical journals and popular articles described how the institutional use of Rauwolfia was reducing the need for electric shock treatment by as much as 90 per cent and almost eliminating the need for drastic brain surgery. One account described a wild-eyed patient who used a bed to batter down her door in a California sanitarium and then attacked everyone in sight. As a result, she had to be kept under forced restraint for a year. After a month on Rauwolfia tablets, she was quiet and co-operative enough to benefit from psychiatric treatment. Another patient spent seven years in institutions and underwent 165 shock treatments without improving. Unusually violent, haggard, and disheveled, she looked sixty years old. After she had taken Rauwolfia for two months, the superintendent of the hospital failed to recognize her when a nurse brought in a neat, smiling young woman obviously only in her twenties.

By 1957, over 1,500 scientific papers on Rauwolfia had been published. It was said to be useful in treating schizophrenia, paranoia, manic states, chronic alcoholism, and withdrawal symptoms in narcotic addiction. Some authorities hailed it as the most important development in the history of psychiatry because it demonstrated that mental disturbances may have a chemical basis and it pointed the way to the control of mental illness through chemical treatment.

At the Second International Conference on Biological Treatment of Mental Illness, held at the New York Academy of Medicine in 1962, scientists from all over the world agreed that the use of tranquilizing drugs, starting with Rauwolfia, had taken mental hospitals out of the horror category. Conference chairman Dr. Max Rinkel said: "The evidence is mounting rapidly to support the view that the biological approach holds the key to all mental illness." And Nobel prize-winner Dr. Linus Pauling remarked that although he had been slow to accept the fact that mental ills were caused by defects in body chemistry and could be treated with drugs, he now believed that this was true and he felt that there should be more intensive research in this direction.

Actually, as early as 1947, Dr. Emil Schlittler, then in Ciba's research laboratories in Switzerland, was studying the alkaloids of Rauwolfia. After he removed some of the already-known substances such as ajmaline and serpentine, there remained a brown residue that produced all of the biological activity of the crude drug. Working with Dr. Johannes Müller, Schlittler concentrated his efforts on separating this resin into various fractions. By using new isolation techniques, they were able to obtain in 1952 a new alkaloid that they named reserpine, because they had been using *Rauwolfia serpentina*.

Reserpine proved to be the most active of all the plant's components. A few grams of shining white crystals—representing five years of labor—were equivalent in effect to more than 10,000 times that weight of the crude drug. Schlittler, Müller, and an imaginative pharmacologist, Dr. Hugo Bein, made a combined study of reserpine. By September, 1952, they wrote that they had isolated the substance responsible for the sedative effect. A few months later, Bein published a second report stating that reserpine also had lowered the blood pressure of experimental animals. In November, 1953, Ciba began to market reserpine as the drug Serpasil. Within the next few years chemists in various companies extracted thirty more alkaloids from *R. serpentina* and one authority said recently, "We still don't have a fraction of them."

Schlittler, now directing further research at the Ciba laboratories in Summit, New Jersey, has recently reported that a new series of reserpine derivatives may offer several potential advantages over reserpine. They have a rapid onset of action and are not cumulative, so that the dose may be better controlled for the treatment of mild psychiatric disorders. Some of these drugs are also being tested in animals by scientists at the National Heart Institute, but it is still too early to predict their usefulness in man.

At the Riker Laboratories in California, which has specialized in Rauwolfia and Veratrum drugs, some very fine animal studies showed that reserpine works on the hypothalamus in the brain and not directly on the nerves that control blood pressure or on the blood vessels themselves. Much of this research was done by Barbara Brown, M.D.

Perhaps the most famous work with reserpine was its total synthesis in 1956 by Dr. Robert B. Woodward of Harvard. Synthetic reserpine based upon his process is being marketed by Roussel Corporation. Whether this will seriously compete with the natural product only time will tell. But knowledge of reserpine's structure proved useful in working with other naturally occurring Rauwolfia alkaloids and with related plants, such as Alstonia from Australia and yohimbé from

Africa. How little is known about some aspects of plant materials can be illustrated by the many variations found in alkaloids isolated from the seeds, leaves, barks, and roots of any one botanical—frequently they are not the same alkaloids at all.

Dr. Maurice Shamma, an organic chemist at Pennsylvania State University, has commented, "It turns out that one of the most interesting natural products so far isolated in the history of organic chemistry is reserpine. What we have been doing here at Penn State is to study fifteen alkaloids that are related structurally to reserpine. These will tell us something about the relationship between the natural product and its physiological activity. . . . We hope that what we learn will help other researchers find out which groups of elements are responsible for what kinds of biological action."

After a very slow start, Rauwolfia products caught on commercially. In 1954, the first full year of reserpine therapy, two dozen companies in the United States were preparing finished drugs. At that time Meer Corporation supplied the bulk of whole root *R. serpentina.* By 1960, Penick, which had become the leading bulk supplier of Rauwolfia derivatives, reported that prescriptions for these items totaled $30,000,000 for the year. The price, meanwhile, had been reduced from $45 a gram to $1, in part because of extensive searches for additional Rauwolfia sources by several companies.

On March 1, 1954, Edson F. Woodward, Penick's chief pharmacognosist, by then a veteran of the 1949 African Strophanthus hunt and other expeditions, flew to India to make a scientific appraisal of Rauwolfia's commercial potential. He was the only American in the area on such a mission and, because he was particularly well informed, he was to play an important part in getting the now-famous Rauwolfia embargo of April, 1954, lifted. His objectives when he left New York City, however, were to fill in Penick's information on the raw material, to expedite purchases, and to uncover and develop new sources of supply. Until this time, attention had been focused upon India's *R. serpentina,* but as many as 175 different species were thought to exist throughout the world, mostly in rain forests and well-watered grasslands at rather low elevations.

Rauwolfia species vary widely. For instance, *R. praecox* grows as a tree to heights of 100 feet in the Peruvian rain forest, while *R. nana* of Rhodesia is fully grown at a mere six inches. One distribution breakdown lists fifty-two species in Central and South America; thirty-nine in Africa; twenty-three in the Philippines and the Far East; thirteen in India and Burma; seven in Hawaii and the Sandwich Islands, with certain species occurring in more than one region. (The plants known as snakeroot in the United States are not Rauwolfias; the senega snakeroot is *Polygala senega* and the button or corn snakeroot is *Eryngium aquaticum.*)

Woodward's jumping-off point was the west coast port city of Bombay, where many exporters had their headquarters and warehouses, called "go-downs." All sorts of information came to light, a conglomeration of fact, fiction, and rumor which Woodward had to sort out and verify. For instance, one shipper explained a delayed delivery by saying, "Our collections are being held up because a wild elephant went on a rampage up in Bengal and killed seventeen collectors. The others have been afraid to go into the forest for days." This story was true.

In making his rounds in rural India, Woodward learned to wait patiently while half a pint of betel-nut juice was expectorated by some of the laborers he questioned, just like the " 'baccy" chewers at home. In rushing from one city appointment to the next he had to allow for the fact that the taxis, while dodging bullock carts, peacocks, elephants, and the like, ran on virtually empty gas tanks until their drivers earned enough to purchase a gallon or two.

In describing the sights, he was sometimes at a loss. One day he wrote: "I am like that legendary traveler in India who sat down to write a letter home. He started off by saying that he had seen two mongeese. But that didn't look right, so he tore it up and began again. 'I saw two mongooses to-day . . .' No, that went into the wastebasket, too. After staring at the paper for awhile, he was inspired to say, 'I saw a mongoose this morning and then I saw another mongoose.' Well, in case you really want to know, the people at the zoo say the plural is mongooses."

Plus the usual petty irritations suffered by travelers, Penick's pharmacognosist had business worries, as well. He discovered that worthless *R. serpentina* stems and roots of other plants were mixed with the valuable roots. Since quite a few of the collectors in certain mountain villages of South India seemed to be on the wrong track, he flew down to investigate. He found that, on the basis of a blurred newspaper picture, they were collecting anything that had light-colored tubular flowers and dark, shiny leaves. Prospective suppliers were given a short course in drug plant identification on the spot.

As he traveled the length and breadth of India and Ceylon, Woodward was almost always off the beaten path; for instance, in Tuticorin, near the southern tip of India, he was the second American ever to be seen by the inhabitants. At another time, he wrote from Bombay, "The rains have been going on steadily for two or three weeks. Thirty inches in the last two days. Don't have an underwater camera, so no pix." He described the plains of the Ganges as "one big lake, tens of miles wide, hundreds long." The cars he rented very often had no glass in the windows, and the private planes he used for aerial reconnaissance were of ancient vintage. As he surveyed areas to be scouted later on foot, he flew at extremely low altitudes, 500 feet or so, to stay under the heavy, black storm clouds.

One night, after battling the monsoons in full fury, he found himself stranded in a town where the bank didn't have enough money to cash a traveler's check, and he wrote: "Now I know from what deep well of experience and exasperation Kipling wrote his poem 'If.'"

When asked to describe how one searches for Rauwolfia, Woodward replied: "Up in the foothills of the Himalayas, you look in areas of secondary growth. This means virgin forests which have been cut down, perhaps cultivated at one time or another. . . . *Rauwolfia serpentina*, from a distance, looks something like a small Azalea. It has dark, glistening leaves and clusters of white to yellowish-pink flowers. Its berries are sparse and blue-black."

After going to the Himalayas, meaning "the home of the snow," Woodward landed in Calcutta, which, he felt, surely must be "the home of the heat." Approaching the city, he read in a newspaper that the temperature was 113° and the humidity over 90. Nevertheless, there were people he had to see in the merchant quarter. But little or no business was being conducted that day, for it was Holi, the season of spring festival. (Instead of coloring Easter eggs, the Indians color each other by carrying vessels of dye water to sprinkle and splash.)

The following day at 7 A.M., with the temperature already 101°, the plant explorer was off in an old DC-3 to Cooch-Behar, together with twenty-two adults, several babies, and a substantial amount of freight piled in the center aisle. He remembers Cooch-Behar, home of the Maharajah famous for his tiger hunts, for its airport terminal "building," a sheet of corrugated iron teetering on a couple of bamboo poles. The ticket counter was a battered table with a cardboard sign announcing improbable destinations. But the Indians were making a laudable effort to link every town with a population of 10,000 or more by air.

He was going on to Jainti, and after an unexplained all-day wait on the railroad platform while the train stood ready to go "any minute," the four-hour trip was finally made. At daybreak the next day, he started a fifteen-mile hike along jungle trails, finding a plentiful occurrence of *R. serpentina.* The plants were a foot high already and he knew that after the rains they would measure a good thirty inches. They would be much easier to dig then, too, for getting the long roots out of hard ground was slow, backbreaking work. It took twenty collectors and about a hundred local diggers ten deep to get a ton of roots, and many tons were needed.

Of his return trip to Calcutta, Woodward wrote: "The train ride was a synonym for slow torture. No seats as we know them, just a wide bench on which you sit cross-legged. In the compartment meant for eight, we were twenty-three adults and three babies. Not out of my clothes for two days. Back in Calcutta, I had a small dinner, a big brandy, and twelve hours sleep." (He was not always this fortunate. In one village where he arrived footsore and tired, there was a sign reading "Punjab Hotel, Very Tasty Meals!" It turned out to be just a restaurant with no place to sleep. Another time it was "Bengali Restaurant, Nice Clean Sleeping Rooms!" —but no food.)

North of Delhi at Dehra Dun, Woodward consulted with the Indian Forestry Service about the possibility of cultivating Rauwolfia. During his six weeks in India he had made many such valuable contacts and had gathered a good fund of information covering just about every aspect of the botany and commerce of the drug plant. All this accomplished, it was time to fly home after stopping in Africa on the way.

Then it happened—an embargo. The Indian government suddenly banned the export of *Rauwolfia serpentina.* One week and one day after Penick's pharmacognosist returned to New York, he was back on a plane bound for India. With him went William J. Heckman, a representative for the Squibb Division of Olin Mathieson Chemical Corporation, of which he is now vice-president. Heckman also acted for the Meer Corporation, one of the major importers of Rauwolfia root, and he had obtained through the Pharmaceutical Manufacturers Association in Washington, D.C., the backing of the United States government. The two men began to make the rounds of one Indian government agency after another, trying to get the ban lifted. They were advised that this might take many months, if it could be accomplished at all. Because it was June, when officials took to the hills to avoid the murderous heat, making and keeping appointments was likely to be doubly difficult, they were warned.

Conferences, statistical presentations, and letter writing, interspersed with delays, filled the nights and days. Recalling this period, Heckman remarked that the Indians had an ingenious method for air conditioning their offices: "They hung thick grass mats outside of their windows and watered these down periodically so that the breezes passing through were cooled."

As it turned out, the Indian officials were on the job and Squibb's representative in India, Frank Eden, helped to establish rapport with them. The botanical surveys Woodward had made just weeks before provided the facts needed for a good case against the embargo; he proved that there was plenty of Rauwolfia and that it was in no danger of extinction then. On the spot the Indian government decided to permit exporters to honor all existing obligations to ship the root. After ten days of steady negotiating, the exhausted Americans returned home. Later the entire embargo was lifted.

Woodward has since commented: "It is basically unreasonable for any country to put a total embargo on a natural product in the hope of keeping an industry all to itself, or in the fear that a plant might be exterminated. Plants are not likely to recognize political boundaries; they can be collected or cultivated and then processed in many another area. In the case of Rauwolfia, the Indian government probably put the embargo on for any of several reasons: For instance, they may have been genuinely afraid that the plant would become extinct. As soon as they established the embargo, we began to search in surrounding countries and we located all of the root we needed. . . . I do not mean to condone careless, rapacious harvesting of forest or field produce. Very often it is necessary to institute a reforestation program to go along with a collection program, but this can be done in practically every instance."

Even with supplies again coming out of India, Penick, Meer, Ciba, Squibb, and others surveyed potential sources in Ceylon, Burma, and Siam, just in case. Several attempts to cultivate the plant were made in India, Pakistan, Indonesia, Central America, and Puerto Rico. Most of these projects were abandoned because it was cheaper and easier to collect the plentiful wild-growing roots. However, as this is written, cultivation is being renewed in East Pakistan under a UNESCO-sponsored program.

While *Rauwolfia serpentina* was receiving all this attention, other species of Rauwolfia were being studied by several companies—Ciba, in particular. One object was to locate better, more economical sources of the alkaloid reserpine, obtained up to then from *R. serpentina* and four other species. The second objective was to find other new alkaloids that might be useful. Another variety of Rauwolfia containing reserpine was known to exist in Africa—but nobody knew just where, how much, or how to set up a chain of supply. Ciba's president, T. F. Davies Haines and two colleagues packed their camping gear and set out on a safari, first to the Belgian Congo, then to French Equatorial Africa. By mid-July, 1954, regular Rauwolfia shipments were being made to the United States where Ciba's facilities operated on a twenty-four-hour-a-day schedule. Reserpine was again readily available for patients.

Rauwolfia vomitoria from Africa turned out to be the best source of reserpine. It is so named because two or three leaves, when swallowed, produce violent vomiting. In appearance it resembles a high-bush cranberry loaded with berries. On a surveying expedition in 1955, Woodward noted that not all *R. vomitoria* yields a high percentage of alkaloids. He mapped its range all across Central Africa from Senegal on the west coast to Lake Victoria in East Africa. At the extremes of the range, the roots contain as little as 0.03 per cent reserpine, but in the best collecting areas in the Congo, at the right time of year, the yield is ten times as much. As a result of this exploration, the ultimate cost of Rauwolfia derivatives was drastically reduced.

One other species of Rauwolfia is important commercially: *R. canescens,* a small bush with leaves occurring in rosettes of four along the stems, two large leaves opposite two smaller ones. The flowers are tiny and white, very inconspicuous and not particularly pretty, but the berries are bright red when unripe, changing to dark purple later. This plant is native to the Caribbean, but about a century ago it was introduced into India accidentally when its seeds were mixed in the ballast of ships. To give some idea of the complexities of botanical identification, the plants growing in India are taxonomically identical with those growing in the Caribbean except that the leaves of the Indian plants are a bit more hairy. Yet the Indian root yields the alkaloid deserpidine, none of which is found in the Caribbean root. It is now commercial practice to refer to the Indian species as *R. canescens,* although the proper scientific name for this plant no matter where it is found is *R. tetraphylla.*

In the spring of 1958, Woodward had a new mission in

India. Deserpidine was of growing importance in medicine and tons of *R. canescens* roots were needed. Before the end of the long hot summer, everything possible had been done to build up supplies on a continuing basis; new areas of plant growth had been discovered, collectors had been trained, and exporters lined up to take care of the shipment. The Indians were eager and quick to learn. As an example, Woodward told of riding out from the almost abandoned airport at Jessore in East Pakistan, formerly used by "hump" flyers in World War II, and finding himself in a procession of "taxis" —gaily decorated tricycle rickshaws. As he and the local botanist, who had come to meet his plane, began to recognize Rauwolfia plants along the side of the road, they called out "There's one, and there's another one." It wasn't five minutes until the cyclists themselves were calling, "Sahib, Sahib, look another one, another one, another one!"

Today *R. serpentina, R. vomitoria,* and *R. canescens* are important sources for drugs that rank sixth among all prescriptions written for natural products, according to the Gosselin Survey. But the men who have explored for Rauwolfias and related plants in tropical lands agree that in this same family there are at least 100 species about which little is known, except their names. And in that reservoir there must be something more of possible value in medicine.

Asked to sum up the Rauwolfia story because of his long and close association with it, Edson Woodward said: "Before the days of Rauwolfia research there had been breakthroughs in medicine against infectious diseases, hormonal imbalance, and a whole host of other medical and surgical problems. Mental illness remained with us, but hidden away. Even before we truly began to understand, we were saying politely that it was a disease. Although a few of us believed this, fewer accepted and almost no one understood. A sick brain? No, we said it was a sick mind. We so readily accepted a sick pancreas—diabetes. A sick liver—hepatitis. A sick colon—colitis. But a sick brain—brainitis? The outward aspects of man had become confused with his spirit. The willingness to reason had become confused with the ability to reason, to think and act rationally.

"*Rauwolfia serpentina* changed all that. For the first time there was an understanding of the biochemical basis for mental illness and mental health. And there was a tool, a drug. Not a drug to correct all mental diseases, but at least to help some of the conditions that had baffled and befuddled doctor and patient. Thus, brains out of chemical balance were put into balance by Rauwolfia, and racing hearts and overworked arteries were put at ease. We had a reasonable explanation for a reasonable happening, adjusted and corrected by reasonable therapy."

Rauwolfia is a most effective drug for lowering blood pressure and it is still indicated in the treatment of mental illness. This drug has also proved useful in studying the functioning of the central nervous system, in particular, the biochemical pathways to the brain. It helps millions of hypertension victims lead useful lives, whether they are in rural India, the Nigerian bush country, or on Park Avenue.

Mental Drugs; From Stone Age to Space Age—and Back

- *Aldous Huxley, Prophet of the Happy Pills*
- *LSD, the Chemistry of Madness*
- *Ololiuqui, Insights from the Devil's Morning-Glory*
- *Extracting the Magic from Mushrooms*

THE REDISCOVERY OF THE 5,000-YEAR-OLD HINDU cure for lunacy, Rauwolfia, revolutionized the Western world's treatment of mental disease in the early 1950's and introduced the era of psychopharmacotherapy, or drug treatment for emotional disturbances. This first "modern" tranquilizer and related compounds have been so successful in calming wildly disturbed patients that the environmental-psychological theory is no longer considered to be a sufficient explanation for human behavior. Freudian psychoanalysis, with its emphasis upon traumatic childhood experiences and family relationships, is being seriously challenged, according to Dr. Fred Elmadjian, of the National Institute of Mental Health Training Branch, and other authorities who study trends in the teaching and practice of psychiatry.

Dr. Sigmund Freud himself foreshadowed these changes. In one of his last papers he wrote, "The future may teach us how to exercise a direct influence, by means of particular chemical substances, upon the amounts of energy and their distribution in the apparatus of the mind."

While Rauwolfia stimulated an all-out search for the biochemical roots of mental disease, certain individual researchers had been working on these relatively unfashionable projects during the years when psychotherapy consisted largely of discussions and few, if any, injections or pills. The research tools of these lone workers often were exotic drug plants, narcotics, stimulants, and intoxicants used by primitives in religio-magical rites. At the time such plants were being rediscovered and botanically identified by modern scientists like Dr. Richard Evans Schultes, of Harvard, they seemed to many others to offer little in the way of practical application in medicine. Many pharmaceutical companies have only recently begun to give this type of research the attention it deserves.

Now scientists in medical centers the world over—particularly in Europe—are making chemical, pharmacological, and clinical estimates of such curious botanicals as "magic mushrooms" from Mexico; peyote, a cactus the Aztecs considered a "divine intoxicant"; hashish; the fungus ergot, blamed for Medieval epidemics of madness; *ayahuasca,* the "soul vine of the Amazon"; iboga, a Congo ordeal poison; cohoba, narcotic snuff of the Caribbean; *ololiuqui,* the so-called devil's morning-glory; and a potpourri of roots and barks named in legendary accounts of witchcraft and sorcery. It is literally a case of black magic for men in white, with medical specialists apprenticing the witch doctors.

What do these weird substances have in common?

They are all members of the plant kingdom with a history of tribal use in what the native regards as "medicine." Some have long been considered a successful treatment for certain forms of insanity, as Rauwolfia actually did prove to be. But their most outstanding shared characteristic is the fact that in normal persons they induce a state that resembles the split personality, or schizophrenia—a feeling of "being outside of one's self and transported to another world." The world may be heavenly or hellish, the brightly colored visions beautiful or terrifying; each experience is unique and usually unpredictable, even in the same person at different times.

This group of drugs is commonly called the "hallucinogens" or the "psychotomimetics," because they mimic psychosis. A pioneer in the clinical application of these agents, Dr. Humphry Osmond, of the New Jersey Neuro-Psychiatric Institute, defined them as "substances that produce changes in thought, perception, mood, and sometimes, in posture. These changes occur alone or in concert without causing either major disturbance of the autonomic nervous system or addictive craving. However, if there is overdosage, some disorientation, memory disturbance, stupor and even narcosis may occur, but these reactions are not characteristic."

Not included in this category are alcohol, opium and its derivatives, cocaine, atropine, benzedrine, barbiturates, anesthetics, analgesics, and hypnotics, although some overlapping is inevitable. And, of course, almost any drug can cause delirium when given in excess or to hypersensitive persons. The psychotomimetics, however, are a distinct class because they have marked psychological action for a limited period of time, with lesser physiological activity. They are what the famous German pharmacologist L. Lewin termed "The Phantastica."

In the realm of pure science, there is interest in these drugs for several reasons. Most of their alkaloids and glycosides have chemical structures known as indole and benzene rings. Because it may be that these configurations are the ones that cause the strange effects, study of the natural products has stimulated intensive research on similar synthetics. In another fundamental area, it is hoped that by studying the biological activity of the substances, particularly in normal persons, light may be shed on the causes of mental disease.

These uses are not the only ones, though. Like the tranquilizers and the older "pep pills," some of these substances are beginning to be used in the actual treatment of mentally ill patients. Now we are getting into an area which is not only extremely controversial, but very difficult to describe. The key word here is "accessibility." The aim of all psychotherapy is to reach the patient and explore the problems; these drugs have enabled psychiatrists to establish better rapport, so that psychoanalytic techniques can be more successfully employed.

Because, as Dr. Osmond said, "The mind cannot be explored by proxy," a growing number of doctors are taking these drugs themselves in order to get a better idea of the fantastic world of their patients. Here "empathy" is the key word. Osmond believes that no doctor should use psychotomimetics on others until he first has taken them himself, preferably several times. These experimental, drug-induced psychotic states are called "model psychoses." They have been utilized in testing the effects of other mental drugs and procedures—"model therapies"—to be used in treating the spontaneous psychoses of the mentally ill.

For a psychiatrist to administer a hallucinating substance to treat hallucinations may seem like carrying the "hair of the dog that bit you" theory to extremes. But reports presented at international conferences have shown some very promising results. For instance, at a recent medical meeting in London, psychiatrist G. W. Arendzen-Hein from Holland discussed his treatment of twenty-one cases of long-standing, severe, psychopathic criminality "quite untouched by ordinary therapeutic contact." Under hallucinogenic therapy "conflicts were revealed, resistance fell, introspection and insight increased: a new capacity for human relationships was formed. The subjects co-operated well and fourteen of twenty-one cases were clinically improved." The doctor summarized: "We should re-think our belief in the intractibility of psychopaths —this method enabled us to penetrate deeply and bring about changes in personality formerly thought impossible." While clinical applications are still in a very preliminary stage of investigation and have encountered some serious obstacles, to be described later, there have been encouraging results with some other disorders most resistant to ordinary methods of treatment—obsessional states, phobias, and depersonalization syndromes.

Mental disease, particularly that most widespread and baffling form, schizophrenia, is the plague of the twentieth century. It fills half of all hospital beds in civilized areas. In the United States alone, an estimated 17,000,000 people suffer from some type of mental illness, and the annual cost is $3,000,000,000, not counting work-time lost. The causes are just as controversial as the cures: is the condition primarily due to disordered metabolism or an upsetting environment? Body or mind? While most authorities agree that there is a complex interplay of nature and nurture involved, a growing number of scientific investigators report evidence of physical abnormality.

Recently, for example, a study of the distinctly different fingerprint patterns of schizophrenics suggested that an inherited genetic deficiency may play a role. Differences have also been noted in the capillary arrangements at the base of the fingernails. Studies of hormones and enzymes known to affect emotional stability are providing additional clues. Independent laboratories have confirmed an earlier finding that there is a unique protein substance in the blood of schizoid patients. One theory holds that erratic behavior is a toxic symptom, the "poison" being brewed in the hapless victim's own body, possibly resulting from an accumulation of abnormal products of metabolism or from an inability to detoxify natural substances, which then induce harmful changes in the body.

Whatever the causes of mental disease prove to be, the trend in treatment is becoming increasingly biochemical. This is not to say that psychiatrists are on the verge of being "synthesized"; there is no over-the-counter "psychoanalytic pill" in the offing. Psychotomimetics are recommended for use *in conjunction with* modified psychotherapy and only under very close medical supervision, for obvious reasons.

Dr. Nathan S. Kline, research director of New York's Rockland State Hospital and a leading proponent of the pharmacotherapy school of thought, stated that the feared risks of addiction and serious physical or emotional after-effects are minimal *when cases are carefully screened and followed up by physicians.* Strange as these new drugs seem, they are surely not as drastic as electroshock therapy and certainly less so than the irreversible brain surgery used as a last resort in mental institutions. Dr. Kline thinks that, thanks to these new drugs, we may possibly solve mental disease problems before we find an answer to cancer: "The major breakthrough may come sooner than most people think, possibly within the next five years." In fairness, it should be pointed out that some psychoanalysts still believe that the only rational treatment of mental disorders is psychotherapy, and they use drugs sparingly, if at all.

Meanwhile, the search for new compounds that might have application in solving our number-one health problem is understandably feverish. While many promising projects are "under wraps" for business reasons, it is safe to say that every leading pharmaceutical company is involved. In addition to humanitarian considerations, there is a business incentive in the fact that tranquilizer sales, surpassed only by antibiotics and hormones, totaled over $200,000,000 in 1961, not including vast institutional purchases. About one in every dozen American adults uses physician-prescribed tranquilizers regularly.

Unfortunately, tranquilizers are only part of the answer. Fewer than half of all schizophrenics are helped by tranquilizers, and depressed patients are sometimes plunged deeper into melancholia by calming medications. Therefore, much research effort is now expended upon central-nervous-system stimulants, which have roughly an opposite effect. These anti-depressants, or psychic energizers, fight despair and apathy without causing the "hopped-up" tensions and dreary "let-downs" experienced with pep pills of the benzedrine type. They not only have the power to elevate mood and overcome fatigue of psychological origin, they also seem to release creativity, improve memory, and even heighten intelligence in reasonably normal persons. Hence their applications extend beyond the pathological.

When Kline tested one of these drugs on himself for several months, he found that he needed only four or five hours sleep, that he awoke refreshed and unusually alert and perceptive, and that he was able to do two days' work in one. Further, "I have seen no evidence whatever of addiction with any of the newer psychopharmaceuticals," he said. However, some hallucinogens and psychic energizers have shown a tendency to aggravate liver disease in certain susceptible persons and to cause skin eruptions, blood disturbances, and other side effects. They are not for self-medication, by any means.

Drug companies, searching for ways to eliminate such drawbacks, have put their chemists to work manipulating molecules and have sent botanical explorers to search for new drug plants with related compounds or similar action. Since some of the best leads so far have been gleaned from Stone Age peoples, anthropologists are sometimes consulted; but the top experts in this work are ethnobotanists like Schultes.

Because vision-producing botanicals are usually considered sacred by the natives who use them, or inhabited by a divinity, they are the most difficult of all drug plants to obtain, identify, and study in their habitat. Yet their use must be carefully noted, for details bound up in their ritualistic context may later prove to have a sound basis pharmacologically. Are fresh or dried plants used? Which parts? How prepared? What are the exact effects? As we have seen, ethnobotanists often need to remain in the field for long periods of time, establishing rapport and participating in tribal cremonials. Taking nauseous concoctions that may stimulate, intoxicate, or perhaps even cause serious illness is one of the occupational hazards.

In probably no other area of pharmaceutical research do explorers, chemists, and clinicians so often also serve as guinea pigs. Obviously, laboratory animals are not suitable for some aspects of mental-drug testing, although they are widely used. For one thing, their hallucinations, if any, must remain a mystery. Hundreds of preclinical papers on the effects of new compounds on animal behavior have been published. A sampling of results shows that, while "under the influence," waltzing mice became dejected wallflowers, spiders changed the angles of their webs, Siamese fighting fish turned pacifistic and hung tail downwards, liver flukes were agitated, the absolute visual threshold of pigeons was raised, and rats were seemingly disheartened in their rope climb for a food reward.

These findings are hardly enough to go on. Dosages intended to restore the sanity of the world's millions of mental patients are not determined by the flailings of liver flukes. Higher animals from cats to baboons are used, but sooner or later, human beings with scientific training have to "see what it's like" and publish their subjective observations so that others may build on their work.

The self-experimenting scientist usually will not be the first human to break this ground. Osmond observed, in connection with a historical survey of the psychotomimetics: "As I list these treasures of 5,000 years of perilous and sometimes fatal searching, I think upon those nameless discoverers and rediscoverers, Aztec and Assassin, Carib and berserker, Siberian and Red Indian, Brahmin and African, and many others whose endeavors even scholars do not know. We inherit

their secrets and profit by their curiosity and their courage—
even from their errors and their excesses. Let us honor them.
They do not appear in any list of references."

The calculated risks taken by self-testers of new compounds, whether in the jungle or in the laboratory, are considerable. We know less about the terra incognita of the
human brain than we do about the unmapped regions of
Amazonas. Brain tissue is composed almost entirely of 10,-
000,000,000 continuously active nerve cells, and its chemical
vulnerability to psychosis is still not charted. But if the scourge
of insanity is to be eliminated, we must continue to explore
unknowns, however strange. In the following pages several
men who have been willing to take the necessary chances in
order to advance our knowledge will be introduced. Many
of them feel that time is running out, that it is becoming a
case of "now or never." Schultes, himself one of these men,
pointed out the reasons:

"The most important methods for discovering new [botani-
cal] drugs are the examination of ancient writings; the scientific interpretation of folklore; and field work amongst primitive peoples still living in close association with the plant
world. We must seize these opportunities now before the few
remaining aboriginal areas are blotted out by encroaching civilization. I am convinced that another quarter of a century will
see most of this ethnobotanical lore doomed to extinction. We
have chanced upon some valuable psychotherapeutic agents,
but only in the nick of time.

"What political leaders call 'progress' is often synonymous
with destruction of natural resources. The accelerated divorce-
ment of primitives from dependence upon their plant environment can be illustrated by what happens when aspirin pills
are made available along the Amazon. This seems to start
an astonishing disintegration of native medical lore. The
rapidity of this is frightening. That the aspirin may be more

beneficial in some cases than the herbs it supplants is not the point. What should concern us is: how can we salvage this priceless medico-botanical knowledge before it is forever entombed with the culture that gave it birth?"

Aldous Huxley: Prophet of the Happy Pills

Forty years ago the brilliant novelist Aldous Huxley* predicted the tranquilizer era. A decade before *Brave New World,* with its imaginary drug *soma,* was published in 1932, he was writing superb satires in which seedy London intellectuals insisted that the day would come when drugs would control the emotions and free the spirit. Underlying all of his writing is an awareness of the biochemical basis of behavior. In his most recent novel, *Island,* described by a reviewer as the "fun in the fungi book," his characters nibble on yellow mushrooms of the type investigated by Schultes in Mexico.

Soma was the name of an ancient Asian intoxicant, now lost. As Huxley detailed the effects of his latter-day *soma,* it seemed to be a combination of mescaline, hashish, and reserpine. "Recently the producers of the tranquilizer Miltown applied the name Soma to one of their products," Huxley told me with a wry smile. It is prescribed by doctors for lumbago and other mundane woes, a far cry from the fantastic uses he described.

There are really two Aldous Huxleys, according to *Time* magazine: "The master novelist whose characters used to be so nasty that his first name might well pass into common usage as an adjective—if someone woke up feeling aldous, he would be liverish, cold to the touch and awfully, awfully acute. But the time came when Aldous did not feel aldous any more; he felt thomas-henry." (Dr. Thomas Henry Hux-

---

* Mr. Huxley died in December, 1963, a few weeks after approving this manuscript. Because his influence will long endure, the author prefers to have all of his statements in the present tense.

ley, the novelist's grandfather, was an eminent biologist.) Much as we all admire Aldous, the writer, it was the scientifically oriented, or "thomas-henrified," Huxley that I wished to interview, for the personal correspondence and published works of Aldous Huxley are cited frequently in the bibliographies of medical-journal articles on the psychotomimetic drugs.

In the spring of 1953, after reviewing seventy years of research on peyote, Huxley was eager to be a guinea pig. He took some mescaline (one of the alkaloids in peyote) in a glass of water and described the results in his book *Doors of Perception,* which has for its theme a passage from William Blake: "If the doors of perception were cleansed everything would appear to man as it is, infinite." Huxley continues to be an active participant in this type of investigation, and because he travels widely in the Orient and elsewhere, he serves as an international contact and inspiration for many scientific researchers in this field.

I talked with him in the home of some of his friends, high in the Hollywood Hills overlooking the city where he has lived for thirty years. (His own house had recently burned to the ground; almost everything was lost except the manuscript of his latest intellectual teaser, the work of nine years.) I recall an effect of almost painful brilliance as sunlight streamed through glassed areas in the living room and was reflected from white walls, a white rug, and white furniture. There was a sense of otherworldliness, but little talk of mystical transports. A very large cat drowsed through it all, blinking only when Huxley strode over to the fireplace and, in his irritation at our present-day values, raised his voice in making his points.

Huxley's features are strong and he has thick locks of gray hair falling over a handsome, lined face. Despite his sixty-eight years, he is charged with restless energy. On that day he was dressed with casual elegance in soft gray—checked jacket, flannels, sweater, silk tie. What is most striking, of course, is that Mind at Work. A court stenographer could not have kept up with it. What follows, therefore, is largely an impressionistic transcription of the highlights, the glints and gleams.

In one of his earlier books he wrote: "Is mental disease due to a chemical disorder? Is chemical disorder due, in its turn, to psychological disturbances affecting the adrenals? It would be rash and premature to affirm it."

My question: "Would it still be 'rash and premature'?" His answer: "Yes, probably."

Hundreds upon hundreds of articles have debated this, but since Huxley knows most of the scientist-authors personally and is familiar with the literature, this, to me, was the definitive statement. He then explained the various schools of thought, describing 1952 as a turning point when a similarity in the chemical composition of mescaline and adrenalin was discovered by three Canadian psychiatric researchers, Dr. Osmond and Dr. John Smythies, at the Saskatchewan Hospital in Weyburn, and Dr. Abram Hoffer, at the University Hospital in Saskatoon. They suggested that schizophrenia might be caused by defective metabolism of the body's own adrenalin and they found that if they injected normal volunteers with synthetic "pink" adrenalin, called adrenochrome, these people became temporarily psychotic. This theory has yet to be proved to everyone's satisfaction. For instance, research conducted by Dr. Elmadjian and his colleagues while he was at the Worcester Foundation for Experimental Biology does not support the hypothesis that there is in schizophrenia a defective metabolism of the body's own adrenalin. But other researchers are working in this area.

Aldous Huxley brought out two important points to consider when we adopt drugs developed by primitive peoples:

first, that man has changed little, anatomically and physiologically, during the last 30,000 years or so; and, second, that the native or genetic capacities of a bright child born into a family of Upper Paleolithic cave dwellers were just as good as those of a bright city child today. Ancient or modern, the two babies are indistinguishable; each contains all the potentialities of the particular breed of human being to which he or she happens to belong. Because of lack of opportunities to develop, the Paleolithic baby could not possibly become anything except a hunter and a food-gatherer. But the most intelligent of these early people were perfectly capable of applying a form of the scientific method in solving their problems. For instance, the Swiss Lake Dwellers experimented with opium-poppy heads in every possible way, chewing them, using them as snuff, and so on.

What does this imply? Enormous curiosity plus an overwhelming desire to escape pain and—for a time—their own lives. As a latter-day Guatemalan primitive, who was using drug plants, once observed, "A man must sometimes take a rest from his memory." The point is, Huxley emphasized, we should stop thinking that we live in *the* Age of Anxiety. Our forefathers also sought release from tension, and they may have had superior methods. Some of our modern man-made stimulants, sedatives, and other drugs do their mind-changing work at ruinous cost to our systems. (Dr. de Ropp wrote in *Drugs and the Mind*: "If Mankind must take an occasional holiday from reality, it is certainly high time the chemists found a more satisfactory 'happiness drug' than that dreary old nerve poison, ethyl alcohol.")

Recently there has been a change for the better. "Pharmacologists still produce plenty of ambivalent miracle drugs with unpleasant side effects almost as remarkable as their healing powers," Huxley said, "but they are now learning to produce drugs from natural products used by primitive people which

Gordon Svoboda adjusts the flow rate of a chromatographic column which is separating *Vinca* alkaloids from a particular fraction. The turntable with funneled bottles is part of an automatic fraction-collecting apparatus, controlled by timer at left.

William Meer studying *Vinca Rosea*

University of British Columbia

Dr. C. T. Beer,
Cancer Research Centre,
University of British Columbia.

University of British Columbia

Dr. R. L. Noble, Director
Cancer Research Centre,
University of British Columbia.

National Institutes of Health

Jonathan Hartwell working with botanical extracts at the National Cancer Institute.

Lindbome-Potter Enterprises

Norman Farnsworth
planting *Vinca*.

T. F. D. Haines, CIBA Pharmaceutical Company president, (far left) with A. Ammann of CIBA-Basle, and Father Callens of the Jesuit Mission in Kisantu, being presented with African Rauwolfia by the local chief (in white cap).

Aldous Huxley,
as drawn by Bachardy
in 1962.

Albert Hofmann (left)
talking with
R. Gordon Wasson
in Basle.

Sandoz

R. Gordon Wasson
eating sacred mushrooms
on first occasion
ever recorded
of a white man
attending the sacred rite.
(Picture was taken
in the dark by
Allan Richardson
with the aid
of a Strobe light
like the one
Wasson is holding.)

Allan Richardson

Allan Richardson

Curandera Maria Sabina
passing the mushrooms
through the smoke
of aromatic plants.

Roger Heim of the
Paris Natural History M
trying to reproduce
the exact coloring
of the mushrooms
in Mexico.

Allan Richardson

Mexican Herb dealer selling
vegetables to be used in the
mushroom rite in Huatla de
Jimenez.

Allan Richardson

powerfully affect the mind without doing any harm, or more than a little harm, to the electro-chemical substratum through which they work on the mind. In certain cases of severe depression, for example, a few doses of one of the synthetic psychic energizers, patterned upon these plant drugs, can totally abolish a deeply rooted and wholly unrealistic conviction of sin, and when carefully administered, can do so without changing the blood picture or upsetting the heart, liver, or kidneys. In a few years it will probably be possible to lift the electro-chemical balance within many *healthy* individuals to a new position of equilibrium and effiicency, causing hitherto latent potentialities to be actualized. And all this at little or no physiological cost. It will also, of course, be possible to induce contentment with their lot even in slaves living under miserable conditions."

Then Huxley pointed out that discoveries in the field of pharmacology undoubtedly have already been used for nefarious purposes; during the Korean war, it was rumored that LSD was employed by North Korean armies in "brainwashing" prisoners. Other unconfirmed reports indicated that as long ago as World War II this chemical was being investigated by Russian and German militarists. (Most brain washing procedures since World War I involved scopolamine and hyoscyamine, plus either morphine or a barbiturate.) "How the fruits of science are to be used is decided not by scientists, but by citizens," he said. "And at any given moment the leading citizen may be called Hitler."

Others have expressed similar concern over the dangers involved in taking powerful drug plants from isolated primitive cultures and then giving them to nations at large, who might become ruthless aggressors. The contemplative Indians, who have had these drugs for centuries, have not used them to grind the helpless faces of the poor. But what if . . . ? There is certainly a strong element of moral responsibility—

on an international as well as personal level—to be faced in research of this type.

"So far as botanical research on mental drugs is concerned," Huxley said, "it is a fascinating fact: modern pharmacologists have not discovered one single mind-stimulant in natural sources. In this country, there has been sporadic work with a few significant compounds already known to primitives, but nothing new directly from nature and nothing like the five-year-plan approach of other countries. These nations know that he who first succeeds in producing a really effective psychic energizer will control the world!"

He feels that our research is hamstrung by our attitudes. Primitives are not interested in the whys, but in the effects. We, however, attempt first to discover how these strange new drugs work; the fact is, nobody knows exactly how even the century-old "wonder drug" aspirin works. We readily accept its usefulness, though, because, after all, *we* synthesized this compound. It is not a heathen concoction or a witch doctor's brew; therefore it is not dope and its users are not fiends.

Huxley strongly believes that more scientific investigators should try the drug plants themselves, and that it is, as he put it, "frightfully important to take them in the context of the native rites," although this is difficult because some natives feel spied upon and fear punishment, and others wish to keep their lore secret. He said that the peyote cult, for instance, has become part of the American Indian's cultural nationalism; members say, "God gave everything to the White Man, but he gave peyote to us."

Huxley concluded: "We need a thorough and *entirely sympathetic* investigation of exotic remedies. I've been talking about this for years; it is absurd how little has been done. The development of drugs that change human behavior may well prove to be far more revolutionary than achievements in nuclear physics."

LSD: The Chemistry of Madness

The modern history of the "chemistry of madness" dates from 1943, when a psychosis-mimicking effect was discovered in LSD, a drug derived from the fungus ergot *Claviceps purpurea*. But it has its roots in pre-Christian times, when the ancient Assyrians used ergot in medicine. More of a deep purple than a green medicine, ergot is a blight that invades fields of rye, wheat, and most grasses, replacing the grain with a fungus growth called the sclerotium. Ergotized grain is toxic, and foods contaminated with it can cause ergotism, a severe form of poisoning. Ergot has been blamed for the epidemic of madness that took such a toll of the peasant population in the Middle Ages and again in Spain just a few years ago. St. Anthony's Fire, a form of mania accompanied by gangrene, is one result of ergotism.

Despite these effects, ergot in many forms has been a stand-by in midwifery for hundreds of years because it has the power to control post-partum hemorrhaging. Modern obstetrical practice makes use of the ergot alkaloid ergonovine as a uterine stimulant. Another alkaloid, ergotamine, is the drug of choice in treating migraine headaches, the pain of which develops from strongly dilated blood vessels in the brain. Ergot gives relief by acting on the sympathetic nervous system to prevent this excessive dilation.

Sandoz, the Swiss pharmaceutical company, got its start with finished drugs from natural products like belladonna and Digitalis, but it made its name with ergot. In 1943 Dr. Arthur Stoll, then the research director, and Dr. Albert Hofmann, a chemist, synthesized the first natural ergot alkaloid. They discovered during the course of this work that lysergic acid is the characteristic nucleus of all the ergot alkaloids; a derivative of this, LSD, was prepared later that same year.

What happened next has been recounted many times, but

not always accurately. Dr. Hofmann said, "Such fantastic versions are current, even in professional circles, that I feel justified now in giving the true story. It was not a pure chance discovery—I planned to synthesize an analeptic [restorative] and in my work on this, I made an observation which was elucidated by a planned personal experiment."

Here are some of the highlights from Hofmann's own account: "On the afternoon of 16 April 1943, when I was working on this problem, I was seized by a peculiar sensation of vertigo and restlessness. Objects appeared to undergo optical changes and I was unable to concentrate on my work. In a dreamlike state I left for home, where an irresistible urge to lie down overcame me. I immediately fell into a peculiar state similar to drunkenness, characterized by an exaggerated imagination. With my eyes closed, fantastic pictures of extraordinary plasticity and intensive color seemed to surge towards me. After two hours, this gradually wore off. . . . I suspected that the lysergic acid diethylamide (LSD) with which I had been working that afternoon was responsible."

Hofmann was perplexed because he could not imagine how he could have absorbed a sufficient quantity of this compound to produce such phenomena. Moreover, the symptoms did not resemble those of classic ergot poisoning. So he decided to get to the root of the matter by taking an extremely small dose, 0.25 milligrams, of LSD. He knew that natural ergot alkaloids produce toxic symptoms in man only with doses exceeding several milligrams. After forty minutes, he noted the following symptoms in his laboratory journal: "Slight giddiness, restlessness, difficulty in concentration, visual disturbances, laughing. . . ." Then his entries became unintelligible.

He asked his laboratory technician to accompany him home. Since it was wartime and no car was available, this historic journey was made by bicycle. It was a trip of four

356

miles and Hofmann constantly complained that he was not making any progress in his peddling, while his companion insisted that he was rolling along at a great clip.

"I was overcome by a fear that I was going out of my mind, and the worst part of it was, I was clearly aware of my condition; my powers of observation were not impaired. Space and time became more and more disorganized, but I was not capable of any act of will. I could do nothing to prevent the breakdown of the world around me. At home, the physician was called. I had a feeling as if I were out of my body. I thought that I had died. My ego was somewhere in space. I even saw my dead body lying on the sofa."

In spite of his caution, Hofmann had chosen a dose that was perhaps ten times too high. LSD is by far the most active and specific psychotomimetic—10,000 times more potent than the same amount of mescaline. Only drugs like ouabain (from Strophanthus) and ergotamine approach LSD's power, and their minimal dose is still five times higher. As little as ten-millionths of a gram of LSD may provoke clinical changes.

In the mid-1940's, chemists at Sandoz began careful studies of the pharmacological properties of LSD. They found that only a small fraction of the total dose ever reaches the brain, and after one or two hours it is no longer detectable there. The drug is excreted from the body during that time, but its effect may last much longer. It would appear, that LSD is mainly responsible for triggering a chain reaction. Well over 1,000 scientific papers have tried to answer the question, how? We cannot possibly go into these theories involving the body's neuro-regulatory agents such as adrenalin and serotonin here, except to say that in the past few years this has been the area that has attracted the greatest amount of interest and controversy in mental drug research.

Ergot's source of supply is, in itself, a research objective because physicians need the alkaloids for their obstetrical and migraine patients and because mental research has increased the demand for raw materials. During World War II, when vital supplies of ergot from Japan, Spain, Portugal, the Balkans, and Russia were cut off, pharmacognosists like Dr. Ross M. Baxter, at the University of Toronto, and Dr. Arthur E. Schwarting, of the University of Connecticut, began to investigate the possibility of growing ergot quickly and efficiently in laboratory flasks. Originally, tissue culture of drug plants had been of academic interest only, as scientists tried to find out how botanicals produced their active constituents by the process of biosynthesis. Dr. Heber W. Youngken, Jr., of the University of Rhode Island, who published his first paper on this subject in 1942, explained to me that the cultivation of ergot in artificial media is a semi-synthetic process similar to the mass-production methods used in manufacturing antibiotics. The nutrient broth contains important amino acids and mineral elements to support the growth of the fungus, which resembles mounds of pussy-willow fluff. There are many difficulties involved, and only a few groups have been able to obtain the important building blocks of alkaloids from which drugs might be produced. Italian, Japanese, Canadian, and American scientists have made important contributions to the voluminous literature on this subject.

The research director of Sandoz Pharmaceuticals in Hanover, New Jersey, Dr. C. Henze, told me that while laboratory cultivation is not yet a complete success, a very good beginning has been made. This is important because the field collection of ergot has always been a problem. In Switzerland, where the temperature and climate are ideal for rye cultivation, whole fields are inoculated with selected strains of C. *purpurea* with the objective of obtaining particularly high yields of the desired alkaloids. The fungus must be picked by hand, however, and they never know just what the harvest will offer. During the wartime shortage mentioned, pharmaceutical manufacturers gleaned what little ergot was available from food grains before they were milled into flour, and in Australia even school children were sent out to search for bits of fungus on wild grasses. Thanks to pioneering work in biosynthesis, and improved extraction processes, such haphazard methods for obtaining life-saving medicinals will never need to be resorted to again.

But supplies of LSD have been curtailed for quite another reason. Somehow shipments of this potent drug, intended only for use by qualified professionals investigating mental disease, fell into the hands of thrill-seekers, via the black market. In the May, 1963, *Archives of General Psychiatry,* the editor-in-chief, Dr. Roy R. Grinker, Sr., warned that mental illness and even death might result unless controls are developed against the unauthorized use of LSD. In the same issue Drs. Sidney Cohen and Keith S. Ditman, of the Veterans Administration Hospital at Los Angeles, described an increasing number of complications stemming from the misuse of hallucinogens. "Until the indications, techniques, and precautions are better understood, LSD therapy should be restricted to investigators in institutions and hospitals where the patient's protection is greater and appropriate countermeasures are available in case of adverse reactions," they wrote, pointing out that in the majority of cases developing ill effects, the drug had been obtained from improper sources. They had cautioned physicians a year earlier in the American Medical Association *Journal* that "antisocial groups have embraced LSD and mescaline in addition to marijuana, the amphetamines, the barbiturates, and the narcotics. Since the LSD state can be a shattering one psychologically, these individuals may sustain severe, undesirable reactions."

During the past few years, books and articles written for laymen extolling what is called "the experience" have caused some persons who are disturbed to seek illusion-producing drugs. Literary beatniks have called the state "instant Zen"; most psychiatrists label it mere "chemical mysticism." All authorities deplore the use of such potent drugs for self-medication. Latent psychotics have been known to disintegrate after a single dose, according to Dr. Grinker, who is director of the Institute for Psychosomatic and Psychiatric Research at Michael Reese Hospital in Chicago. Psychic addiction can develop—even psychiatrists and psychologists are not immune —and as a result, small LSD sects have been established in which the leaders are quite successful in controlling others, according to Drs. Cohen and Ditman.

To protect irresponsible persons from themselves, Sandoz has voluntarily suspended LSD shipments while safeguards against improper use are being strengthened in this country. Unfortunately, this has brought some vital research to a standstill, for *The Archives of General Psychiatry* emphasized that these drugs "are unique tools in the study of altered states of awareness, perception, and ideation." That qualified investigators must be denied these important drugs because of a few bootleggers is a truly maddening disruption of progress in the scientific understanding of the "chemistry of madness."

Ololiuqui: Insights from the Devil's Morning-Glory

In 1941 Schultes made order out of chaos by identifying the Mexican morning-glory, *Rivea corymbosa,* as the ancient Aztec narcotic *ololiuqui.* Then, as he was quoted in Chapter 3: "This contribution was so earth-shaking that my monograph on the subject gathered dust for more than a decade." The scientist who finally put this information to practical use in studying mental disease was a thirty-six-year-old psychiatrist at that time in charge of a mental hospital in Canada— Dr. Osmond, previously mentioned in connection with the adrenochrome theory.

Osmond and his colleagues had been investigating the similarity in chemical composition between adrenalin and mescaline from peyote, and they were anxious to find other compounds that might mimic psychosis. When he heard about the work of Schultes, Osmond obtained some of the seeds from Harvard and embarked upon the first experiments with *ololiuqui* conducted for the sole purpose of psychological observation.

He described these in the July, 1955, *Journal of Mental Science*. The following notes are abstracted from that report: He first stated that he was in good health at the time and had never suffered from jaundice (some of these drugs have an adverse effect upon damaged livers). He was experienced in model psychoses, having taken mescaline, adrenochrome, and LSD. In his first *ololiuqui* experiment, he took fourteen of the brown, lentil-like seeds and found that they had a bitter taste; chewing them was tedious, for they have a hard coating. On three following occasions, he took twenty-six, sixty, and one hundred seeds, smashing these with a hammer and grinding them in a mortar. (It may be recalled from Chapter 3 that a Mexican physician "gulped a handful of seeds" and concluded that they were devoid of action. Osmond and Schultes believe that this was due to the seeds not being sufficiently chewed.) And as for the number thirteen, Osmond said, "Despite their sacred significance, thirteen seeds had little effect upon me. There may be more subtle explanations, but I suggest that Red Men, from bitter experience, have found it prudent to mislead White Men, lest they once more prohibit the sacred seed and persecute its devotees."

After Osmond swallowed the finely powdered seeds with ice water, he noticed a rapid onset of symptoms similar to those described for mescaline and LSD, although he did not experience any hallucinations. At times everything seemed "fresh and new as on a May morning when you are twenty-one." There were also periods of apathy, or absence of mood

—not depression—when he lacked the energy to record his observations despite his keen interest in doing so. His bodily sensations were less than with mescaline, but there was some epigastric burning, a tingling in the face and hands, and a slight headache.

"Four hours later," he said, "there was a period of alert, calm, relaxed well-being that lasted many hours. This was a condition I had not seen described before, wakefulness without tension. It was very different from the touch-me-not after-effects of mescaline or the bruised bluntness after alcohol. The lack of caffeine or benzedrine tension is remarkable. The next day, there was slight mouth dryness, but no hangover. . . . this preliminary experiment suggests that *ololiuqui* differs from mescaline, adrenochrome, and LSD. A full pharmacologic investigation would be very welcome. . . . I hope this small reconnaissance will encourage larger and better equipped expeditions into this strange territory."

Of what practical value are experiences of this sort? Osmond noted some very significant things. For instance, he found that he was indifferent to the people around him, including his wife, his four-year-old daughter, a psychologist, and a nurse. But he held a little puppy in his lap and he found its warmth and nearness very comforting. At the time he mused, "Shouldn't psychotic people have pets? Wouldn't they be more helpful than humans? Probably. Why? Because they are not self-conscious, hardly selves at all. Self gets in the way—even 'H' (Osmond's daughter). But not the puppy, no self intervenes. Animals are alive but undemanding." And then he quoted from Walt Whitman's poem *Song of Myself*: "I think I could turn and live with animals, they are so placid and self-contain'd. . . ."

Later in the report, he wrote that the comfort he derived from the little dog deserves further investigation because few studies of the relationship between animals and humans have been made. This is often dismissed as just being a substitute for another relationship, a human one. But in Osmond's view, this is superficial and misleading. "The relationship between man and dog has developed over tens of thousands of years and seems based on deeper levels of understanding than words. Perhaps, then, when words fail us this is why dogs can be so comforting."

In referring to his dismaying "paralysis of the will," he pointed out that "this happens to many unlucky folk labelled schizophrenic. When they complain about their lack of energy, they are looked upon as being bizarrely hypochondriacal. When they are forced to overcome their lack of energy, they often become irritable and sometimes their behavior seems to be impulsive." At one point, Osmond intended to give his little daughter a gentle push and found that he had knocked her flat. "The effort once made resulted in action that was not fully controlled. At the height of the experience, so much effort was needed to do even the smallest thing that there was a temptation to remain totally immobile. During the fourth experiment, about an hour and a half after the hundred seeds were taken, a curious thing happened. I raised my hand above my head and couldn't get it down. No urging or verbal pressure by my colleagues made any difference, neither did voluntary effort on my part. It was a strange, unpleasant feeling. Eventually, I pulled it down with my other hand."

In the phase of schizophrenia described as catatonic, patients become unresponsive and refuse to move or to talk. There is a tendency to hold the limbs in unnaturally awkward positions for long periods of time. Clearly, then, psychosis-mimicking effects are not limited to hallucinations, and a model psychosis that does not happen to produce hallucinations may still provide valuable insights.

Osmond and other psychiatrists have used these experiences in planning their treatment of patients. One of the areas being explored is the phenomenon of pain that recurs at the site of old, long-forgotten injuries. Normal persons under the influence of psychotomimetics like LSD frequently complain of this. So do acutely psychotic patients. Upon physical examination there "seems to be nothing at all wrong." But now doctors are wondering whether there might not be a metabolic disturbance of some kind which reawakens symptoms in areas that appear to be completely healed. (Paradoxically, Chicago Medical School researchers have found that LSD gives superior relief in cases of extreme pain and may prove to be the pain-killer of choice in many cases.)

In case reports on the use of LSD-type drugs, published by authorities like Dr. R. A. Sandison in England, and Dr. Oscar Janiger in Los Angeles, one reads of patients saying such things as, "I'm laughing because The Fool is jostling me." Senseless mirth is a characteristic of the hebephrenic phase of schizophrenia—but if, with the aid of drugs, the patient can explain that he feels he is actually being tickled, it doesn't seem quite so senseless. Nor does terror remain inexplicable when it is noted that in hundreds of cases normal volunteers taking the drugs said they felt that everything was "alive." Furniture seemed to have rippling muscles, the walls breathed, paintings were composed of colors with an independent life of their own—much as the mad artist Vincent van Gogh saw his world.

In August, 1960, Dr. Hofmann announced that he had isolated and identified three of the active ingredients in *Rivea corymbosa*: d-lysergic acid amine, d-isolysergic acid amide, and chanoclavine, all in the LSD family of substances and previously known to exist only as ergot derivatives. The same alkaloids were found in related morning-glory seeds of the *Ipomoea tricolor,* reportedly used as a kind of *ololiuqui* in Oaxaca, Mexico. The entire morning-glory family is now being scrutinized. Rhode Island's Dr. Youngken, using radioactive

C_{14} compounds, has found that the active principles are localized in the seeds, and that *I. tricolor* contains by far the most of these. One of the substances studied also occurs in the "magic" mushrooms.

The incredible suggestion—that the same narcotic properties are shared by a lowly fungus and an "innocent" ornamental vine—is now a confirmed fact. At long last, the Spanish chroniclers of the ancient Aztecs have been proved correct in their observations that *ololiuqui* has the mysterious power to make clear "all things which cannot be fathomed by the human mind." Because the plant's drugs are providing insights into mental illness, Schultes' early hope—that it might serve mankind in a less satanic way than that which bedeviled church fathers of old—is well on the way to becoming fully realized.

Extracting the Magic from Mushrooms

One of the best-known "mushroom men" in this country is a layman who has made such important contributions to science that he is now a research fellow of the Harvard Botanical Museum. R. Gordon Wasson is a self-taught ethnomycologist, or specialist in the uses of mushrooms by primitive peoples. After being graduated from Columbia's School of Journalism, he studied at the London School of Economics and became a financial reporter for the *New York Herald Tribune* before going into international banking. He has lately retired from his post as a vice-president of Morgan Guaranty Trust Co.

Until 1927, if he thought of mushrooms at all, it was with revulsion. But then he met a charming White Russian pediatrician, and in a romance that is in some ways reminiscent of that of Dr. Withering, he, under the influence of the pediatrician, learned to love these lower plants. Dr. Valentina P. Wasson introduced him to fungi in the Catskill woods on their honeymoon in 1927. She accused him of being a myco-phobe, or one who fears mushrooms; most Anglo-Saxons are. However, they soon were sharing a tender mycophilia, or love of mushrooms, which caused them to give up most of their social activities in order to spend their free time studying all aspects of this subject. In the course of their more than thirty years together, the Wassons traveled the world over, gathering mushroom lore during their vacations. He said, "We were amateurs unencumbered by academic inhibitions; therefore, we felt free to range far and wide, disregarding the frontiers that ordinarily segregate the learned disciplines."

What they produced was a pioneering work of scholarly knowledge and a very practical lead for further investigation of hallucinogens in mental-illness research.

Wasson, today, is a striking-looking man with thick gray-ing hair and a sharp, piercing glance. His apartment over-looking the East River in Manhattan is filled with archeologi-cal specimens and beautiful, rare books; one of the collectors' items is the two-volume work *Mushrooms, Russia and History,* which he wrote with his late wife. It was published in 1957 in a limited edition of 512 numbered copies priced at $125, but two sets recently sold in London for $500 apiece. The Wassons discovered some unpublished mushroom paintings done by the great Jean Henri Fabre between 1885–1895 lying neglected in his home at Sérignan in the south of France. These became the perfect illustrations for their book.

Before interviewing Wasson I had read his scientific pa-pers, including a 362-item bibliography, published by Harvard University, on the anthropological, botanical, chemical, and clinical aspects of the hallucinogenic mushrooms. I was al-ready familiar with some of the details of his field work in Mexico, having recently returned from the area myself. I knew that it had not been physically easy for him to make his way by mule pack to the chill heights of the Sierra Mazateca, where he and the society photographer Allan Richardson were the first Americans to partake of the sacred mushrooms, on the night of June 29, 1955. His experiences are fully described in his book and in the May 13, 1957, issue of *Life* so they need not be repeated here.

What seemed to be the untold story was the "before and after" part. How was he led to the hallucinogenic mushrooms and what has happened since their discovery?

"We—my wife and I, that is—drew heavily on our betters in the field," Wasson said, "especially Professor Roger Heim, director of the Paris Natural History Museum. But it was not until 1952 that our attention was turned to Mexico through an article sent to us from Majorca by the poet Robert Graves. It was from the Ciba *Symposia* of February, 1944, and it mentioned the then recent work of Schultes in connection with the Aztec mushrooms, *teonanacatl*."

This was hearing about things the long way around, but it was sufficiently important to cause the Wassons to delay publication of their book, already in galley proofs. After talking with Schultes, recently returned from his long stay in the Upper Amazon, they decided to pick up the trail where he had left it. Five years later the result was Volume II, dealing with the Mexican mushrooms.

In 1953 the Wassons and their sixteen-year-old daughter, Masha, set off for Oaxaca, feeling as if they were "pilgrims seeking the Grail." "To this attitude of ours, I attribute such success as we have had," Wasson said. They had various goals, but their main objective was to collect samples of the mushrooms used by the Indians in their ceremonies. First they had to persuade the Indians to show them where the sacred mushrooms grew. Then they set to work taking colored photographs of the mushrooms in the ground. Next they made spore prints by putting white or black paper under the caps overnight. With water colors they tried to capture the true tints. "All mycologists should be good water colorists," Wasson said. After the mushrooms were bisected, the cross sections were photographed again in color and and then the plants were pickled in alcohol—in large jars so that they wouldn't be crushed. When the Wassons didn't pickle their specimens, they dried them in the sun or over fire and tagged them.

They had to return year after year to this area before they were finally able to gain the confidence of a woman shaman, or *curandera,* who permitted them to participate in the ceremony. This is, essentially, a celebration of "holy communion" in which the mushrooms are first adored and then consumed in a rite mingling Christian and pagan elements of worship. Wasson has written:

"For more than four centuries the Indians have kept the divine mushroom close to their hearts, sheltered from desecration by white men. Today, we know that there are many curanderos who carry on the cult, each according to his lights, some of them consummate artists, performing the ancient liturgy in remote huts before minuscule congregations. . . . To them, performing before strangers is a profanation. Do not think it is a question of money. 'We did not this for money,' said Guadalupe after we had spent the night with her family and the curandera, Maria Sabina. . . . After all, would you have it any different? What priest of the Catholic church will perform Mass to satisfy an unbeliever's curiosity? The *curanderos* who today, for a big fee, will perform the rite for any stranger are prostitutes and fakers. Their insincere performance has the validity of a rite put on by an unfrocked priest. Religion in primitive society was an awesome reality . . . pervading all life and culminating in ceremonies that were forbidden to the profane. This is what the mushroom ceremony is in the remote parts of Mexico."

Wasson himself unwittingly started a journalistic landslide with his 1957 story of the effects of the mushrooms. Since

Mary Belle Allen preserving "living soup" aboard the *Stella Polaris*.

Don Ollis

Dr. R. Robichaud

"The Table Cloth is Impatient," an oil painting by Dr. Marvin Malone, painted and named while under the influence of mescaline in a scientific experiment. The figure's face is bright red, hair is purple, table cloth is a shimmering mass of blue, yellow, green, and purple.

Heber Youngken, Jr., examines microscopically the cells of ergot strains from which alkaloids are extracted.

E. Yale Dawson
collecting marine specimens
on the sea floor.

Don Ollis

Today's Health

John Sieburth holding
ringed penguin making
tests that led
to discovery of
antibacterial activity
of marine algae
(Deception Island).

Ross Nigrelli
working with
a sea cucumber,
Bimini, Bahamas.

Lerner Marine Laboratory

Sir Henry Wellcome
going down the Nile
with the floating
tropical disease
research laboratory
he established in 1906.

tache-less Edson Woodward
eets bearded Russell Polden,
otorcycled around the world
collecting soil samples
for antibiotic studies.
The plant hunters
had last met in Ceylon.

Metro Photo Service

African native drug market.

E. F. Woodward

Richard Schultes
feeding a young
Amazonian manioc flour.

Finn Sandberg
with a
small African
friend.

Bruce Halstead
checking a feverish
little Campa.

then almost every type of publication has picked up some aspect of the discovery as good copy. One hears about the mushrooms on television and can even buy a phonograph record of a *curandera* chanting in Mazatec, "I am a good woman, a doctor woman, a wise-in-the-way-of-plants woman." With the international set, "having a go at the mushrooms" has become "a thing." Hollywood writers have made the most of it. (When one considers that this glamorization may lead to legal curtailment of vital tools for mental-disease research as has happened already with LSD and, to a certain extent, with mescaline, the implications are serious.)

On the other hand, scientific workers the world over were stimulated to further research by Wasson's first article, which, because he is a layman, was published by a popular magazine, *Life.* At that time it was unlikely that scientific journals would have accepted his account. In fact, it was this story, in an international edition, that caught the eye of the one chemist perhaps best suited to work on the mushrooms—LSD discoverer Albert Hofmann, in Switzerland. He succeeded in getting in touch with Wasson, who went back to Mexico to collect properly preserved specimens for him. From these the Swiss chemist extracted and isolated two active agents, psilocybin and psilocin, from the species *Psilocybe mexicana.* After the molecular structure was defined, Sandoz scientists synthesized the "magic mushrooms." The eminent French psychiatrist, Professor Jean Delay, was the first to experiment clinically with these drugs, at the Hospital Ste Anne in Paris; since then, many hundreds of trials on human subjects have been reported in the medical literature.

Research in many other areas has also been stimulated. Drs. Varro E. Tyler, Jr., and Lynn Brady, of the Drug Plant Laboratory, College of Pharmacy, University of Washington, and Dr. Marvin H. Malone, of the Pharmacy Research Institute at the University of Connecticut, are collaborating on a series of creative experiments in pharmacognosy involving many different mushroom species. In summarizing the extensive literature on the beautiful but toxic fly agaric, *Amanita muscaria,* first cousin to the destroying angel, *A. phalloides,* Dr. Tyler noted that Oliver Goldsmith in 1762 reported that Siberian peasants drank a broth from stewed Amanita which caused a much-sought-after type of intoxication. Because the mushrooms are rare in the extreme north of Siberia, the primitive tribes inhabiting these wastelands still go to extraordinary and revolting lengths to conserve the active principle in this broth: they have learned it passes through the kidneys of three or four successive imbibers without losing its potency.

One hundred years later, when Lewis Carroll was writing *Alice in Wonderland,* Siberian explorers again called attention to mushroom intoxication, which, in addition to producing intense excitement, caused the size and shape of objects to appear distorted. Tyler suggested that the scholarly, scientifically minded writer of the fairy tale used these facts as the basis for the scene in which the wise old caterpillar tells Alice to eat from one side of the toadstool if she would grow large, and from the other, if she wished to grow small.

The intoxicating or hallucinogenic principle of fly agaric has defied all attempts to identify it up to the present time. In 1869 German chemists isolated a poisonous sirupy base that they called muscarine. This slows the heart, causes a marked fall of blood pressure, increased salivation, and other symptoms, but it does not produce the initial central-nervous-system stimulation and hallucinations that result from eating the whole Amanita. Because of the difficulty of obtaining and testing pure muscarine, Malone, Tyler, and their colleagues devised a rapid, uncomplicated bioassay method for muscarine activity which can be used with even unidentified samples of crude botanical materials. The results of their tests on laboratory animals have practical application so far as wild mushroom collector-gastronomists are concerned: now the look-alike species can be identified by either bioassay or chemical means, and the more muscarine they contain, the more deadly they are likely to be.

Tyler and Brady studied a closely related species of the fly agaric, *A. pantherina,* responsible for most of the cases of mushroom poisoning in the Puget Sound area. They were able to prove that the active principle in this species was not bufotenine (a derivative of serotonin) or hyoscyamine (a constituent of the deadly nightshades) as had been previously reported, but was in fact an unknown principle. Authorities agree that one of the most difficult accomplishments in pharmacognosy is to prove, beyond any doubt, the absence of a particular compound from a particular botanical specimen.

Malone and Tyler were the first to report that the mushroom *Panaeolus campanulatus,* formerly considered synonymous with one of the "magic" Mexican mushrooms, contained serotonin, a neuro-regulator that occurs naturally in the human brain. However, they do not at this time believe that serotonin causes hallucinations. Tyler tried the mushrooms on animals and ate them himself in carefully controlled experiments and wrote that they were devoid of psychic effects. (For one thing, serotonin and bufotenine have never been known to be active when taken orally. Cohoba snuff, containing bufotenine, must be sniffed.) No one has the answer yet, but it is thought that the active principles will be related indole compounds, such as psilocybin and psilocin, already isolated from the Mexican hallucinogens, which are mostly of the Psilocybe species. It is interesting that the extensive screening programs for the identification of active principles in mushrooms of the Pacific Northwest has already turned up a Psilocybe species, limited to western Oregon, which contains the hallucinogenic principle psilocin; two others with the same property, plus psilocybin were found growing in a yard in Seattle. This work extends the reported occurrence of these compounds to North American mushrooms of three genera: Conocybe, Panaeolus, and Psilocybe.

In addition to these studies, Tyler and his co-workers have succeeded in the difficult task of cultivating the mushrooms in Erlenmeyer flasks, a particular boon to researchers because wet, miserable, day-long mushroom-collecting trips can often result in only a half a dozen tiny specimens.

One of the graduate students assigned to the problems of culturing the fungi stumbled upon an almost unbelievable coincidence when another student consulted him about the typical effects of eating certain mushrooms. After eating several specimens of inky-cap *Coprinus atramentarius,* and then drinking some wine, the latter student had become ill with the same type of symptoms as those experienced by alcoholics who take the drug Antabuse (disulfiram) and then forgetfully consume liquor. After a series of inky-cap experiments, Tyler and Malone reached the conclusion that there is a disulfiram-like substance in these mushrooms that reacts with alcohol, but is innocuous by itself. European investigators are also working on this fascinating problem.

The reports on the Mexican mushrooms also stimulated botanical research in mycology, regarded as something of a stepchild by plant specialists. As Tyler said, when speaking of the difficulties of obtaining fresh specimens, "The dark-spored Psilocybe can be identified with certainty by only a few men. . . . The nondescript, brownish Inocybe are familiar to practically everyone, but identifiable by practically no one."

Professor Heim, of Paris, is an acknowledged authority in these matters and R. Gordon Wasson has been grateful for his help on mushroom hunts in Mexico. While Heim will continue this work in his scientific specialty, for Wasson the mushroom obsession has ended. When he returned from his last trip he told me that he was now deeply involved with an investigation of plants used by the Mazatecs when the mushrooms are out of season. These are surely the greenest of all green medicines, belonging as they do to the mint family. The Harvard Botanical Museum has recently published an account of Wasson's experiments with a species of mint new to botanists—*Salvia divinorum*. The Indians propagate these plants from cuttings and hide them away from prying eyes in remote ravines. Wasson found his reaction to eating the leaves similar to the initial symptoms of "being be-mushroomed"; he saw elaborate, three-dimensional designs and so forth. One wonders how many more hallucinogenic botanicals remain to be uncovered by this tireless researcher!

His part in the mushroom saga ended in a dramatic introduction of two friends. One of them, Albert Hofmann, talks a special language of complicated formulas and abstract concepts that only other chemists can fully fathom. The other, Maria Sabina, an unschooled *curandera,* speaks only Mazatec, an unwritten language. Wasson brought these two poles-apart individuals together in Mexico in October, 1962. During this incredible bridging of many barriers, the *curandera* accepted Hofmann's gift of "synthetic mushrooms," pure crystalline tablets of psilocybin.

When she employed them that night in her ceremony, she and the other Indians found that they preferred them to the legendary "God's flesh" that their people had been gathering during the rainy seasons since before 1500 b.c. Maria Sabina was particularly delighted with Hofmann's gift because, as she said, "Now I can respond to calls at any time of the year."

Whether this would be an unmixed blessing can't be explored here. It does illustrate, though, the fate of some natural products destined to be replaced by synthetics, and it brings full circle the discussion of Stone Age mental drugs, which, in this instance, have been to the Space Age and back.

Drugs from the Sea

THE SEA—INSPIRATION TO WRITERS, ADVENTURE-
land of sportsmen, battleground for militarists—is the realm
of Inner Space, a challenge to oceanographers and our last
frontier on this planet. More and more authorities are pointing out that man cannot hope to understand the physical
environment on the moon, Venus, and elsewhere until he
knows his own world better. Yet some two decades after a
concerted effort to explore marine regions was begun, the
sum of what we know is insignificant compared with what
we do not know.

At the 1962 American Institute of Physics Seminar on
Oceanography, the theme song seemed to be, "We must stand
in awe of our ignorance." The eminent scientists agreed that,
in the light of discoveries made since 1957, the first International Geophysical Year, the whole body of long-standing
"facts" about the marine world must be reinvestigated now
in quite different ways.

The magnitude of this task? The oceans occupy about
71 per cent of the surface of the globe; four-fifths of the
animal life dwells there, as does the unestimated bulk of the
vegetation. These plants grow at the prolific rate of 4,000
tons per square mile, and the oxygen in our atmosphere is
largely supplied by these aquatic plant communities.

Oceanographic research forms a strong common link for international co-operation, as has been demonstrated by IGY results and by the current International Indian Ocean Expedition. The seas lying beyond the territorial waters of nations belong to all men; without these seas, none can survive.

The new field of marine pharmacology—drugs from the sea—has just begun to receive the attention and financial support it needs. A symposium at the New York Academy of Sciences helped to stimulate interest in 1960, and various bills to advance all marine sciences are now being considered by Congress. When passed, these measures will establish a comprehensive ten-year program designed to explore the sea for solutions to some of mankind's major problems. The cost of the entire project has been estimated at $2.3 billion.

While vast expanses of water do not at first seem to offer much to medicine, a surprising number of important discoveries have come from this source:

—In 1901, experiments with Portuguese man-of-war jellyfish stings unraveled the mystery of shock reaction, called anaphylaxis, and formed the basis of our present concept of allergies.

—The process by which white blood cells protect the body from invading organisms was understood after studies of young sea urchins.

—Work on the electric eel has resulted in the synthesis of PAM, an antidote for nerve gas.

—Important vitamins concentrated in the livers of cod fish and sharks pointed the way to better nutrition for all of us.

—The iodine in sea water and plants gave an early clue to thyroid function and goiter therapy.

Dr. Albert Szent-Györgi, the Nobel laureate who discovered vitamin C some thirty years ago, is now studying mollusks at the Institute for Muscle Research at the Marine Biology Laboratory, Woods Hole, Massachusetts. Speaking of his work, he said, "I hope that some day my studies on mussels will yield a clue to muscular dystrophy. We must study the basic phenomena of life in order to solve problems like this and like cancer. The ocean, cradle of life, offers immense possibilities for the approach to basic problems, as well as to our immediate needs."

Marine scientists are making progress in our battle with disease. They are also looking for the answers to such vital questions as, What is life? How does it begin? But first the raw materials for this research must be collected far from land. Here is an eyewitness account of a typical search for drug sources in the sea:

Shortly after dawn on a tropical March morning in 1959, an unorthodox fishing party cast off from Panama and headed out into the Pacific. Over the horizon, sixty miles away, lay the Las Perlas Islands. In their vicinity giant sailfish and black marlin could be caught, but the "fishermen" aboard the 110-foot *Stella Polaris* were after much smaller game. On the fantail of the yacht stood a pleasant, soft-spoken brunette, Dr. Mary Belle Allen, Director of the Kaiser Foundation Comparative Biology Laboratory in Richmond, California. She was tying a seventy-five-foot nylon line to a stanchion, and on the end of the line was a small net which she tossed astern. The net was towed along beneath the surface of the water in order to collect plankton—the microscopic plants and animals that drift with the currents on the open sea.

Also on the fantail were three men. One of them, husky Dr. E. Yale Dawson, a University of Southern California professor who is an authority on marine plants of the tropical and temperate North Pacific, was carefully marking a series of anchorage spots on a navigation chart. He planned to collect his specimens, algae, by diving down to the sea floor. But since working alone in the depths is a risky business, seated beside him was his diving partner, and the group's official photographer, Don Ollis, a trim, seasoned veteran of many scientific explorations, including the Halstead Expedition to Peru. Underwater photographs by Ollis have won many international first prizes. The third man was Palmer T. Beaudette, of the Beaudette Foundation for Biological Research in Solvang, California. At the moment he was rapidly spinning a hygrometer to measure the air's humidity.

The owner of the *Stella Polaris,* after having finished a vacation cruise from California to Panama, had flown back to the United States. In the interest of pure science—and since his yacht had to return to California anyway—he had loaned his boat and crew to the marine biologists. Unfortunately, in the United States there are only seventy-six research vessels, and these have a limited amount of modern equipment with which to investigate all aspects of oceanography: ocean boundaries, bottom topography, the physics of the sea, the chemistry of sea water, types of currents, and the many phases of marine biology. Marine pharmacologists are grateful for any opportunity to collect specimens, wherever and however they can.

The objective of this particular expedition was twofold: to determine the abundance and types of marine plants along the coasts of Panama, Costa Rica, Nicaragua, El Salvador, Guatemala, and Mexico; and to collect specimens of algae that might contain antibiotic substances for use in medicine.

The marine biologists had decided to use a stop-and-go program. Dr. Allen would sift the surface of the sea whenever the yacht was under way, while Dr. Dawson's field work would be performed around each anchorage. The first stop was the Las Perlas Islands. From there on, the yacht would anchor at intervals approximately 100 miles apart until the last collecting station was reached at Cabo San Lucas on the tip of Baja California Sur, 2,400 miles away.

Meanwhile, as powerful twin diesel engines drove the

craft through 80° water, Dr. Allen began the second phase of her collecting. Her net, riding along in the yacht's wake, looked very much like those used by butterfly fanciers; its fabric, though, was much finer: 200-mesh. But even this fine mesh allowed many forms of plankton to slip through. To collect these microscopic specimens, she turned to laboratory filter paper.

Lowering a plastic bucket into the sea, she scooped up sparkling, clear ocean water and poured it into a transparent cylinder of lucite that stood up on the deck. The cylinder, eighteen inches high and six inches in diameter, had a water-tight base. When the cylinder had been filled almost to the top, she attached a large filter paper to the end of a smaller lucite cylinder. She placed this unit, filter-end down, inside the larger one. Its weight caused the paper to sink, condens-ing the microorganisms in the sea water beneath it. When the filter was within an inch of the bottom, she siphoned off the water, removed the filter, and repeated the whole process.

After about five gallons of water had been filtered, the remaining liquid had the appearance of a thin, tomato-colored chowder. This "living soup" was preserved for future re-search in two-ounce bottles, kept in the light from a porthole. All samples were carefully labeled so the scientist could re-late them to the locality where they were collected. The yield from the plankton net ranged all the way from gelatinous goo embedded with fish eggs to shrimplike crustaceans and tiny, evil-looking monsters with fanglike teeth. Specimens to be preserved were stored in bags in the freezer.

In the afternoon, the throbbing hum from the diesels abruptly stopped and the yacht coasted slowly into calm water on the lee side of Saboga, one of the Las Perlas Islands. It was now Dawson's turn to collect. He and Ollis quickly put on their aqualungs and adjusted their face masks. Hardly had the anchor been dropped before they too plunged into the water. Just below the surface they encountered hundreds of tiny jellyfish, whose threadlike tentacles inflicted sharp, stinging prickles on the divers' bodies until they sank beneath the layer of drifting creatures. Visibility, they found, was about thirty feet in each direction. A small school of sierra mackerel sped by, then vanished. The two men, following the anchor chain, descended slowly into the gloom, clearing their ears as the pressure increased. The depth gauges registered seventy feet when they touched bottom.

Dawson first collected some pinkish-grey "pebbles"—a red alga, *Lithophyllum imitans,* that forms a hard, thin, coralline crust over the surface of rocks and old shells, sometimes completely covering them. At that depth, however, the red rays of the sun were filtered out and the surface colors of pink and red were replaced by light tan, grays, and black. The two men swam side by side, gathering dozens of other species and putting them into plastic bags. Some algae displayed feathery fronds; a few had the appearance of thick-leaved succulents; now and then there was one resembling a nondescript back-yard weed. But on the whole, attached algae remind one of miniature shrubs and trees of great delicacy. When they found an especially luxuriant cluster, Ollis, using flash attachments on his underwater camera, took pictures of this fairyland of shadings, form, and motion. Surge currents moved the plants, usually anchored by a single stipe, to and fro in the dim light. This swaying of the "forests" surrounding divers intent upon making scientific collections causes a certain amount of tension as they keep one eye on the vegetation and the other on the lookout for possibly dangerous sea creatures. Every few moments Dawson and Ollis peered into the water around and above them, because in tropical seas barracuda and sharks are an ever-present menace. For this reason, and others, well-trained divers never go down alone and are extremely safety conscious. They know and respect the sea. On this dive, only one small white-tip shark was seen; he circled them once and moved on into deeper water.

As the men worked toward shore, the water became shallower and plant and fish life more abundant. At only fifteen feet the whole bottom blazed with color. Gaudy butterfly fish darted in and out of crevasses and algal growths glinted with hues of blue, green, brown, and purple in the dancing light reflected from sunshine on the waves overhead. Flash bulbs were no longer necessary. Dawson, using a knife, scraped algae from sunken boulders, or, if the growths were hard coralline species, chipped them free with a prospector's hammer. By the time the men had broken through the gentle surf along the shore, they had collected six plastic bags full of specimens. By banging loudly on their aqualung tanks, they signaled to the yacht for an outboard motorboat to pick them up. While waiting, they gathered additional algae clinging to outcroppings of rock along the beach.

Upon returning to the yacht, they rinsed their equipment in fresh water and themselves in hot showers, then settled down on the fantail for some hard work. As Ollis took close-up identification pictures of different species, Dawson recorded the date, location, depth, temperature, and name of species, if known, on slips of paper. These were inserted, along with the algae, into small plastic bags and deposited in the freezer. Larger specimens to be preserved for identification purposes only were placed in five-gallon tins of formaldehyde solution or in pint Mason jars of alcohol. It was 10:30 P.M. before they finished with the day's collection.

At dawn the yacht headed for its second anchorage, at Punta Naranjas, a promontory on the mainland northwest of the Panama Canal. The third stop, on the next day, was at Isla Coiba. And so, day after day, the biologists alternately probed the ocean floor and skimmed the surface of the sea. A month and a half later the yacht reached its home port in

California. From the collection standpoint, the expedition had been exceedingly worthwhile. Now the time had come for exhaustive laboratory tests to see whether the specimens contained substances that could combat harmful bacteria.

Eleven months later a joint report by Mary Belle Allen and E. Yale Dawson, entitled "Production of Antibacterial Substances by Benthic Tropical Marine Algae," was published in the March, 1960, *Journal of Bacteriology*. Portions are quoted here to indicate techniques of laboratory analysis and the results obtained:

"Recent studies have shown that planktonic marine algae may produce antibiotic substances that can account for the well-known bactericidal activity of sea water. . . . These investigations suggest that production of antibiotics may be widespread in marine algae. . . . Algae were collected in intertidal and infratidal areas. . . . When samples of thalli [stem and leaf-like parts of various seaweed] were thawed and placed on nutrient agar plates that had been seeded with representative bacteria [such as the hospital-plaguing *Staphylococcus aureus*], typical inhibitory zones resulted." In other words, substances produced by the algae had slowed down the growth of the bacteria. The report continued: "The patterns of inhibition obtained suggest the presence of at least four different antibacterial substances in the algae studied."

The work of the Dawson-Allen expedition is typical of many other research groups conducting a world-wide search for drugs from the sea—a vast new frontier for "green medicine." For instance, as this is being written, Dr. John M. Sieburth, chief scientist aboard the University of Rhode Island's new research vessel, the *Trident,* is directing a marine microbiological survey along the entire track from San Diego through the Panama Canal and back to the School of Oceanography's Narragansett Marine Laboratory. Dr. John T. Conover and others are working with him on a study of the antibiotic activity of the gulfweeds *Sargassum natans* and *S. fluitans,* as related to the burden of parasites and epiphytes (non-parasitic plants growing on other plants) that increasingly collect on the Sargassum as it drifts farther and farther from the Sargasso Sea in the Atlantic Ocean. A pilot project indicated that the program was well worth launching.

The relationship between an algal host plant and its parasites and epiphytes is largely unknown ground. Dr. Conover explained: "Here is an opportunity to test a hypothesis with a genetically stable pair of populations, since both species of Sargassum apparently lost their ability to reproduce by spores or egg and sperm many millenniums ago. By collecting, the weed first at the southern fringe of its distribution, then in the center, and finally at its northern fringe over a 3,500 mile transect, we found a spectrum of antibiotic activity directly correlated with the load of 'free riders' infecting the host plants. The gulfweed represents a very large biomass of plant material. If found to contain valuable antibiotics, the sea might be harvested for a crop over many years."

Algae, the vegetable matter of the watery world, grows almost entirely in depths of less than 150 feet. Below 5,000 feet there is only the light from bioluminescent organisms, and only specialized plants are found. Many species of algae exist on land, some even on icebergs; others coexist with fungi and become lichens, clinging to trees and rocks. During the past sixty years, over 17,000 species of algae have been described. Their variety staggers the imagination, for they range in size from single-celled diatoms and some violently toxic dinoflagellates too small to be seen by the naked eye—millions in a cubic inch of water—to giant kelp, which grows up to fifty feet in a year and can reach the tremendous length of 600 feet. The principal algal groups are: green, brown, red, and blue-green. Despite their variations, algae include the simplest form of plant life, though they may have one cell or many. They are called "simple" because they possess no true seeds, leaves, stems, or roots, and because their basic metabolic processes, nutrition and reproduction, generally take place in the individual cell. Anatomically, some groups are quite complex.

Common to most algae is the property of photosynthesis— utilizing sunlight, they convert water, nitrogen, carbon dioxide, and minerals into proteins, carbohydrates, and other life-sustaining matter. Exactly how they do this, what they produce, and why, is the subject of some of the most exciting fundamental research being done anywhere today. Such investigations were stimulated by Dr. Robertson Pratt of the University of California, and others, who discovered that certain algae produce antibiotics, as well as vitamins and many important minerals. In addition, certain hormone-like enzymes seem to exert a profound influence, not only upon the species which produce them, but also upon life in the surrounding waters. Because these changes are of a genetic nature, involving cell division and development, including the conversion of one sex into the opposite sex, this research has far-reaching consequences.

Despite this abundance of vital elements, the sea's potential has been scarcely tapped as a source for finished pharmaceuticals. Mankind's delay in making use of them has not necessarily been caused by a lack of interest, but rather by the difficulties involved, lack of knowledge, and a natural fear of the unknown. In some respects, ocean jungles are more inaccessible and hazardous than the most impenetrable tropical rain forest. It may seem inconsequential, but just finding researchers who are not subject to seasickness during a three- to four-month tour of duty presents a problem. There is also the obvious question of survival in an "atmosphere" that men cannot breathe. In addition, divers face the perils of compression and decompression. On land, humans withstand pressures of fifteen pounds to the square inch; deep-water fish may endure pressure on the order of six tons per square inch. A diver equipped with scuba (self-contained underwater breathing apparatus) who forgets the cardinal rule to inhale and exhale normally may suffer a crippling or fatal embolism, or air-bubble obstruction of the lungs. (However, this can happen even in a deep swimming pool if the scuba diver holds his breath while surfacing rapidly.)

Lest potential scientist-divers be discouraged from considering an exciting, worthwhile career, I should point out, having taken scuba training in preparation for expeditions, that the well-instructed diver has little more to fear in the ocean than on the average turnpike. As one marine biologist put it, "The sea, to divers such as myself, seems a safer habitat than the corner of Times Square on a Saturday night. It is not true that there are a *great many* deadly creatures always lurking about. There are some mean ones, but with proper caution and equipment the risks are reduced. The gravest enemies of the diver are extremes in water temperature and himself. The limits of the diver's equipment, of his own physical strength and endurance, and of his self-control and psychological stability constitute the real hazards."

It is not absolutely necessary to be a skin or scuba diver to work at sea, because collections can be made on or near the surface, where plant life flourishes. And incidentally, the oceanographers who make six-mile bathyscaphe descents into abyssal depths are chiefly concerned with geographical exploration, at the present time, and not with drugs from the sea.

Since the dawn of history, man has attempted to find medicinal uses for the comparatively few marine plants he could obtain. In the most ancient Chinese writings, species of seaweed were prescribed for dropsy, abcesses, and cancer. Primitive tribesmen in the South Seas and in America made seaweed extracts to treat skin diseases, stomach disorders, and inflammations. The use of seaweed for goiter has been very widespread: Peruvian Indians high in the Andes chew on compressed seaweed "goiter sticks"; among the Irish, Chinese, and Japanese, who today use mineral-rich seaweeds in their diet, goiter and other deficiency diseases are practically unknown. (The iodine used in medicine now comes largely from nitrate mines in Chile, and brines in the United States and Japan, rather than from the declining kelp industry.) The Indians of Sitka, Alaska, make ingenious use of the tubelike stipes of bull kelp as an instrument for treating earache: the thin end is placed in the ear, and the bulb put on a hot, wet stone, thereby allowing steam to enter and soothe the auditory canal.

If the island-dwellers of the world could be studied for their utilization of marine plants, the list would probably seem endless. The Japanese alone would make a staggering contribution. Considering the potential, the few adaptations we have made are rather insignificant. For instance, it has long been known that seaweeds make good poultices for bruises and cuts. During World Wars I and II, sphagnum peat moss was steam-sterilized and made into gauze-covered pads; wounds healed more quickly than with cotton bandages because the moss contains disinfecting substances in addition to its draining qualities. Old herbals mentioned Irish moss, or carrageen, for diseases of the lungs. In World War I these remedies were revived to ease the throats of soldiers who were gassed in combat. Dr. J. C. Houck recently reported that carrageenin, derived from the moss, is valuable in treating peptic ulcers. Agar, a vegetable gelatin from algae, is indispensable in bacteriology, serving as a culture medium. And algin, first extracted in 1885, is still used in manufacturing delayed-action drugs, because alginates are not digested by stomach juices. For this reason, they are also used in laxative and reducing preparations. A few years ago Professor

Takemoto, of Osaka University, discovered kainic acid in *Digenea simplex,* a seaweed traditionally taken as a vermifuge. After clinical trials, Takeda, a Japanese drug company, began marketing a product containing kainic acid. But prescription drugs derived from marine sources are few in number so far.

One of the first contemporary researchers to see the results of his work on algae appear in drug form is Dr. Paul R. Burkholder, the distinguished botanist who provided a treatment for typhus and typhoid fever when he discovered in a Venezuelan soil sample an organism that produces the antibiotic chloromycetin. Chloromycetin was the first antibiotic to be synthesized (by Parke, Davis & Company). Dr. Burkholder has also made important contributions in the vitamin and food-preservation fields. But it is his pioneering investigation of lichens—the algae-fungi combination—that concerns us here. A few lichens grow in maritime places, even in intertidal zones. The lichens resemble the symbiotic relationship between plants and animals that produce coral reefs.

In 1944–45 Burkholder and his associates at Yale University reported that they had found antibiotic properties in usnic acid derived from Cladonia and Usnea species of lichen collected on Cape Cod, in New Hampshire, and even from the Alcan Highway. Their tests showed usnic acid to be active against several kinds of bacteria, including the deadly staphylococcus species. Today, in Turku, Finland, a usnic-acid, broad-spectrum antibiotic is prepared from reindeer lichen by the Lääke Oy Pharmaceutical Company. It is exported to neighboring countries, Africa, and the Far East for use by physicians in treating tuberculosis and serious skin infections. Medical-journal reports state that it has been successful in clearing up conditions that resist treatment by antibiotics derived solely from fungi. It is not known for sure just how the algal and fungal components produce their special antibiotics, which are responsible for the improvement in treating fungus infections. Dr. O. Erik Virtanen, manager of Lääke Oy's Biochemical Division, wrote that usnic acid has been found valuable in treating a common, stubborn female complaint, a mixed infection caused by protozoan and yeastlike organisms. Professor Savicz, in Leningrad; Dr. H. J. Koornhof, in Johannesburg; and Professor Peter Ark, of the University of California, are among the scientists doing further work on usnic acid.

Professor Augusto Capriotti, of the University of Perugia in Italy, pointed out in a review paper that lichens were used in medicine by the ancient Egyptians, according to evidence found in a vase in the Nile Valley. Thanks to Burkholder, he said, this age-old remedy has been revived. From 1600–1800 A.D. lichens were considered an outstanding cure for pulmonary tuberculosis—the most successful field for usnic-acid therapy today. This "gift from the Northland" is not toxic, according to the clinical-trial literature cited by the manufacturer. Reindeer lichen, which gets its name from its antler-like branches, has been used as a famine food in Scandinavian countries, and it is eaten by reindeer without apparent ill effects.

Burkholder, continuing his studies of the occurrence of antibiotic substances in marine organisms, reported in 1958 on gorgonian corals, an algae-animal combination. These corals, collected off the coast of Puerto Rico, showed definite antibacterial action.

With Dr. Sieburth, Burkholder next went to Antarctica in December and January of 1958–59, the antarctic summer. Contrary to what one might think, the antarctic waters are full of life and provide marine biologists with some of the best "hunting" in the world. As soon as the pack ice began to break up, the scientists started towing their nets and lowering their buckets to gather samples of plankton, which they examined under a microscope set up in a makeshift laboratory aboard the Argentine hydrographic ship *Chiriguano*.

The clue to a new antibiotic came through the study of penguins. Sieburth was intrigued to find that the intestinal tracts of the penguins were virtually bacteria free. In tracing the birds' diet, he found that it was largely composed of shrimplike Euphasia, which had, in turn, been feeding upon gelatinous globules of Phaeocystis, a type of plankton that formed a yellow-green slime on the tow nets. Laboratory tests with various indicator bacteria showed that Phaeocystis was clearly associated with the antibacterial activity. Further testing is underway on possible human applications. Meanwhile, in veterinary medicine natural acrylic acid from Phaeocystis acts as a broad-spectrum "antibiotic" and is now being used in poultry feeding; other plankton is used to improve the butterfat of cows and to invigorate race horses.

Since the antarctic expeditions, Burkholder, now chairman of the Biology Programs at Columbia University's Lamont Geological Laboratory, has been studying the ecology of many algal antibiotics—how these organisms relate to their environment. One approach is to test them against marine bacteria in the same way that they had been tested against laboratory strains of staphylococcus and other routine indicator bacteria. A model experiment was devised to show whether or not a marine microorganism *while growing in the sea* could produce an antibiotic inhibitory for other microorgansmis *in the sea*. Experiments with Gonyaulax, collected near Puerto Rico, and other algae demonstrated that the antibiotics inhibited both laboratory strains and bacteria in the ocean. As with most scientific research, this raised more questions than were answered. Burkholder and others are now trying to determine whether antimicrobial substances are excreted by living algae, whether they have survival value for these plants, or whether they are given off only from the dead remains.

A new approach to the interrelationships between microscopic and macroscopic (much larger) marine organisms is developing. It is believed that antibiotics, vitamins, and enzymes are *the* dissolved substances in sea water that may be responsible for the growth of one population and the decline of another—a vast chemical check-and-balance that strongly influences seasonal growth and reproduction cycles.

Laboratory technicians can make artificial sea water by dissolving proper amounts of various chemical constituents in pure distilled water. Tests will prove the salt content of this solution to be identical with that of natural sea water; nevertheless, certain species of salt-water algae will not grow in it—unless some sea water is added. We now know that certain vitamins are involved. Strangely enough, not all sea water has this life-giving quality. Water collected offshore at one time of year will stimulate the algae's growth, while samples obtained at other times, or from other locations, will not. Therefore all sea water is not the same.

Dr. H. W. Harvey, who made a study of this phenomenon in the open sea near Plymouth, England, calls this life-sustaining liquid "fertile water." It is still not known whether "fertile water" moves about in currents, causing seasonal variations, or whether it is formed, dissipated, and then re-formed in the same location. Experiments elsewhere have shown that this mysterious substance deteriorates on standing; some, but not all, of it is stopped by fine filters; and it is destroyed by heat. The effect is strongest in fresh sea water collected where the population of marine bacteria is most concentrated.

Bacteria are among the most numerous organisms in the seas and are important scavengers of organic wastes. Sparkling "clear" oceanic water contains only about a hundred bacteria in a teaspoonful, but millions of these microorganisms, which live by the deaths of others, can be seen in a drop of water taken from a polluted maritime harbor. Bacteria are classified as plants, related to fungi on one side, algae on the other, and sharing many life properties of both. They have no chlorophyll, so they cannot manufacture food. In the sea, where the big fish devour the little fish, and so on, endlessly—bacteria are engaged in a gigantic feast, working away on everything that dies. As in our own atmosphere, a few of them may cause animal and plant diseases.

Since the oceans were first formed, they have been a catch basin for organic and inorganic chemical substances eroded or discharged from the land. Added to these are the products of decomposition and excretion from living creatures. Matter from underwater volcanoes—more numerous than those on land—and cosmic dust from Outer Space also contribute to the complicated formula. Chemists estimate that each cubic mile of sea water contains about 200,000,000 tons of chemical compounds, including elements such as silver, gold, sulfur, aluminum, and radium.

Is it not probable that drugs as diverse as those found in land plants might also be available in the sea?

What could be considered an international information exchange for this vital research exists in a loft-type building near the United Nations Headquarters in Manhattan. Haskins Laboratories, a nonprofit research group, is reached by a creaky freight elevator. The first room one enters is a combination office-library overflowing with scientific journals and correspondence in every language. By following a corridor lined with refrigerators in which plants are growing under fluorescent light, one finds in a maze of small laboratories, the white-coated researchers and their student-assistants, a number of them girls in their teens.

On the day he was interviewed, Dr. Luigi Provasoli, a distinguished-looking Haskins scientist, was surrounded by page proofs of a highly technical monograph. With the characteristic modesty of such researchers, he and his colleagues spoke chiefly of important advances being made elsewhere. It was learned from others that this group of biologists has developed techniques whereby marine microorganisms can be grown at will. For instance, Haskins has large fish tanks containing artificially nurtured live coral reefs—not too impressive to the casual passerby, perhaps, but they supply materials for research that have made Haskins a world center for studies in nutritional protozoology.

Various marine microorganisms grown at Haskins have been put to work as highly efficient "laboratory assistants" that test for the presence or absence of substances in sea water. Much more sensitive and accurate than man-made devices, they are able to detect such tremendously dilute amounts as one part in one quadrillion. These bio-assay organisms are known as auxotrophs, meaning that they need specific factors for life. Haskins scientists were among the first to establish that such plants have nutritional requirements just as animals do; most plants produce vitamins, but these need them to grow. One of these laboratory helpers from the plant kingdom is Euglena, an alga discovered in 1674 by the Dutch microscopist Antony Leeuwenhoek. It is one of the organisms responsible for the greenish haze, called water bloom, which forms on quiet bodies of fresh water during the summertime. Euglena needs, but does not contain, vitamin B_{12}, one of the most complex naturally occurring nutritive elements. It was isolated in 1948 as the active anemia-fraction of liver, and the human body requires one-millionth of a gram daily. Euglena research may provide answers for important nutritional questions related to resistant anemia and leukemia-type disorders, to name just two possible applications.

Some laymen might find it hard to believe that people who turn out sentences like: "An O.D. of 1.0 (cm. light-path) is permitted by 10 $\mu\mu$g. (*i.e.,* 10^{-11}g. B_{12}/ml.)[17]" could be delightful, but the atmosphere at busy Haskins is charged with excitement and good humor. Graduate students in the New York area fight for a chance to work here as minimum-wage technicians under the guidance of Dr. S. H. Hutner, the peppery past president of the Society of Protozoologists.

When Dr. Hutner was asked at the tea break, "Which of these tiny marine organisms are plants and which are animals?" he gave this answer: "Most textbook discussions of plants versus animals are fogged by timidity, unless the subject is oaks versus elephants. How very handy to assign *this* group to the orthodox plant kingdom and *that* one to the main animal lines, just as in Gilbert and Sullivan's *Iolanthe* each child born alive is either a little liberal or else a little conservative. But then take *Ochromonas danica,* that fast-swimming, deep green, photosynthetic, voracious chrysomonad you see over there—"

"What is a chrysomonad?"

"Many chrysomonads and some dinoflagellates are amazing organisms in plankton that combine the decisive attributes of plants (they contain chlorophyll and they photosynthesize) with those of animals (they are self-propelled eaters). It seems that we investigators must call such creatures plant-animals. The organisms themselves do not care."*

Ochromonas is now widely used as a replacement for rats and chickens in biological testing and several pharmaceutical companies are using it as a screening method for anticancer agents.

Some dinoflagellates, such as Gonyaulax species, contain substances that are deadly to marine life. An outstanding example of their effect is the "red tide," wherein the mass blooming of dinoflagellates colors large expanses of the sea at certain seasons. The very high concentration of these creatures—up to three and four hundred million per liter of sea

* And in the balance of this chapter, the line between plants and animals in the sea will not be underscored.

water—removes oxygen from the water and produces toxins. However, Gonyaulax is not harmful to mollusks that *eat* it, but the mollusks themselves become poisonous to human beings. Resembling botulism in its effect, one-millionth of a gram of this poison injected into a mouse will kill it. Some excellent new work on the chemistry of Gonyaulax toxins has just been completed by Dr. E. J. Schantz, who showed that the nerve poison accumulated by shellfish is identical with that grown by Gonyaulax laboratory cultures. This poison is several times more toxic than the most virulent nerve gas. Perhaps this deadly substance, like the jungle's curare, will be used some day for the benefit of mankind. It is possible that marine agronomists will cultivate a live stockpile in temperature-controlled salt-water farms. What a fascinating pharmacopoeia is the sea!

Sometimes it is difficult for the nonscientist to see the "reason" for painstaking research drawn out for many years. There is a tendency to ask: What is this good for? At this point Hutner said kindly, "I don't want to inflict involved biochemistry on you, but the supply of assayable small molecules is limited. We have only a few. We should continue such research as this, independent of commercial concern because we may find many new molecules."

Another unlikely spot to find researchers at work on fundamental questions is the New York Aquarium, just off the boardwalk at Coney Island. Few visitors would guess that behind the glass tanks of beautiful or amusing sea creatures progress is being made toward better understanding of heart and kidney diseases, cancer, mental illness, and viral and bacterial infections. The New York Aquarium leads the public aquariums of the world in its contributions to scientific knowledge, its staff having published some 283 scientific papers and 136 abstracts. The director of the Aquarium's Laboratory of Marine Biochemistry and Ecology, Dr. Ross F. Nigrelli, is a comparative pathologist and a past president of the New York Academy of Sciences. He may be found somewhere roughly in the area below the shark tank. His book-lined, triangular office is wedged behind a laboratory at the end of a subterranean passage.

On the day that he was interviewed, Dr. Nigrelli was upset over the loss of Ookie, the playful walrus, which had died that morning of a tusk infection. An autopsy was being performed by doctors at Beth Israel Hospital. Nigrelli was also in the midst of checking page proofs of a booklet for science students, and his office was a clutter of papers, pipes for smoking, and laboratory specimens. We left all that for a quick tour of his domain, which included a stop at a tank inhabited by prickly-looking sea urchins.

Here Nigrelli explained, "In testing drugs we use sea-urchin eggs because the fertilization cycle is well known and results are available within forty-eight hours. We introduce various substances into the water, then watch what happens to the eggs. The substances are effective in amounts so small that it staggers the imagination. The eggs may be stimulated to develop without fertilization—what is known as parthenogenesis. Or there may be deviations in cell division, with results similar to those that the much-publicized drug thalidomide had on the human fetus. We could have told them about thalidomide very quickly, had we tested it on sea-urchin eggs."

Since fish suffer from cancer no different from the forms occurring in man, the Aquarium staff is making tissue cultures of fish cancer cells. Fish also have virus infections, tuberculosis, even cirrhosis of the liver. As at Haskins Laboratories, marine plants and animals and plant-animals are being used as "laboratory assistants." One project has to do with a Mediterranean sea worm called Bonellia, the female of which produces a very powerful hormone. This hormone changes all Bonellia larvae that come in contact with it into males.

Preliminary studies have shown that this water-soluble hormone can also affect the development of eggs in totally unrelated creatures. Its chemical structure is being studied with the idea of testing it on cancer cells.

When Aquarium scientists go on expeditions, some of their work is done on the island of Bimini in the Bahamas, at the American Museum of Natural History's Lerner Marine Laboratory. Founded in 1948 by Michael Lerner, a big-game fisherman who formerly headed a chain of women's apparel shops, this Inner Space exploration station has come up with an extremely potent antibiotic which they are now testing further. The Lerner Laboratory, directed by Dr. Robert F. Mathewson, is in a very good location adjoining the Gulf Stream, where more than twenty "sea terraines" meet. In large outdoor pens, marine species are studied by means of underwater television, and much information, some of it valuable to the armed forces, is being collected. Co-operating in many projects is the nearby Institute of Marine Science at the University of Miami, a graduate school for training oceanographers.

At the New York Aquarium, most of the research materials are collected in the ocean off Coney Island by volunteer skin-diving laymen. One chilly November day while I talked with Nigrelli, two barefooted young men, wearing black rubber "wet suits" to protect them from the cold, brought him several bucketsful of strange-looking creatures. These hauls have yielded Long Island sponges which showed antibiotic activity.

Some of the most interesting work at the Aquarium is concerned with sea cucumbers, which produce a toxic substance called holothurin. For centuries, Pacific Islanders have used this to kill fish. Nigrelli said, "We have injected holothurin into malignant tumors that normally would kill mice in twelve days and the mice live out their life spans. The

spread of the growth is arrested. Our problem is learning
the chemistry of holothurin so that it can be purified and
modified to make it less poisonous, while still retaining and
intensifying its anticancer properties." Holothurin, which
works somewhat like Digitalis from the land plant foxglove,
may prove useful in treating heart disease. Because it acts as
a nerve-blocking agent, it may also help to relieve the pain
suffered by amputees as a result of severed nerves.

A number of new drugs from the sea are currently being
employed in the treatment of human patients, but the physicians who are conducting these clinical trials are not yet
ready to release their findings. However, for some time doctors in Japan have been using the drug tetrodotoxin, a numbing chemical from poisonous puffer fish, to ease the terminal
stages of cancer. It seems to work faster and to do a better
job than most anesthetics in general use for that purpose. It
is also helpful in relaxing muscular spasms. Other diseases
have been reported as responding to carefully controlled dosages of tetrodotoxin—carefully controlled because this substance is the second most powerful biotoxin known, surpassed
only by that which causes botulism from faulty canning
methods.

One of the strangest of all poisons in the sea is the one
connected with ichthyosarcotoxism. This jaw-breaker means
fish-flesh poisoning, which comes after eating certain fish.
Bruce W. Halstead, the skin-diving physician who is director
of the World Life Research Institute of Colton, California, is
considered by many of his colleagues to be the foremost
authority on poisonous fish. In discussing his specialty, marine biotoxicology, Dr. Halstead recalled observing many
cases of fish-flesh poisoning, which produces symptoms entirely different from any others known to medical science.
The victim feels as if his teeth are loose and he experiences
a weird reversal of sensations. There is no known specific anti-

dote or antitoxin for this poisoning, and recovery from one attack does not confer immunity to another. It is a form of poisoning quite different from that which comes from eating spoiled, contaminated fish or from being stung by venomous ones.

An interesting case occurred during fleet maneuvers off the Virgin Islands, when twenty members of the officers' mess feasted on one of two large amberjacks, which are usually considered good to eat. These two were caught the same day and seemed to be identical in every respect, except that one was poisonous and the other was not. The latter was eaten by the crew with no ill effects.

The amberjack served to the officers was broiled for twenty minutes and then baked in the oven for almost three hours. The men ate heartily, some of them commenting on the unusually fine flavor. But shortly after this noon meal, all but one diner became acutely ill. First a peculiar tingling, then a numbness crept over them. This was followed by violent headaches, dizziness, weakness, and aching of the arms and legs. When they drank cold water, it burned their mouths like fury; urinating was sheer agony. Fortunately, all of these men recovered, but it was slow going and the mixed-up hot and cold sensations hung on for weeks, as they blew on their ice cream to "cool it off" and complained that steaming cups of coffee were too icy to drink.

In other similar attacks, an Air Force captain on Tarawa nearly died after eating seven pieces of red snapper fresh from the sea, two Filipino workers on a Saipan construction crew died after eating black moray eel, and the same fate befell a Navy man at Kwajalein.

Why this poison should occur only in some of these normally edible food fish, and only in certain areas of tropical seas, has long been a puzzle to ichthyologists. Researchers such as Halstead, who has led many expeditions to the South

Pacific in search of a solution, and Dr. Albert H. Banner, director of the Marine Laboratory at the University of Hawaii, are convinced that a "food-chain" is involved and that the most likely suspects are poisonous algae, (one reason for including "animals" in this chapter along with plants.) Red snappers, barracuda, sea bass, and amberjack do not feed on algae; they eat only other fish. But some of these "other fish" which form their diet do graze in beds of algae. How much they graze is almost unbelievable: it has been estimated that a pound of codfish represents 100,000 pounds of phytoplankton eaten! Toxins from poisonous algae are transmitted to the larger fish, with neither the smaller fish-carriers nor the predators harmed in the process. But when humans become involved in the food chain, the results may be fatal to them. A well-known and documented example is the seasonal "poisoning" of the edible black mussel, *Mytilus edulis,* by a dinoflagellate.

In addition to the strange reversal of hot and cold sensations, algae and fish toxins cause many other hallucinations or delusions. Halstead has obtained from a fish a hallucinogen which could have military applications. The drug has what he calls a "built-in surrender quotient," in that the victim goes into a profound depression and for about twelve hours is convinced that death is imminent. There is an aftermath of memories that are quite terrifying. He hopes that drugs of this type can be used constructively in the study of mental illness.

In Japan special restaurants serve the flesh of fugu, a very toxic puffer. When properly prepared by trained fugu cooks, who carefully remove the poisonous parts—the liver, skin, and gall bladder—this dangerous delicacy gives the diners a sensational meal. They experience a feeling of well-being and seem to be floating on air. As Halstead put it, "Some of them are literally sent 'out of this world.'" Natives in the South Pacific seek a similar effect by eating certain goat fish which give them fantastic nightmares. Scientists have now catalogued more than 300 kinds of poisonous fish from the deep. These powerful agents must be useful somewhere, somehow in medicine—the problem is to find out where and how.

Halstead has discovered some clues: In the poisonous weever fish and the equally venomous stonefish, he has noted anticoagulant action on blood. The poison of the sting ray slows heart action. Toadfish venom burns up sugar in the blood and may eventually have some application in diabetes.

Other promising work is being done elsewhere:

—Scottish doctors report that brown and red seaweeds produce anticoagulant action which seems as good as or better than that of heparin obtained from animal tissues. Furthermore, the effect can be stopped immediately by the injection of another drug.

—Researchers in Venezuela are experimenting with pond scum as a possible therapeutic addition to the diet of lepers.

—At the National Institutes of Health, Dr. C. P. Li and his associates have isolated from abalone and oysters an extract they call paolin. Animal experimentation shows paolin to be one of the rare agents known to inhibit polio virus.

—Drs. E. S. Beneke and Y. Lingyappa, University of Michigan, have found that a certain water mold is an excellent test object for potential anticancer drugs.

—Serotonin, found in the blood, brain, and certain tumors in man, is known to be abundant in clams, octopus, jellyfish, and many other marine invertebrates. Dr. Irvine H. Page, of Cleveland, one of the pioneer investigators in this field, has stated, "Serotonin may well become a capital clue to the biochemistry of sanity and insanity."

—Murex, a substance extracted from snails, acts very much like curare, the arrow poison useful in surgery as a muscle relaxant and in electroshock treatments of the mentally ill.

While almost in a science-fiction category, these phenomena are nevertheless being scrutinized by scientists with the idea of putting them to use in future space travel. Some researchers believe that when expeditions to distant worlds become commonplace, there will be a need for drugs that will relieve boredom or prevent conflict between passengers and crew. These emotional hazards could be greatly minimized if soothing sensations and pleasant dreams were induced by means of drugs—and these drugs may well come from the sea.

Finally, problems of food and oxygen replenishment in space may also be solved by using marine plants. At the School of Aerospace Medicine in San Antonio, Texas, experiments with algae and mice are being conducted to develop a system whereby astronauts could live in a sealed cabin indefinitely. Recently, four brown mice—Hickory, Dickory, Dock, and Sock—were placed inside a small, airtight "space cabin" that also contained algae of the type found in green pond scums. The mice were able to live very comfortably: all the oxygen they needed was provided by the algae, and the carbon dioxide exhaled by them was in turn used by the algae in their life process, thus completing the cycle.

Scientists themselves have also spent many hours in sealed capsules breathing no other oxygen than that released by algae. (In a United States Navy project at the University of California, work is being done to adapt algal cultures to control the oxygen and carbon dioxide in atomic submarines.) It is calculated that in future spaceships each man will require about forty-five gallons of water containing twenty-five pounds of algae. This will yield not only the oxygen required, but over a pound of food a day. While efforts to convert algae into mouth-watering planktonburgers have not proved too successful—it looks unappetizing and tastes like hay, with fishy overtones—biochemists of the Boeing Aircraft Company in Seattle, Washington, have somewhat improved palatability and appearance by blanching the algae under fluorescent lights. (Of course, the Japanese cuisine makes extensive use of marine

400

algae in soups and other dishes.) When future space stations are established on the moon, Venus, Mars, and other planets, algal gardens may be the primary means of raising food where there is none to be had useful to earthlings.

Many scientists believe that life began in the sea. And they agree that what we have learned so far is "just a drop in the ocean" compared with the unexplored potential still locked in the world's briny depths. As mankind reaches out toward space, drugs from primitive marine organisms could be key factors for maintenance of life. Man's curiosity about the universe and his need to survive in it are causing him to return to the very seas from which he himself may have evolved.

The World-wide Search Continues[*]

JUST AS THERE IS THE FLYING DUTCHMAN LEGEND, there is the Flying Finn of Pharmacognosy—Finn Sandberg, M.D., of Sweden—a symbol of good will rather than ill omen as he jets around the world in his capacity as advisor to the United Nations Economic and Social Council (UNESCO). This robust, happily energetic physician-pharmacognosist is not alone in his globe-trotting, of course, but he is probably the outstanding cosmopolitan catalyst in the complex field of botanical drug research.

An enthusiastic supporter of the (actually, international) American Society of Pharmacognosy, he may well be its most versatile member: first, a botanist, then, a pharmacologist, a phytochemist, and now a professor at the Pharmaceutical Institute in Stockholm, where one of his specialities is gynecology. Dr. Sandberg's winters are usually spent in the laboratories and clinics there, but his summers are filled with explorations and research consultations in many countries.

[*] The author is continuing to collect information on botanical drug research throughout the world for a book dealing with countries other than the United States. It will be an expansion of this chapter, which focuses largely upon less industrialized areas; but it will also include more detailed information on the outstanding work being done in England, Europe, Japan, etc., which could not be fully covered here.

For example, in June, 1962, after being the featured speaker at the ASP annual meeting at the University of West Virginia, he went to Central Africa via United Nations headquarters in New York and Paris; then, back to Sweden, followed by a dash over to Prague, Czechoslovakia, to attend the Second International Symposium on the Chemistry of Natural Products. He had been to similar meetings in Kuala Lumpur, Malaya, Canberra, Australia, and Hong Kong within the past few years.

Several summers ago, he was in the South Seas, following almost two centuries in the wake of Captain Cook's good ship *Resolution*. He wanted to investigate *Piper methysticum,* a fascinating member of the pepper family used to prepare a drink called Kawa Kawa. This drug plant was first scientifically described by a father and son team of botanists named Forrester who accompanied Cook on his second voyage in 1776. Both Sandberg and Cook's men were welcomed in the same way by the natives of Fiji: they were given a coconut shell filled with a strange greyish-brown liquid with a faint lilac odor—Kawa. At first it tasted pungent and rather soapy, but next came a fresh feeling in the mouth lasting several hours. Even the Islanders did not relish the taste for they made faces and shivered as they drank it. What they sought was its strange narcotic effect, unlike any other. A small quantity made everyone relaxed and friendly, but for those who took too much, Kawa became a Polynesian Mickey Finn! This substance has been called the most powerful soporific in existence —a wineglassful can produce within half an hour a profound, dreamless sleep with no morning-after grogginess. In contrast to alcohol, the drug does not impair mental alertness; it is a spinal rather than a cerebral depressant and apparently no ill-effects have resulted from moderate amounts. But if imbibed too freely and too frequently, strong Kawa can cause scaly ulcerations of the skin, eye troubles, and an alarming weight loss.

Sandberg was particularly interested in the fact that these

reactions were most common in areas where the fresh, undried rootstock of the plant was consumed in a drink prepared in the "old-fashioned way." This is a most peculiar procedure in which the beauty of young maidens, selected for their rosy lips and white teeth, is supposed to counteract the unappetizing method of making the brew. The chosen girls (always unmarried) wear hibiscus flowers tucked in their long, dark hair, but little else, as they sit in groups of four or five around ornately carved wooden bowls with piles of the snarled roots beside them. They are obliged to chew these into a soft mass, taking care not to swallow in the process. The quids are deposited in the bowls and stirred by hand until the liquid portion takes on the appearance of milky soap suds, which is then strained through a sieve made of narrow strips of bark before being passed around in a communal cup to the guests. Because it tends to destroy the teeth of the industrious chewers, this traditional method of producing Kawa is being abandoned. But it has not seemed to be a source of infection, despite its unhygienic manufacture; possibly it contains a self-purifying or antibiotic property. In the modern method of preparation, the roots are pounded between two stones, rather than masticated by virgins. This is said to produce a far less potent drink and one actually quite different in its action.

Since *P. methysticum* was first investigated chemically in the 1850's, at least eleven compounds have been isolated from it and several have been synthesized. Riker scientists M. W. Klohs, F. Keller, G. E. Cronheim, et al, have published a number of reports; the most recent cited the results of clinical trials (*Lloydia,* March, 1963). One of the botanical's constituents, dihydromethysticin, while ineffective in treating schizophrenia, did appear to be active as a mild tranquilizer of the Miltown type. Much of the biological evidence collected to date seems to be highly contradictory. As Dr. Norman Farnsworth (who, with his colleagues at the University of Pittsburgh, has also studied the plant) summed up the situation: "Perhaps the most potent ingredient is still unknown." The question that intrigues Dr. Sandberg, as a specialist in female endocrinology, is this: must a certified maiden chew the roots to insure maximum drug potency? Could there be transitory "virginal" hormones or unique salivary enzymes involved? Is fermentation chemistry a factor? Or is it just the moon of Monakoura that adds that special something?

Finn Sandberg's field experiences are not always so delightful. Much of the time he is deeply involved with the miseries of people in less-favored, more turbulent parts of the world. For instance, he wrote that during the summer of 1962–63, he "visited the Central African Republic and the Republic Congo /Brazzaville, where I collected each year about 120 species of plants used in folklore medicine for screening by the Swedish pharmaceutical industry. Out in the savanna there is an absolute lack of comfort, of course, but I had wonderful practical daily help from Swedish missionaries. The French botanist B. Descoings, who has surveyed medicinal plants in another part of the former French Congo, assisted with the botanical identification. The Brazzaville Institut de Recherches Scientifiques au Congo is doing important work on the ethnographical aspects of plants of the area. And Abbé André Walker in Libreville has published a survey of medicinal plants in Gabon. All this despite obvious difficulties."

In small countries, such as those in Africa, college graduates may number from two to a dozen—an almost impossible situation for establishing research projects for any purpose unless there is outside help. One co-operative effort a short distance from Bukavu in Kivu Province, a thousand miles east of Léopoldville, is the Central African Institute for Scientific Research. Belgian institutions pay the staff, and the Congolese government pays the 250 workers, but it seems almost a day to day existence.

Africa is typical of the countries where only a trickle of modern medicines reach the inhabitants outside of the larger cities, and even in these the few pharmacies are precariously barren. The diseases, on the other hand, are rampant and devastating. There are no large pharmaceutical manufacturers operating anywhere near the areas of greatest need in Africa, and often the local drug plants of proved scientific value are collected in quantity mostly for export, as is the case with Rauwolfia, Strophanthus seeds, Calabar beans, and Cola nuts. As for cultivation, about 1,500 tons of Cinchona bark are said to be harvested a year in Burundi (formerly, Ruanda-Urundi), but this is almost the only botanical drug crop destined for consumption by the natives. Papain is grown to be swapped for finished foreign goods. Dr. W. J. Peal at Makere College, Kampala, Uganda, is currently concentrating on cultivation problems of yams used as hormone starting materials, but here again the goal is primarily a crop for export.

The natives must depend upon roots, barks, and herbs sold in crude drug markets in the villages or gathered as needed in outlying districts. Some of these may be efficacious remedies, but scientific investigation of the pharmaceutical possibilities in the great, green "physic garden" that is Africa is in its infancy. Authorities agree that there are probably only one or two competent botanical collectors in the whole of East Africa, for instance. And the most distinguished, Dr. Peter J. Greenway of Nairobi, is in semi-retirement.

From Tananarive, Dr. R. Pernet has written: "Madagascar (Malagasy) is magnificently situated from the botanical point of view: it has 10,000 different species of which almost 6,000 are endemic. On the other hand, chemical research, already begun in the nineteenth century, has only taken wing very recently." A 1957 book by Pernet summarized previous research on this flora, which includes such medically important plants as species of Vinca used in cancer therapy. From an old Madagascarian folk remedy for sores, made from the plant

Centella asiatica, the substance asiaticoside has been obtained. Sandberg reports that this is useful in treating leprosy lesions.

Pernet may well be speaking for other scientists in far-flung laboratories when he says, "My ideas for the future are very precise and ambitious but unfortunately, it depends only on me to see them realized. . . . I would like to see the creation of a vast ensemble of phytochemical and pharmacological research encompassing the whole country—but man proposes and God disposes, as we say. . . ."

It is possible, however, to leave Africa on a note of hope that within the next few years useful new botanical drugs may be developed and mass produced. In 1957, Dr. Robert Raffauf of Smith Kline & French in Philadelphia, arranged a long-term co-operative program with the Council for Scientific and Industrial Research, a unit of the South African government. Botanical collections are underwritten in all parts of the Republic from Northern Transvaal to the Cape Province. The Council makes preliminary checks for active substances, then crude extracts of the promising ones are shipped to the Pennsylvania laboratories for evaluation. The time between lab screening and availability of a new medicine has been estimated at about five years. In addition to turning up possible treatments for some of the scourges that ravish this land, African students are being brought to the United States for intensive scientific training so that they can return home and make the most of the natural products available. Similar programs are underway in East Africa, Brazil,* and Australia.

In a unique co-operative effort of a few years ago, the

---

* Since 1959, the Rockefeller Foundation has helped subsidize the training of Brazilian graduate students in the field of natural products, with grants totaling $235,000. The program is directed by Stanford Chemistry Professor Carl Djerassi, working in co-operation with Dr. Walter Mors, at the University of Brazil in Rio de Janeiro. In addition to training students, botanicals are being collected and analyzed, according to Dr. Robert B. Watson, of the Rockefeller Foundation's Medical and Natural Sciences Division.

Government of the Federation of Malaya and the University and Botanic Garden of Singapore worked with Smith Kline & French on a survey of the flora of the Malayan Peninsula. Almost a thousand species were collected, many of them having a history of native use as medicine or poison; the aborigines were invaluable in this phase of the work. Later, Dr. A. K. Kiang of Singapore worked with Dr. Bryce Douglas of the American company on the laboratory follow-up. Douglas spent two years as a Visiting Research Associate in the Chemistry Department at the University, lecturing to advanced students and scientific societies. He also was technical secretary of the 1957 Symposium on Phytochemistry, sponsored by the Malayan government and UNESCO, and attended by delegates from nine Southeast Asian countries. The Malayan project was the beginning of a systematic survey that received much stimulation from the outstanding work done in neighboring countries by Drs. L. J. Webb in Australia and Papua-New Guinea, H. R. Arthur in Hong Kong, and N. Bisset in South Moluccas.

In talking with Douglas about the international aspects of his work, one gets the impression that here is a modest servant of science who happens to wear a Madison Avenue suit. But along with the combination of ivory tower intellectualism and big business, there seems to be an aura of the inscrutable East when he is asked for specific details. With a positively Oriental smile, he alludes to preliminary findings as "rather interesting."

Of all the areas in the world where commercial firms search for plants, there is the greatest reluctance to speak of ventures in Australia; but academic sources and scientists employed by not-yet-involved companies have agreed that this continent, almost as large as the United States, is a "hot bed" of botanical exploration, with drug hunters from many countries plucking their way through the bush, almost leaf by leaf.

There are sound reasons for this extraordinary interest: one of the big botanical success stories of recent years came out of Australia, and while its unique flora has been studied by systematic botanists, the medicinal potential is still virtually unknown. Prior to World War II, Australia imported all of its drugs from England or America, but when Japan cut off its life-line, it had to search "out back" for native plant substitutes. The Council for Scientific and Industrial Research (CSIR) co-operated with the Universities of Sydney and Melbourne on this investigation. As one result, Australia became almost overnight the world's leading supplier of two important drugs, scopolamine and hyoscyamine, formerly obtained entirely from European belladonna and Egyptian henbane. These medications proved indispensable in keeping invasion troops from becoming seasick in the landing barges, and in treating certain types of "bomb shock," as well as many other conditions requiring muscular relaxation and sedation.

The new source of the narcotic alkaloids was the genus Duboisia, which grows only in Australia and has three species. The two most important, *D. myoporoides* and *D. leichardtii,* supply the present commercial quantities of the drug, which is extracted from the leaves of trees growing in wild stands mostly on the east coast. However, Duboisia is being cultivated experimentally and seeds have been sent to other countries. Because the plant has a scattered natural distribution in Australia, it is expected that it will ultimately grow elsewhere. The third species, a scrubby desert tree, *D. hopwoodi,* has been prized by the aborigines for centuries. The leaves, which contain nicotine, but little of the other alkaloids, are chewed for their stimulating effect. When the natives tire of chewing, they park their quid behind their ears just as some of their primitive counterparts do in our bubble gum set. Like the betel-nut chewers in India and the coca-chewing Andean Indians, they mix ashes with the plant leaves to increase the drug's potency, causing one to wonder how they all hit upon this trick in such widely separated parts of the globe.

When Australian natives have trouble bagging enough game with their boomerangs, they use Duboisia to poison the water holes of animals such as the emu. The government currently is very much interested in investigating other toxic plants—they, too, may have medicinal application. Dr. J. R. Price of Melbourne, who directs the CSIR Division of Organic Chemistry, has supervised much of this work.

A second new drug to come out of Australia since World War II is rutin, derived from Eucalyptus, the genus that produces the tallest trees known—some actually reach the incredible height of 480 feet. The leaves of the blue gum, *E. globulus,* have long been a source of pungent Eucalyptus oil, so helpful in clearing stuffy noses. But it is another variety, *E. macrorryncha,* that gives us rutin for strengthening capillaries. Leakage through these one-cell thick walls can be dangerous, especially in the brains of older persons, so, to guard against fragility in vital blood vessels, rutin is frequently prescribed along with a diet high in vitamin C. Less important rutin sources have been buckwheat and buds of *Saphora japonica,* native to China.

While a good many drug plant investigators headed "down under" to see what else might be discovered, one of the experts in this field, Dr. Douglas E. White, of the University of Western Australia, traveled in the opposite direction to Bangkok to teach organic chemistry for a year under the auspices of the Southeast Asian Treaty Organization, SEATO's activities not being strictly confined to matters militaire. Commenting on the Australian situation, Dr. White wrote, "We still have a long way to go before we have looked at all of our native plants, and even then there will be plenty of unsolved problems. After that we can turn to studies of plant metabolism. We need to increase the tempo of botanical work just to keep up with the removal of our flora in the interest of expanding agriculture. There may not be anything in the future to equal Duboisia, but who can tell?"

Traveling northward from Australia, one passes through the islands of Indonesia, scattered like pieces of a jade necklace. In the days when two of these were called Sumatra and Java, they were focal points for the cultivation of such plants as Cinchona for quinine. The Dutch botanists, who started these profitable plantings and founded botanic gardens in the interest of science, were unrivaled in their knowledge of tropical agriculture; but the rise of nationalism drove out many skilled Europeans just when their abilities were most sorely needed to rebuild war-ravaged plantations. A sad situation, but, in the case of Dr. A. J. G. H. Kostermans of Bogor, not without its wryly humorous aspects. When he was faced with ejection from his post as keeper of the herbarium in the famous botanical garden Kebun Raya (formerly, Buitensorg) someone came up with an acceptable solution—he could stay, but henceforth he is to be known by the strictly Indonesian name of "Achmed Amir Daeng Matarang."

The island hopping Dutch botanist Rumphius, who examined the folk use of more than 700 species of East Indian plants in the eighteenth century, probably had no such problem as he went about verifying "fables, superstitions and old women's babblings." He explained that "in these faery tales always some grain of truth, some unseen natural virtue lies hidden . . . and to excite amateurs to diligent search, I assure them that in these lands many secrets of nature are revealed daily, erstwhile unknown to Europeans and seemingly unworthy of belief."

Today, after crossing the South China Sea and reaching Hong Kong, diligent searchers are brought to a full stop, whether they are "excited amateurs" or experienced professionals like Dr. Sandberg, who told me, "I was invited to go to Mainland China to confer with scientists in 1961, and I applied for a visa. Then the visa was suddenly denied."

What happens behind the Bamboo Curtain is far more

mysterious than life behind the Iron Curtain. There are no co-operative exchange agreements, for instance, such as those made in 1959 between American and Soviet scientists who have been working together on cancer, polio, and heart disease projects. According to a leading authority in the United States Department of Agriculture, "We exchange botanical research material with the Russians on an eye-for-an-eye basis and they often send representatives to international meetings to report their research findings. They also explore for plants in other countries. But we have no official exchange of communications or material with Red China and I know nothing of their activities with respect to medicinal plants."

The estimated population of China exceeds 700,000,000, according to the Population Reference Bureau. One out of every five persons in the world is Chinese, but the actual living and dying conditions of these people have always been an enigma. Dr. Charles H. La Wall wrote in his encyclopedic survey, *4,000 Years of Pharmacy:* "We know less about the pharmacy of ancient China than we do of that of either the Egyptians or Babylonians . . . because there has been less research into the ancient literature of this living nation than into the literature of races that have disappeared."

There are many indications that the Mainland Chinese today are feverishly searching through these ancient documents for clues in the treatment of malaria, tuberculosis, leprosy, parasites, diseases of the eye like trachoma, and vitamin and protein deficiencies. Not long ago, the prohibition against birth control was reversed, so investigations of hormonal starting materials on the order of the Mexican yams are probably underway, as they are in Russia, certain informed sources have told me.

The first Chinese herbalist is said to have been Emperor Shen Nung, who recorded his observations of 365 drugs around 2800 B.C., later published as the *Pen Ts'ao Ching* in the golden age of Chinese medicine, 206 B.C. to 220 A.D. This was revised many times down through the centuries. A biography of the most famous revisionist, titled, *Li Shih-chen—Great Pharmacologist of Ancient China,* was published in Peking in 1960. The editor's preface states: "In the past ten years, the people's government of China has begun paying particular attention to the centuries-old Chinese art of healing and has called upon the medical profession to study and develop this art. In this development, Li Shih-chen's work has a special significance. . . . He was the author of the most important medical work of ancient China, *The Compendium of Materia Medica,* a summing up of the pharmacological knowledge accumulated in the two thousand years before his time, but also the prototype of the science of plant morphology. In his book we see clearly that his methods of observing and experimenting with drugs, biologically and chemically, are very similar to methods used in modern science."

Li Shih-chen was born in the middle period of the Ming dynasty near Chichow, in what is now Hupeh province in the central Yangtse basin. The son and grandson of physicians and a medical doctor himself, he devoted his life (1518–1593 A.D.), to correcting and supplementing the medical lore in 1,000 old documents, Shen Nung's among them. His beautifully illustrated treatise was continually revised as he struggled to compress some ten million words into one million, at the same time discarding remedies that he found to be worthless and adding hundreds of new ones. The appendix of this monumental work (52 volumes) contains 10,000 prescriptions!

He collected these wherever he went, noting them down on the spot with his brush pen. When he treated a patient, he preferred to be paid with a home remedy formula, saying that any therapy that had stood the test of time among the people was "worth more than a hundred taels of gold." Although he studied at the Imperial Academy of Medicine in Peking, he felt that the peasants were his best teachers. Once, while crossing a windswept mountain pass, he asked why the heavily burdened porters were boiling pink-flowered bindweed.

"We are prone to muscular injury," they explained. "This is an ancient secret remedy of our ancestors. We eat it and it protects us from these injuries." (Perhaps there is a "Project Bindweed" underway in some Chinese laboratory today.)

Li Shih-chen never enjoyed official approval during his lifetime because he was always out of step with the current vogue in medicine. When the alchemists were favored by the court, he bravely attacked their reliance upon cure-alls compounded from arsenic, lead, and tin, branding them dangerous and superstitious. The emperor went on consuming "Ninth Incarnation Pills" and such, anyway, until they were the death of him. Then, his avenging son banished the alchemists; doctors were not even permitted to discuss how to make saltpeter. This was going too far in the other direction to suit Li Shih-chen, who pointed out that the alchemist quacks had hit upon some valid therapies such as calomel, and mercury and lard ointment for certain skin diseases.

It was not enough to study all the available books, collect folklore medicines and utilize the laboratory techniques of the chemists of the day—Li Shih-chen believed that "One must also use one's eyes, ears and brain, do one's best to make direct observations of nature." A true pharmacognosist in every sense, he collected and identified many thousands of rare botanical specimens, using some of these to start herb gardens. Later, he conducted experiments with the drugs he compounded. His cures are still recounted today—how he saved scores of dying dysentery victims with light doses of the poisonous croton-oil bean, for instance.

In 1590, the first edition of his work (fifty copies) was printed in Nanking by using engraved wood blocks. Copies of this still exist in good condition, according to the 1960 biography. Repeated printings and hand copyings have been made in the 370 years since his death. Today, his work is considered a standard reference for both medical practice and basic research in his country. Li Shih-chen, as the subject of a popular paperback book, is one pharmacognosist who may be said to rank as a national hero!

The classical Chinese materia medica contains around 1,500 drugs of vegetable origin and 500 or so of animal and mineral composition. An estimated 75 per cent of our plant drugs originated in China. One of the best known of these is Ma Huang, meaning yellow astringent, a mixture of several species of the genus Ephedra. This shrub was listed in the Chinese dispensatory of 1569 as a valuable remedy to produce sweating in fevers, and as a circulatory stimulant and cough sedative— but it was also used for thousands of years for many other ailments. While particularly associated with the Orient, Ephedra long has been popular in Russia for treating respiratory diseases and rheumatism; and, American Indians made "squaw tea" from a species whose scientific name denotes the condition for which it was used, *E. anti-syphilitica.*

From earliest times, the herb was always collected in late autumn. Modern studies confirmed the wisdom of this practice by showing that the alkaloid content reaches its maximum just before the frosts. Not until 1887 was the alkaloid ephedrine obtained in pure form by the Japanese chemist N. Nagai. In 1923, Dr. K. K. Chen of Eli Lilly and his co-workers introduced the drug to Occidental medicine, reporting in a series of studies that are classics on its cardio-vascular effects, its similarity to the body's epinephrine (adrenalin), and its absorption from the intestinal tract. The drug may now be injected and applied to the mucous membranes, as in nasal inhalers, as well as taken orally. It is a decongestant, a central nervous system stimulant, an aid in eye examinations, and a standby in asthma therapy, to cite a few uses. In America, commercial supplies are largely synthetic, but in many other countries the green growing shrub is still the most important—or the only—chemical factory.

In such vast areas as China, the cost of manufacturing man-made drugs is too great, the people too isolated and poor, to sustain pharmaceutical production and distribution as we know it. Another reason for reliance upon herbal remedies is the extreme shortage of well-trained physicians. There is said to be only one medical doctor for every 10,000 Chinese, so the Communists emphasize the need for close co-operation between graduate physicians and village healers.

Not long ago, an issue of the *Peking Review* told of the revival of an ancient herb center, Changsuchen, in South China, where secret recipes for the extraction of curatives from poisonous plants are being translated into modern terms and disseminated by the government. Dr. Sandberg planned to visit the Institute of Materia Medica of the Academica Sinica in Shanghai, and other leading scientific centers in Nanking and Nanning, where old cures such as the fruits of *Brucea javanica* for amoebic dysentery have proved to be effective and economical. These fruits are also used to treat various types of malaria: "tertian—95 per cent cured, quartan—78 per cent cured, and malignant—46 per cent cured," according to a report received by Sandberg, who said that Brucea compares favorably with the synthetics atabrine and plasmoquine.

Some aspects of traditional Chinese medicine have a long way to go before even all the Chinese doctors will accept their merits: coffin fungus for tuberculosis, dried seahorses for glandular disorders, deer tails for kidney disease, to name a few. One of the basic tenets of herbal practice the world over is the doctrine of signatures, which originated in China, spread to Europe during the Middle Ages, and was popularized by Paracelsus. This theory holds that for every ailment, there is a specific plant remedy—the clues being found in the shape, color, taste, or other physical characteristic of the botanical. Many common plant names hark back to these early uses, such as the red juice of the blood root for anemia. Heart-shaped leaves indicated value in heart disease, yellow flowers were prescribed for jaundice, quaking aspen for palsy, and so forth.

At least one of these quaint beliefs had a fragment of truth in it. Willow bark tea was taken for stiff joints and rheumatic pains because the willow was so supple and graceful. The most widely used synthetic drug today is aspirin, a specific for these conditions by modern standards. Its chemical structure was based upon salicylic acid, a substance related to extracts of willow bark.

The best source of information on Chinese botanicals is probably Harvard's Arnold Arboretum and Gray Herbarium, containing the world's largest collection of living and preserved Oriental specimens. Here, Dr. Lily M. Perry, a pleasant, energetic woman, is completing a definitive study of the medicinal uses of the plants of Red China, Vietnam, Burma, Thailand, Malaya, Indonesia, New Guinea, the Solomon Islands, the Philippines, Japan, and overlapping areas.

"The literature of this folk medicine," Dr. Perry explained, "is widely scattered in the journals of travelers, botanists' field notes, and documents in many languages. By translating and analyzing these, we hope to find a *pattern of consistency* in the use of plants from different geographical areas. Highlighting the most important ones should help medical investigators in their search for new curatives."

As an amusing though frustrating sidelight, Dr. Perry found that when some early botanical collectors, unfamiliar with the native language, asked the name of a plant, the answer in the local dialect was the equivalent of "I don't know . . . No comprendo . . . Je ne sais pas . . .," which was then dutifully recorded as the common name of the botanical! Despite such obstacles, she and her assistants have worked their way through a bibliography of 1,500 references, including textbooks and research reports published by Red China for the guidance of its own scientists. These sources indicate that very good work is being done there, not only in re-evaluating folk remedies, but also in correcting errors in basic botany.

"In fact," Dr. Perry said, "They are way ahead of us!"

It was intriguing to learn that the number one botanical drug cited in current Chinese medical books is ginseng, a species of which, *Panax quinquefolium,* grows wild in the United States and Canada. But our entire supply of the root is promptly exported. We have no use for the drug, yet an emperor once paid $10,000 for a single, perfectly formed root. (The stems and leaves are not used in medicine.) *Jin-Chen,* the Chinese name for ginseng, means "man-like," referring to the shape of the underground part which resembles a root doll, a whole body with arms, legs and head. Harking back to the doctrine of signatures, it is supposed to be good for everything that ails you. The generic name, Panax, is derived from the same word source as panacea, for this reason.

In Chinese medicine, the root is taken as a preventive as well as a cure, to preserve strength and vigor and "to stay young." Family doctors are supposedly paid to keep their patients well in China; if someone in their care falls ill, they have failed, and they are not paid anything until the patient is on his feet again. This calls for a high consumption of ginseng! Obviously, the highly prized variety Panax Schin-seng from northern Asia, must be reserved for special cases and the millions of others have to make do with poorer quality roots. Wild-growing varieties are always preferred to any cultivated ones. As a matter of fact, the plant is very difficult to grow because it requires practically virgin soil and is prone to disease. Nevertheless, many promotional brochures on how to make a fortune raising ginseng have been sold to prospective farmers— a rewarding business for the publishers of these tracts, at least.

Wild "Seng" digging has been a profitable sideline among hunters and mountain dwellers, especially in the Ozark and Blue Ridge country, for generations. Father Jartoux, a Jesuit who had been in China, started the ginseng export business in 1679, after he noticed American Indians employing it as a medication. Following this lead to the source, he began shipping the botanical down the St. Lawrence to England, where the East India Company sent it around the Cape of Good Hope and on to the Orient. The first American ship went to Canton in 1784, no doubt with some ginseng aboard. All this was long before another botanical, the narcotic poppy *Papaver somniferum,* was credited with really opening up the China trade as a result of the infamous Opium War of 1839.

Ginseng today is not considered a commercially important drug plant, although it is the most expensive one listed in suppliers' catalogues.* Its market price, as this is written, hovers around thirty dollars a pound, but a relatively small amount of the American root is available for trading. Eager purchasers abroad have little competition in this country: there is a marked absence of interest in ginseng among botanical drug investigators here. The feeling seems to be that "cure-alls . . . cure nothing." Some preliminary chemical testing was reported in the Dutch journal, *Acta Phytotherapeutica,* by German Doctors Alfred Mosig and Gottfried Schramm—Dr.

---

* At the Penick crude drug collecting station in Asheville, North Carolina, ginseng was locked up in the manager's office, along with his first edition of *"Look Homeward, Angel,"* by Asheville's Thomas Wolfe. I was curious to try ginseng myself, just for fun. Over a period of weeks I consumed a precious root doll in tiny nibbles. On the days when I had ginseng, I seemed to have very vivid, complex dreams at night. (Not daytime hallucinations.) A Stanford University neurophysiologist suggests that dreams may have a chemical basis, being initiated by the body's efforts to rid the central nervous system of some naturally created poison. Could it be that ginseng achieves its results by augmenting this process?

Schramm of Berlin being one of the few Europeans to have visited Communist China—but no extensive scientific investigation of the drug's activity in human beings is being conducted in the Western hemisphere, so far as I have been able to determine.

Does it really work? We have only such clues as this one, provided by Finn Sandberg, who said: "Whenever I am in Singapore, I have lunch with Han Suyin, author of *A Many Splendored Thing* and other best selling novels. As Elizabeth Comber, M.D., she practices medicine in Johore Bahru, near Singapore, prescribing mostly European and American drugs for her patients. But when she is sick herself, the only remedy she uses is ginseng root."

One can't help wondering how any absolutely inert substance could for ages, and in widely-separated lands, maintain so high a reputation. As one observer of Eastern peoples, Sir Edwin Arnold, wrote: "Can all those generations of Orientals who have praised heaven for ginseng's many benefits have been totally deceived? Was humanity ever quite mistaken when half of it believed in something never . . . advertised . . .?"

The inscrutable Chinese, indeed. If only because we know not why *they* see what most of us do not. Who is wearing the emperor's invisible new clothes now?

Sandberg reported, "Of the Asian countries, Japan and India are the most important as regards medicinal plants and natural products as drugs. There is a lot of wonderful chemical work performed in Japan, much of it stimulated by Professor Tatsuo Kariyone, Director of the National Institute of Hygienic Sciences in Tokyo." During World War II, the Japanese developed a valuable tuberculosis drug from moonseeds. Since then they have concentrated on antibiotics, vitamins and enzymes. As described in an earlier chapter, they are particularly adept in obtaining drugs from the sea. Even their big pharmaceutical manufacturers are very much involved with botanicals—adjoining the Takeda Laboratory is the Kyoto Herbal Garden where thousands of species are cultivated for experimentation. The Fourth International Symposium on the Chemistry of Natural Products convened, most appropriately, in Kyoto in April, 1964.

The 3,000 islands of the Philippines are struggling with the responsibilities of independence, but even here a nucleus of competent scientists carries on the work inspired by Professor Eduardo Quisumbing, now retired, who wrote the basic book on the flora. Dr. Gertrude Aguilar-Santos at the University of Manila is one of these. She completed her doctoral studies in Germany—another example of the international spread of knowledge in this field.

As for India, where to begin? Kipling's India was split apart January 26, 1950, with the extreme eastern and western portions becoming the disjointed country of Pakistan, the world's largest Moslem state. West Pakistan, stretching up to the wild, rocky borders of Afghanistan contains 85 per cent of the land, mostly arid and sparsely populated. When Sandberg last went through the Kyber Pass on UNESCO business, he photographed ferocious-looking warriors with archaic weapons, venturesome traders, and caravans that appeared unchanged from the days when spices from the Orient were the most highly prized medications. It almost seemed as if Marco Polo—quite a botanical collector himself—might come round the bend any minute. More likely, it would be Dr. O. H. Volk of Würzburg, Germany, making his studies of medicinal plants in Afghanistan; or, from the other direction, Dr. George M. Hocking of Auburn University in Alabama, surveying botanicals in West Pakistan for the United Nations.

Before 1950, Professor N. A. Qazilbash of the University of Peshawar was almost alone in working on West Pakistan's drug plants. He was the only person holding a doctor of science degree in pharmacognosy in the Indo-Pak subcontinent. So far, he has completed thirty-four major research projects under the most trying conditions imaginable. Believing, with Lord Kelvin, that "The soul and life of Science consists in its practical applications," his discoveries resulted in the "golden drug of Pakistan," *Artemisia kurramensis* Qazilbash, a species of wormwood now regarded as the most important source of santonin. This drug is used against the intestinal parasites that plague populations throughout the tropics. In addition, the cultivation of Artemesia in the Kurram Valley, and the production of more than 1,000 tons of santonin annually by a Lahore factory, have brought needy people a source of income. Qazilbash is also noted for his work on the alkaloid-rich Ephedra species he discovered growing in Baluchistan. According to a UNESCO report by Sandberg, a factory in Quetta now extracts about 18,000 pounds of ephedrine from this plant each year, an amount corresponding to the world's total consumption of the natural drug.

About 1,500 miles across India lies East Pakistan, running from the Bay of Bengal, through lush forests, and on up to the Himalayas. It is heartening to learn that in the midst of this abundant and varied flora, UNESCO and the government of Pakistan will build an International Research Center in Chittagong. Intended for the use of scientists the world over, it will be devoted to the study and development of medicinal and aromatic plants of the humid tropics. Although Pakistan lacks a national herbarium and pharmacopoeia, it is known that of the 271 drug plants growing in East Pakistan alone, 28 are already employed in western medicine. Many others are extremely promising. In addition, from the annual tea waste in the country, over four tons of caffeine could be salvaged— many a life has been saved by an injection of the heart stimulant caffeine sodium benzoate. Cardiac glycosides could be produced from strophantidin in now wasted jute seeds. Research Center plans call for laboratories and pilot plants where pharmaceutical manufacturing procedures will be worked out and personnel trained.

Rauwolfia plantations have been started and it is hoped that 24,000 acres of drug plants will be under cultivation within the next six to nine years. The large scale cultivation of ipecac, *Cephäelis ipecacuanha,* native to Brazil, has already begun to improve the health of Pakistan's people. (This age-old remedy of South American Indians was re-discovered by the eighteenth century pirate surgeon Thomas Dover and became the main ingredient in his Dover's powder.) Emetine, an alkaloid extracted from wiry ipecac roots, is most valued for treating amoebic dysentery. As an example of the endless need for this one drug: over 90 per cent of East Pakistan's population alone is ravaged by the disease. In order to give each infected person just one treatment per year, twenty-five tons of emetine from 1,250 tons of root are required.

In the United States, where we are inclined to be choleric over cholesterol, rather than cholera or other plagues, billions of dollars are allocated to research and development of various types. In Chittagong, they speak gratefully of budgets of a million or so. One of Sandberg's jobs is to help them spend it wisely.

While Kipling was in India, British botanists G. Bentham and J. D. Hooker described the flora, paying not too much attention to herbal remedies favored by the natives. As the Raulwolfia chapter demonstrated, we have the Indians to thank for some of our most important modern medicines; nowhere else are the people harder at work to obtain from their own fields and factories the life-extending, health-restoring drugs so desperately needed.

Pharmacognosy Professor C. S. Shah of Ahmedabad provided this summation: "The honor of creating medicinal plant-consciousness at the scientific level in India goes to Colonel Sir

Ram Nath Chopra and his co-workers, who have carried out mostly pharmacological and clinical investigations of crude drugs and published many basic references. . . . As for pharmacognosy, in the old days it was mainly descriptive—the physical characteristics of plants, macroscopic and microscopic, were recorded. While many of these works were beautifully illustrated with drawings and color plates, they were not always too dependable. The resurgence of pharmacognostic interest has shown other aspects of the science to be important; particularly, the employment of new techniques to determine the chemical constituents in plants. Our evaluation of saponin-containing drugs by haemolytic index and froth number, for instance, resulted in deletions and corrections in the Indian Pharmacopoeia and in clarification of botanical identities." (From the Yam Chapter it will be recalled that saponins affect the blood and are soapy or frothy.)

Dr. L. D. Kapoor, who worked with the Chopra group on the botanical side, wrote from the Regional Research Laboratory, Jammu & Kashmir: "The Indian government is encouraging drug research in a very liberal way through grants for surveys of the flora and investigations of folklore cures; promising plants are then subjected to phytochemical analysis and biological assay. Many indigeneous botanicals are cultivated on a commercial scale, while exotic ones are being introduced and acclimatized in suitable localities. One of the goals is to find medicinals that could be substituted for British Pharmacopoeial drugs." Other leading research centers specializing in botanical drugs are in New Delhi, Calcutta, and Lucknow, where a maharajah's palace with an umbrella-shaped dome on the tower has been converted into a modern laboratory.

Such laboratories, in what we think of as "the other side of the world," are sometimes amazingly well-equipped. While in Burma, pharmacognosist Edson Woodward visited the Applied Research Institute on the outskirts of Rangoon and noted:

"In this area—where you can see hungry people stalking rats as 'game' with their slingshots around the beautiful pagodas— I was pleased to find that Dr. Arnold Nordal, United Nations expert from Oslo, and his Burmese colleague, botanist U. Thein, had infra-red and ultra-violet spectrophotometers for their work on such plants as *Clerodendron serratum,* used to stop childbirth hemorrhaging."

Nations involved in boot-strap operations require very specific help from more developed areas, not just "more money and equipment." The lack of a trained staff at all levels is a major handicap. "The botanical and chemical work is often excellent," Dr. Sandberg pointed out. "But then projects may bog down because there is no pharmacologist available to test the extracts. Or, there are too few physicians who know how to conduct clinical trials. In Chittagong, the local medical college will co-operate in training doctors to perform the double blind test with code-numbered medications. (Neither patient nor doctor knows which is the drug being tested and which is the placebo, or sugar pill.) Ever since the thalidomide tragedy, there has been increasing emphasis on experimental therapeutics, as this medical specialty is called. Without such expert follow-through on clinical trials, previous hard work on promising new drugs can end in bitter frustration."

In addition to the assistance rendered by international organizations like UNESCO, student exchange programs, and religious and philanthropic efforts, increasing numbers of pharmaceutical companies are finding it good business practice to help these people help themselves. Some approaches have already been cited, here are a few other examples: Back in 1901, Henry Wellcome, the American co-founder of Burroughs-Wellcome of London, was so moved by the plight of the Sudanese that he established the Wellcome Tropical Research Laboratories and Historical Museum Library. These have been important sources of information for researchers and physicians all over the globe. Ciba, the Swiss drug company, has a scientific laboratory in Bombay where Indian scientists, collaborating with St. Xavier's College there, have studied the physiological activity of 175 Indian plants and found 64 worthy of further investigation. (Various Indian investigators have reported some fascinating clinical findings: "Sterile" women given an extract from poisonous mandrake, which has a "man-shaped root" like ginseng, have consistently given birth to boy babies. In another report, seeds from a plant belonging to the soapberry family have produced a substance which, when taken orally, is said to be 100 per cent effective in fertility control.) A number of large companies like Pfizer, Sterling-Winthrop, Lederle, Wyeth, Feigy, etc., have overseas branches such as the one established a few years ago in Karachi by Warner-Lambert and Pakistani investors. These modern factories are commercial enterprises, but the finished products that leave their loading docks by camel cart and other primitive conveyances seem particularly humanitarian in countries so starved for medications that doctors write three different prescriptions in the hope that just one might be filled.*

Benefits flow in both directions. Dr. Qazilbash, while lecturing at Arizona State University's Institute in Desert Biology, noted many similarities in the two floras and suggested ways in which his West Pakistan research might be applied to make our arid wastelands more productive. Traveling pharmacognosists have a way of becoming citizens of the world, deeply concerned about conditions in other lands and eager to help.

---

*INTERPHARM, an international research organization, was founded in 1963 at Grafing, near Munich, by thirteen drug companies which agreed to pool results of basic research conducted in co-operation with various universities. Countries represented include: Norway, Finland, Belgium, the Netherlands, France, Spain, Great Britain, South Africa, Canada, Venezuela, Argentina, Mexico, Brazil, the United States (Endo Laboratories), as well as Germany (Roland). Drs. Enders and Richter will direct the German research group.

So far as deserts are concerned, it is interesting that when Finn Sandberg determined that the Swedish flora is surprisingly poor, he headed first for the Desert Institute in Cairo. With Dr. Vivi Täckholm, a woman botany professor, he explored the desert, valleys, and exotic native bazaars. The herb dealers claimed that they had a miracle drug which "positively rejuvenated the old Pharaohs." It turned out to be that awful smelling vegetable gum, *Ferula assa-foetida,* which American grandmothers used to insist would ward off colds when worn in a little bag hung round the neck. (It would ward off coughers and sneezers, along with everyone else!) From his Egyptian collections, Sandberg is now testing the alkaloid retamine, which his group isolated from *Retama raetam;* it produced good results in laboratory animals and is now undergoing clinical tests for its effect on certain gynecological disorders.

In Israel, of the fifteen children of Oizer Weizmann, seven became scientists, including the noted Dr. Chaim Weizmann, one of the country's founders. His sister, the late Professor Anna Weizmann of the Daniel Sieff Research Institute, devoted fifty years to searching for valuable pharmaceuticals among the native plants. She studied Syrian rue, *Peganum harmala,* which contains harmine, one of the fascinating hallucinogenic substances used in mental disease research. First mentioned by Dioscorides, it was utilized by the Germans in World War II as a "truth serum." In excessive amounts, harmine depresses the central nervous system, but in therapeutic doses it has had a good effect when used as a stimulant in cases of encephalitis, or inflammation of the brain.

Some other leading scientists working on medicinal plants in the Middle East are Professor Shalom Sarel in Jerusalem; Dr. Ali Al-Rawi of the Baghdad Experimental Station in Iraq; and Dr. Turham Baytop of the University of Istanbul, Turkey. While Sandberg was discussing botanicals in the garden of Beirut's French University during the 1958 civil war, soldiers suddenly made an attack and began shooting all around: "Professor P. Lys made a very French gesture, saying, 'Voilà la grande bataille!" Sandberg recalled, commenting, "You see, pharmacognosy has its distractions." At the American University there, Professor Charles Abou-Chaar, managed to carry on his important work with ergot and other plants, despite interruptions. In a letter to me he has predicted: "In the next quarter of a century, our knowledge of plant constituents will increase tremendously, filling a great gap in our present knowledge"; adding graciously, "your book will, I hope, fire the imagination of countless readers and spur many a young student to 'get on the band wagon,' if I may be pardoned the expression. I have used it only to underline the present interest in this field."

The hardships of war take a toll in this research. From the University of Thessaloniki, Dr. G. C. Phokas reported that only in the last twenty years have systematic studies of the 5,000 medicinal plants in Greece been resumed (since ancient times) and these were twice interrupted when the botanical gardens in Athens were destroyed in World War II; the second bombing occurred just as the tender new shoots were coming up.

At the 1962 International Symposium on the Chemistry of Natural Products in Prague, Czechoslovakia, it was learned that the Russians are working with *Solanum laciniatum,* related to deadly nightshade. It is cultivated on a large scale in south Russia for use as a starting material for cortisone, manufactured at the All-Union Institute of Medicinal and Aromatic Plants (VILAR) just outside Moscow. There is a heavy concentration of botanical drug experts at the Central Asian State University in Tashkent, among them Professor A. S. Sadykov. One of the Russian successes was the isolation of galanthamine from *Galanthus woronowi,* the white snowdrop of the Caucasus Mountains. Professor Mikhail Mashovsky, head of the Moscow Chemical Institute, directed this work which re-sulted in a product used for treating the paralysis of polio and myasthenia gravis, a muscular disorder characterized by ex-treme weakness. In Czechoslovakia, itself, there are two large research centers devoted to natural products in Prague, as well as the Biochemical Institute in Bratislava, where Professor Dr. A. Jindra advised me that he is carrying out a systematic study of the flora of the steppes, especially alkaloidal plants related to buttercups.

In Hungary, Director György Szollar of the National Me-dicinal Herb Trading Center reported that 600 co-operative farms collect wild drug plants as part of their operation. In 1961, 30 botanicals were also cultivated on some 35,000 acres. The poppy, for morphine production, was most important, but Digitalis, belladonna, and chamomile plants were also grown extensively and exported to 25 countries.

Professor R. Paris wrote from the University of Paris, that while the new eighth edition of the French pharmacopoeia has some old botanicals deleted, important new ones have been added, such as *Ammi visnaga,* of the parsley family, the source of khellin used to treat asthma, angina pectoris, and other conditions. Some 10,000 tons of medicinal plants are used in that country every year, and there is an active research program operating with branches in the French colonies.

Strangely, it is in several European laboratories that con-siderable work is being done on an Amerian plant with a beautiful name and a beautiful flower: *Passiflora incarnata,* the passion flower. The symbolism of the flower's structure was used by the Jesuits to explain the life of Christ and His Cruci-fixion to the Indians. At the base of the petals is a corona or circle of spines representing the crown of thorns. The flower has three brilliant spots of color standing for the stigmata caused by the three nails of the cross. Five anthers represent five wounds. The petals and sepals have ten parts, one for each of the Apostles, but excluding Peter who denied Him and Judas who betrayed Him.

Down in the Blue Ridge foothills, the passion flower vine creeps over briar patches, making the job of collecting a scratchy one. The total extract made from the whole vine is not widely used in the United States. However, several laboratories are re-evaluating its long record in medical publications of bygone days when it was recommended for epilepsy, tetanus, convulsions, and other muscular spasms. In a 1920 French medical journal it was cited for use in the emotional disorders of the menopause, including insomnia. Since then, there have been other studies and now volcanic Italians and passionate Parisians of both sexes calm themselves with tranquilizers from passion flowers.

As for botanical drug investigation in the rest of Europe and parts of the Western Hemisphere not touched upon earlier—even the drug plant explorers whose adventures we have followed must stop, sometime. There is always another botanical that should be collected, as there is, in this instance, the work of outstanding researchers in England, Brazil, Canada, and elsewhere that should be reported. But every book must have an end. However, the world-wide resurgence of scientific interest in medicinal plants continues unabated—that is the important thing.

Flying Finn Sandberg has returned to his Stockholm clinic after visiting the USDA experimental station at Tingo Maria, Peru, on the eastern slopes of the Andes. His plant hunting colleagues, whose methods were described in introductory chapters are busy with their own follow-up work: Richard Evans Schultes has come back to his students and research projects at Harvard after a worthwhile summer in Colombia. Robert Raffauf in Philadelphia is involved with the problems of producing finished drugs. Bruce Halstead, at the World Life Research Institute near Colton, California, has temporarily put aside his skin-diving gear in order to complete his treatise on poisonous marine organisms. And in his office near Wall Street, the first botanical explorer introduced, Edson Woodward, copes with the current export/import crisis. This may involve a trouble-shooting trip by taxi to a dock-side warehouse, where bales of aromatic crude drugs are unloaded —or a flight to Ceylon, to expedite raw materials to pharmaceutical manufacturers.

In this story of the search for plants that heal, we have met only a few of the men and women who energetically mix basic science, commerce, education, and international good will to produce new "green medicines" from the universal plant kingdom. But the results of their labor benefit all mankind.

Bibliography

The quest for a new botanical drug begins and ends with the literature. Even plant hunters en route to the rain forest must first stop in at the library. For all concerned—scientist, professional bibliographer, or interested layman—searching the sources for elusive references to medicinal plants can be a time-consuming, frustrating task. As Pharmacognosist Edson F. Woodward noted in his article, "Literature Searches for Uses of New Botanical Drugs," (*Advances in Chemistry Series* No. 12, Amer. Chem. Soc.):

"About 900 plant species are used in the American drug trade. . . . Diversity in botanical character, geographic origin, and medical use makes difficult the systematic classification of plant drugs. . . . The literature is not as well organized as it is for law, chemistry, or physics. The sources of information about new botanical drug uses, unfortunately, have no general category of title."

Students of this subject should be prepared to pick their way card by card through catalogs titled: "Herbs, Medicinal; Botany, Medical; Chemistry, Pharmaceutical; Drugs, Vegetable; Plants, Medicinal; Materia Medica; Herbals . . ." etc. Experts fare little better as they try to find out what is known about one particular plant, or a specific pharmaceutical requirement, such as "botanicals used for pain relief." Woodward explained that a literature search could be commenced from several points, but he implied that the quest was endless: "If the list [of possible references] were inclusive, even to a modest degree, it should include almost every book ever published on economic botany, exploration, plant chemistry and pharmacology, and hundreds of other fields as well . . . for example, anthropology and theology. . . . Such searches are in the province of pharmacognosy and its many ramifications."

Professor George M. Hocking pointed out in *A Dictionary of Terms in Pharmacognosy* (Thomas, Springfield, Ill., 1955) that there are at least 592 technical and scientific serials related to this subject. Appendix C in his book lists some of these. He wrote that he had found it extremely difficult to make a selection because "pharmacognosy cuts across so many divergent fields of interest. . . . Even within the field of pharmacognosy proper, there is much variety of specialization: some pharmacognists are particularly interested in morphology, others in histology and microscopy, some again specialize in phytochemistry, others genetics. Individuals sometimes go into cultivation and commerce, and so on."

Readers of GREEN MEDICINE undoubtedly have even more diverse interests, but I sincerely hope that from my selections every reader will find at least one reference that is new and useful, or interesting. Because of space limitations, it was not possible to publish the full bibliography compiled to document my sources for the text. This would constitute a fair-sized monograph. What follows is clearly a compromise, with all the inherent faults of being at times too general and elementary, at others, too specific or technical. (The book is intended primarily for the layman, although some pharmacognosy professors have said that they will be using it as supplementary material in their courses.) Fortunately, the subject matter is fascinating and one finds extremely "readable" writing in this field—more so than in any other scientific discipline, in my opinion. Many of the leading journals are edited in a lively fashion, with the author's personal style retained. Professor R. B. Woodward of Harvard and his co-authors introduce their methods for "The Total Synthesis of Strychnine" with a brief but sparkling account of the plant's history (*Tetrahedron,* Feb., 1963); "Folklore and Plant Drugs" by the late Professor E. H. Lucas (*Papers of the Michigan Academy of Science, Arts, and Letters,* Vol. XLV, 1960) is not to be missed. Something for everyone here.

After general libraries are explored for basic material, one turns to specialized collections in schools of pharmacy, botanical gardens, horticultural societies, drug companies, hospitals, museums, and historical societies—if one lives in a very small town, the local pharmacist may have some of the following references in his personal library, or know where they may be obtained. Retired physicians are another good source of information on what used to be known as Materia Medica when they were in medical school.

434

The Lloyd Library and Museum in Cincinnati, Ohio, is noted for its outstanding collection of literature in the pharmaceutical sciences, particularly in eclectic medicine. They have the largest collection of Pharmacopoeias in the world, and the first pharmaceutical book ever set in type, published in Venice in 1493; as well as the only copies in America of many obscure or foreign titles. The Lloyd Catalogue lists thousands of periodicals from many countries. Mrs. Corinne Miller Simons is the librarian. *Lloydia,* the quarterly journal of pharmacognosy and allied biological sciences, edited by Univ. of Conn. Professor A. E. Schwarting, is published jointly by Lloyd Library and the American Society of Pharmacognosy. (The Dec., 1962, issue is particularly interesting because it contains papers presented at a symposium on "The Search for New Medicinal Agents from Plants." Interviews with the authors of these papers provided much of the background for GREEN MEDICINE.)

The Oakes Ames Library at Harvard's Botanical Museum specializes in economic botany and has a fine collection on narcotic drug plants. The Univ. of Miami's Morton Collectanea, under the direction of Mrs. Julia Morton in Coral Gables, Fla., also focuses on economic plants. The Liberty Hyde Bailey Hortorium, Cornell Univ., Ithaca, N.Y., places emphasis on the taxonomy and nomenclature of cultivated plants of the ornamental type. Some of their publications include: *Hortus Second: A Concise Dictionary of Gardening* (Macmillan, 1946); *The Standard Encyclopedia of Horticulture* (6 Vols., Macmillan, 1919); *How Plants Get Their Names* (Dover paperbound), all by Liberty H. Bailey. One of the best collections of books and periodicals on poisonous plants is found in the libraries at Cornell and in the personal library of John M. Kingsbury, there, whose book *Poisonous Plants of the U.S. and Canada* (Prentice-Hall, May, 1964) contains 600 pp. and 1,700 cited references. More than 700 species of plants are mentioned.

Other libraries consulted in the preparation of GREEN MEDICINE: N.Y. Academy of Medicine; National Library of Medicine, Bethesda, Md.; Boyce Thompson Institute for Plant Research, Yonkers, N.Y.; Library of Congress; The Smithsonian Institution; National Agricultural Library; The N.Y. Botanical Garden and the Brooklyn Botanical Garden; the N.Y. Horticultural Society; The N.Y. Historical Society; The American Museum of Natural

History; and the Penick, Meer, Squibb, Lederle, and other drug company collections.

A number of researchers are at work compiling bibliographies that will help future investigators. Pharmacognosy Professor Anna H. Koffler and Librarian Geneviẹve Wheelock have prepared *A Guide to Pharmacognosy and Related Subjects,* which lists pertinent books in the Ohio Northern Univ. Library, Ada, Ohio. The Sept., 1961, issue of *Special Libraries* noted that *The World List of Pharmacy Periodicals* had been compiled by Winifred Sewell as the first step toward establishing an international abstracting service. A useful check list, "Books, Reference Works and Periodical Literature recommended for College of Pharmacy Libraries," appeared in the *American J. of Pharmaceutical Education* (Vol. 19, p. 480, 1955). "A List of Herb Literature" by Elizabeth Hall was published in The Herb Society's *Annual Report* in 1948. *Library of Medicinal Plants* by Henry G. de Laszlo, contains 50 pp. of book listings (Heffer & Sons, Cambridge, England, 1958). *Union List of Periodicals in Pharmaceutical Libraries* (Special Libraries Assn., 1952) lists the periodicals available in drug company libraries at that time. *Chemical Abstracts Service* (Ohio State Univ.) lists the scientific journals abstracted, with keys to their location in libraries. In addition to *Chemical Abstracts,* information on botanical drug research may be found in *Biological Abstracts;* in the USDA index, *Plant Science Literature;* and in the *Quarterly Cumulative Index Medicus,* published by the American Medical Assn.

The Jan. 1, 1964, edition of the *J. of the American Pharmaceutical Assn.,* edited by G. B. Griffenhagen, listed colleges of pharmacy, professional organizations and their officers, as well as pertinent publications. The American Pharmaceutical Assn., 2215 Constitution Ave., N.W., Wash., D.C., supplies information on pharmacy as a profession to prospective students. The advanced study of pharmacognosy is undertaken as part of this curriculum.

Books written especially for young readers include: *Plants That Heal,* M. E. Selsam (Morrow, 1959); *Plants That Changed the World,* B. S. Dodge (Little, Brown, 1959); *Plant Hunters,* F. L. Jewett & C. L. McCausland (Houghton Mifflin, 1958); *Plant Explorer: David Fairchild,* B. Williams & S. Epstein (Messner, 1961).

Bibliography

Metabolites of the Sea is a pamphlet written by Ross F. Nigrelli, whose research was described in the "Drugs from the Sea" chapter. (Available from D. C. Heath, Boston, for 48 cents.)

At the beginning of my research, I found *Orientation to Pharmacy,* ed. by H. M. Burlage, C. O. Lee, & L. W. Rising (McGraw-Hill, 1959) very helpful. It lists professional organizations and publications, as well as collateral readings. "The Scientific Status of Pharmacology" by Chauncey D. Leake, (*Science,* Dec. 29, 1961) is the text of the eminent pharmacologist's address as retiring president of the Amer. Assn. for the Advancement of Science. Another interesting review article is "Advances in Pharmacognosy" by W. C. Evans of the Univ. of Nottingham (*Manufacturing Chemist,* Sept., 1963), which describes research trends, the activities of international societies such as the Medicinal Plants Section of the Federation Internationale Pharmaceutique, and current textbooks.

A Textbook of Pharmacognosy by George E. Trease (Baillere, Tindall and Cox, London, 8th. ed., 1961) has a valuable section on the history of pharmacognosy, of special interest to those new to the field. Also published in Britain is *Textbook of Pharmacognosy* by Thomas E. Wallis (J. & A. Churchill, London, 1960). Widely used in America: *Pharmacognosy* by Edward P. Claus (Lea & Febiger, 1961), a continuation of Henry Kraemer's *Scientific and Applied Pharmacognosy,* first published in 1916. This was revised by E. H. Wirth and E. N. Gathercoal in 1936—there is a list of classical references in this edition on pp. 11–12; *Modern Pharmacognosy* by Egil Ramstad (Blakiston, 1959); *Pharmacognosy* by Robertson Pratt and Heber W. Youngken, Jr., (Lippincott, 1956); and *Textbook of Pharmacognosy* by N. M. Ferguson (Macmillan, 1956). Basic earlier books include: Heber W. Youngken, Sr.'s *Textbook of Pharmacognosy* (Blakiston, 1948), and his *Pharmaceutical Botany* (Blakiston, 1951); *Medical Botany* by Alexander Nelson (Williams & Wilkins, 1951).

The late Dr. Youngken, Sr., said that modern pharmacognosy began with the work of Theodor W. C. Martius, a German apothecary who published the results of his studies in 1832 in a book titled *Grundriss der Pharmakognosie des Pflanzenreiches,* which classified drugs morphologically. Histological pharmacognosy had its beginning in 1838, when German botanist Mathias J. Schleiden reported that the cell is the fundamental unit of plant structure and that all tissues are combinations of cells. Schleiden's most important work, *Grundzüge der Wissenschaftlichen Botanik,* appeared in 1842. Dr. Youngken, on pp. 19–20 of his *Textbook of Pharmacognosy,* lists several dozen foreign and American classics, among them: *Pharmacographia* by F. A. Flückiger and Daniel Hanbury, a history of the principal drugs of vegetable origin in Great Britain and British India (Macmillan, London, 1874); *American Medicinal Plants* by C. F. Millspaugh (2 Vols., Phila., 1887); *Organic Materia Medica* by John M. Maische, who was editor of the *American J. of Pharmacy* for thirty years (Lea Bros., 1895); *Origin and History of All the Pharmacopeial Vegetable Drugs, Chemicals and Preparations, with Bibliography,* (707 texts listed) by John Uri Lloyd (The Caxton Press, 1921). Dr. E. H. Lucas said that *The Medicinal Plants of the Various Peoples and Ages* by Dragendorff (c. 1898), listing 12,700 species, was "one of the most comprehensive compilations of medicinal plants in modern times." Others have mentioned the *Materia Medica* of Jonathan Pereira (London, 1839) as an "early monument in medical pharmacognosy."

Dr. John M. Fogg, Jr., Director of the Morris Arboretum, Philadelphia, supplied the following references to taxonomic literature: *Geographical Guide to Floras of the World,* Blake & Atwood, USDA Misc. Publications. (Part I, N. & S. America, Africa, Australia, Islands of the Atlantic, Pacific, and Indian Oceans, 1942. Part II, Western Europe, Scandinavia and Gr. Britain to Switzerland and Italy, 1961.) *Bibliography of Eastern Asiatic Botany,* Merrill & Walker, (1938; Suppl. 1960.) *Genera Siphonogamarum,* Dalla Torre et Harms. An index to genera of seed plants, (1958). *Index Kewensis,* Parts I & II (1895) plus 12 suppls. (to 1955). An index to specific names of seed plants. *Index Londonensis,* Vols. I to IV (1929–31) plus 2 suppls. (1941). A guide to illustrations of plants. *Index Herbariorum,* a geographically arranged index to the herbariums of the world with a list of taxonomic botanists and their fields of special interest. *International Directory of Specialists in Plant Taxonomy with a Census of Their Current Interests.* (Regnum Veg., 1958). *Syllabus der Pflanzenfamilien,* Engler & Diels,

(Ed. 11, 1936). A synopsis of all plant families on a world basis. *Die Naturlichen Pflanzenfamilien,* Engler and Prantl. (1887–1915 Ed. 2. 1924) A more exhaustive treatment of plant families. *Das Pflanzenriech,* ed. Engler & Prantl. A series of monographs by world authorities.

Dr. Gordon H. Svoboda said that he "would be lost" without The Royal Horticultural Society's *Dictionary of Gardening* (Vol. I–IV, 1 suppl., Oxford at the Clarendon Press, 1956). This serves a somewhat different purpose than *Index Kewensis.* It gives brief descriptions of the families, tells approximately how many genera they contain, as well as where they grow. And most importantly, it describes each species listed and cites its uses, when known.

Dr. Melvin R. Gibson, president-elect of the American Society of Pharmacognosy, who edits the "News and Events" section in *Lloydia,* called attention to "one of the most significant contributions of this generation to our literature from a pharmacognosist": *Chemotaxonomie der Pflanzen,* a five-volume work on chemotaxonomy of plants by Dr. Robert Hegnauer of the University of Leiden (Vols. I & II, 1962–3, Birkhäuser Verlag, Basel).

Among the many other basic references consulted by professionals: *Gray's Manual of Botany,* by Merritt L. Fernald (8th ed., American Book Co., 1950); *Taxonomy of Vascular Plants,* G. H. M. Lawrence (Macmillan, 1951); *Flowering Plants and Ferns,* J. C. Willis (Cambridge Univ. Press, 1897); *Botanical Ready Reference,* L. M. Nickell (Chicago, 1911); *The Arboretums and Botanical Gardens of North America,* Donald Wyman (Chronica Botanica, Waltham, Mass., Vol. 10, 1947); *The Lynn Index,* an annotated bibliography of phytochemistry, published by Drs. J. W. Schermerhorn and Maynard W. Quimby at the Massachusetts College of Pharmacy. Four monographs out of an estimated number of sixty have appeared. When completed, users will be able to determine what work has been performed on a given plant; what substances have been reported in the plant; and what plant or plants contain a substance in which the researcher is particularly interested. *Origin of Cultivated Plants,* Alphonse de Candolle (1886, reprinted, 1963, Hafner, N.Y.).

Drug Plants of Africa, Thomas Githens (Univ. of Penn. Press,

1949); *Poisonous Plants of the U.S.,* Walter C. Muenscher (Macmillan, 1951); *Indigenous Drugs of India,* R. N. Chopra (Dhur, Calcutta, 1958); *Plants and Plant Science in Latin America,* ed. by Frans Verdoon (Chronica Botanica, 1945); *Las Plantas Medicinales de Mexico,* Maximino Martinez (Ediciones Botas, Mexico, 1959); *Medicinal Plants of the Arid Zone* (UNESCO, Paris, 1960); *Medicinal and Poisonous Plants of Southern and Eastern Africa,* J. M. Watt and M. G. Breyer-Brandwijk (Livingstone, Edinburgh, 1962); *Soviet Research in Pharmaceutical Chemistry, Part III—Pharmacognosy* (English transl. Consultants Bureau, Inc., N.Y., 1959); *Pharmacognosy,* A. F. Gammerman (Govt. Publ. of Med. Lit., Leningrad, 1960).

Technical references with emphasis on laboratory procedures include: *Encyclopedia of Chemical Technology* (Interscience, 1963). Vol. 1. contains a section on "The History, Preparation and Use of Alkaloids," by Gordon H. Svoboda, with bibliographies for each alkaloid. *The Plant Alkaloids,* Thomas A. Henry (Blakiston, 1960); *The Plant Glycosides,* Robert J. McIlroy (Arnold & Co., London, 1951); *The Alkaloids,* R. Manske (Academic Press, 7 Vols., 1960); *Advanced Organic Chemistry,* Louis F. and Mary Fieser (Reinhold Publ. Corp., 1961); *Medicinal Chemistry,* Alfred Burger, Ed. (Interscience, 1960); *The Chemistry and Pharmacy of Vegetable Drugs,* Noel L. Allport (Chemical Publ. Co., 1944); *Drugs from Plants,* Trevor Williams (Sigma Introd. to Sci. No. 10, London, 1947).

Two basic texts pertaining to tissue culture and biosynthesis: *The Structural Relations of Natural Products,* Sir Robert Robinson (Oxford, Clarendon Press, 1955); *The Cultivation of Animal and Plant Cells,* Philip R. White (Ronald, 1963).

Useful references of a miscellaneous nature: *Style Manual for Biological Journals* (Amer. Inst. of Biol. Sci., 2000 P. Street, N.W., Wash. 6, D.C., 1961); *Pharmaceutical and Medical Latin,* W. F. Gidley and J. R. Moreno (Hemphill's, Austin, Texas, 1959); *A Glossary of Botanical Terms and Their Derivation and Accent,* B. D. Jackson (Hafner, 1960); *A Gardener's Book of Plant Names,* A. W. Smith (Harper, 1963).

Sources on pharmacology and therapeutics: *Pharmacopoeia of the USA* (Mack Publ. Co., Easton, Pa. 1820 to 16th Rev., 1960);

Amer. Medical Assn.'s New and Nonofficial Drugs (Lippincott, 1959); *The Homeopathic Pharmacopoeia of the U.S.* (Otis Clapp & Son., Boston, 6th Ed. Rev., 1954); *Dispensatory of the U.S.* (Lippincott, 1834 to 25th Ed., 1960); *Pharmacopoeia Internationalis* (World Health Organ., Geneva, 2 Vols. & 1959 suppl.); *National Formulary* (Amer. Pharm. Assn., 1888 to curr. ed.); *The Pharmacological Basis of Therapeutics*, L. S. Goodman and A. Gilman (Macmillan, 1955); *The Merck Index of Chemicals and Drugs* (Merck & Co., 7th Ed., 1960); *Remington's Practice of Pharmacy*, E. W. Martin, ed. (Mack Publ. Co., 1961); *Modern Drug Encyclopedia and Therapeutic Index*, Harry D. Fein, Ed. (Donnelley Corp., 1961); *The Pharmacologic Principles of Medical Practice*, J. C. Krantz, Jr., and C. J. Carr (Williams & Wilkins, 1958). *American Drug Index* (Lippincott, 1956–to date).

Regarding the development of the pharmaceutical industry: *The Merchants of Life*, Tom Mahoney (Harper, 1959); *American Chemical Industry*, Williams Haynes, (6 Vols., D. Van Nostrand, 1945–1954); *Drug Research and Development*, Austin E. Smith, with A. D. Herrick (Revere, 1948); *The Toadstool Millionaires: A Social History of Patent Medicines in America Before Federal Regulation*, James Harvey Young, Chairman, History Dept., Emory Univ. (Princeton Univ. Press, 1962); *Drug Store Days*, My Youth Among the Pills and Potions, Richard W. Armour, (McGraw-Hill, 1959). The stories of individual companies have been told in such books as: *The Long White Line*, Herman Kogan (Random House, 1963), about Abbott Laboratories; *Doctor Squibb*, Lawrence G. Blochman (Simon & Schuster, 1958); *Medicine Makers of Kalamazoo*, the History of the Upjohn Company, Leonard Engel (McGraw-Hill, 1961); *Three Score Years and Ten*, Roscoe Clark (Eli Lilly, 1946); *A Sketch of Medicine and Pharmacy*, S. E. Massengill (Massengill, 1943); *Lydia Pinkham is Her Name*, Jean Burton (Farrar, 1949); etc.

Histories of science are often entertaining, as well as informative. Only a few can be listed here: *Four Thousand Years of Pharmacy*, C. H. LaWall (Lippincott, 1927); *History of Pharmacy*, Edward Kremers and George Urdang (Lippincott, 1951); *A Short History of Medicine*, Charles Singer and E. Ashworth Underwood, Dir.,

Wellcome Historical Library, (Oxford Univ. Press, 1964); *Source Book of Medical History,* compiled by Logan Clendening (Dover, paperbound, 1960), consists of 124 papers, including William Withering's "On the Foxglove . . ." James Lind's "Treatise on Scurvy," Thomas Sydenham's "On Peruvian Bark," and excerpts from the Ebers Papyrus.

Two guides to inexpensive editions: *A Guide to Science Reading,* H. J. Deason, Ed. (Signet Science Library Original, 1963). An annotated bibliography selected by AAAS from 18,000 paperbound titles on botany, biochemistry, medicine, etc. Includes addresses of publishers. (New American Library, PO Box 2310, Grand Central Sta., N.Y. 17, 60 cents, plus 5 cents postage.) The R. R. Bowker Co., Box 617, Times Square Station, N.Y. 36, issues *Paperbound Books in Print,* with supplements.

A few reprints dealing with drugs: *Understanding Drugs,* Donald G. Cooley (Pocket Books, 1963); *Medicine and Man,* Ritchie Calder (Mentor Books, 1958); *The Shocking History of Drugs,* (The Eternal Search), Richard Mathison, (Ballantine, 1958); *The Astonishing History of the Medical Profession,* (Call the Doctor), E. S. Turner, (Ballantine, 1961); *Poisons* (Dictionary of Poisons), Ibert and Eleanor Mellan (Pyramid, 1962); *Drugs and the Mind,* Robert S. de Ropp (Grove, 1960); *The Doors of Perception* and *Heaven and Hell* (in one vol.), Aldous Huxley (Harper Colophon Ed., 1963); *Narcotics: Nature's Dangerous Drugs* (Flight from Reality), Norman Taylor (Dell, 1963); *Phantastica: Narcotic and Stimulating Drugs, Their Use and Abuse,* L. Lewin (Dover, 1963). In a hard-cover edition is: *The Drug Experience,* D. Ebin, Ed. (Orion Press, 1961).

Books or monographs on a single botanical drug include: *The Fever Bark Tree,* M. L. Duran-Reynals (Doubleday, 1946); *Curare, Its History, Nature, and Clinical Use,* A. R. McIntyre (Univ. of Chi. Press, 1947); *Curare and Curare-like Agents,* ed. by D. Bovet, et al. (Elseveier, 1959); *Colchicine—in Agriculture, Medicine, Biology, and Chemistry,* O. J. Eigsti and P. Dustin, Jr. (Iowa State Coll. Press, 1955); *Rauwolfia: Botany, Pharmacognosy, Chemistry, and Pharmacology,* R. E. Woodson, H. W. Youngken, Sr., E. Schlittler, and J. A. Schneider (Little, Brown, 1957); "Papain," M. L. Tainter, et al. (*Annals,* N.Y. Acad. of Sci., Vol. 54, 1951–2); *Piper Methysticum (Kava),* E. F. Steinmetz, (Steinmetz, Amsterdam, 1960); "The Hallucinogenic Mushrooms of Mexico and Psilocybin: a bibliography," R. Gordon Wasson (*Botanical Museum Leaflets,* Harvard Univ., March 10, 1963).

Some special categories: *The Search for New Antibiotics,* G. F. Gause (Yale, 1960); *Seaweeds and Their Uses,* V. J. Chapman (Methuen, London, 1950); *The Role of Algae and Plankton in Medicine,* Morton and David Schwimmer (Grune and Stratton, 1955); *Dangerous Marine Animals,* Bruce Halstead (Cornell Maritime Press, 1959); *A Bibliography of Psychedelic and Related Research* (Intern'l. Fed. for Int. Freedom, Cambridge, Mass., 1963); *Psychopharmacology Frontiers,* Nathan S. Kline (Little, Brown, 1959).

The literature on botanical expeditions is vast, but I found only one book about a scientist searching specifically for medicinal plants, *Jungle Memories* (McGraw-Hill, 1933), by the late Prof. H. H. Rusby of Columbia University. Many books mention medicinal plants in passing, but the emphasis is on basic botany. *Plant Hunters in the Andes,* T. Harper Goodspeed (U. of Calif., 1961), for instance, focuses upon the search for tobacco plants and ornamentals, but he also reports on coca chewing by the natives. Two books written by explorers describe personal adventures while searching for native medicinals in the Amazon: *Witch Doctor's Apprentice,* Nicole Maxwell (Houghton Mifflin, 1961), tells of a lone woman's courageous efforts to collect secret remedies; and R. C. Gill's *White Water and Black Magic* (Holt, 1940) is a dramatic story about his quest for curare constituents.

The World in Your Garden, Wendell H. Camp, Victor R. Boswell, and John R. Magness (National Geographic Society, 1957), is a beautiful book about the exotic origins of flowers, fruits, and vegetables. The foreword, by Melville Bell Grosvenor, recaptures "The Romance of Plant Discovery." *Green Cargoes,* Anne Dorrance (Doubleday, 1945) explains how plants have spread from their places of origin. *Spice Ho!* is a story of discovery by Agnes D. Hewes (Knopf, 1941). *Of Herbs and Spices,* Colin Clair (Abelard-Schuman, 1961) contains a wealth of background information. *Folklore and Odysseys of Food and Medicinal Plants,* Ernst and

Johanna Lehner (Tudor, 1962), has 200 illustrations. Most books of this type mention the early use of herbs and spices as medications.

Personal recollections of scientific expeditions include: *The World Was My Garden,* David Fairchild (Scribner's, 1943); *Notes of a Botanist on the Amazon and Andes,* Richard Spruce, ed. by Alfred R. Wallace (2 Vols. Macmillan, London, 1909); *The Naturalist on the River Amazons,* H. W. Bates (U. of Calif., 1962); *Wanderings in South America,* Charles Waterton (Macmillan, London, 1879); *Plant-Hunting in China,* E. H. M. Cox (Collins, London, 1945); *A Botanist in South Africa,* John Hutchinson (Gawthorn, London, 1945); *Plant Hunting,* E. H. Wilson (Stratford, 1927); *Three Years' Wanderings in the Northern Provinces of China,* Robert Fortune (Murray, London, 1847); *Joseph Banks's Journal . . . During Captain Cook's First Voyage* (Macmillan, London, 1896); and many others. *White Waters and Black* by Gordon MacCreagh (Doubleday Anchor Book, 1961) is an amusing account of a 1923 Amazon expedition, which Director James A. Oliver of the American Museum of Natural History introduces in the foreword as "a sardonic lesson in how *not* to conduct an expedition." He feels that it should be required reading for all about to embark on overseas collecting trips.

There are many good books on the early explorer-naturalists: *The Green World of the Naturalists* (Greenberg, 1948) and *South America Called Them,* (Knopf, 1945), both by Victor Von Hagen; *Green Laurels* (Simon & Schuster, 1936) and *Cargoes and Harvests* (Appleton-Century, 1936), both by Donald Culross Peattie; *John and William Bartram's America,* Helen G. Cruickshank (Doubleday Anchor Book, 1957; *John Torrey, a Story of North American Botany,* A. D. Rodgers, (Princeton Univ., 1942); *Voyage of the Beagle,* Leonard Engel, ed. (Doubleday Anchor Book, 1962).

I found *Some American Medical Botanists,* H. A. Kelly (Appleton, 1929) extremely interesting, as were the old botanically-oriented "Family Doctor Books," such as *American Practice of Medicine,* Wooster Beach (N.Y., 1833), and *Thompsonian Materia Medica,* Samuel Thompson (Albany, 1841, many editions).

Herbals, Their Origin and Evolution, A Chapter in the History of Botany (1470–1670), Agnes Arber (Cambridge Univ. Press, 1938), is a good starting point for this extensive literature. An oft-cited reference is Maud Grieve's *Modern Herbal,* ed. by Mrs. C. F. Leyel (2 Vols., Hafner, 1959). (The Stechert-Hafner Publishing Co., 31 E. 10th St., N.Y. 3, specializes in botanical books and scientific journals in the field, both new and used.) Some old herbals: *The Badianus Manuscript* (Aztec) transl. by Emily W. Emmart (Johns Hopkins Press, 1940); *The Greek Herbal of Dioscorides,* R. T. Gunther, ed. (Hafner, 1959); *Herbs for the Mediaeval Household For Cooking, Healing, and Divers Uses,* Margaret B. Freeman (The Metropolitan Museum of Art, 1943). Some new ones: The many books of Mrs. Leyel in England, among them one called *Green Medicine,* brought to my attention after my own book's title was set. Her publisher is Faber and Faber, London. Mary T. Quelch's herbals include *Herbs for Daily Use* (Sterling, 1959); *Medicinal Herbs:Their Use in Canine Ailments,* Juliette de Bairacli-Levy (Sirius House, 1948); *Using Plants for Healing,* Nelson Coon (Hearthside Press, 1963); and, *Stalking the Wild Asparagus,* Euell Gibbons (David McKay, 1962), contains a chapter on herbal medicine, although the book is basically concerned with "living off the land and loving it." *British Herbs,* Florence Ranson (Penguin, 1949), a manual of herb recognition, has an interesting section on W. W. II efforts to obtain needed drugs from rose hips, etc. *The Medical Herbalist,* J. R. Yemm, ed., is issued by the National Assoc. of Medical Herbalists in Gr. Britain. A revised, enlarged edition of Joseph E. Meyer's *The Herbalist* was printed by Rand McNally in 1960. Also of interest: *The Physick Garden,* Edith G. Wheelwright (London, 1934); *Plants of the Bible,* H. N. and A. L. Moldenke (Chronica Botanica, 1952); *Garden Spice and Wild Pot Herbs,* W. C. Muenscher (Cornell, 1955); *A Cordiall Water,* M. F. K. Fisher (Little, Brown, 1962); and issues of *The Herb Grower,* a quarterly edited by Gertrude B. Foster, Falls Village, Conn. (Vol. XIV, No. 4, 1962, had articles on the healing substances in *Aloe vera* and Dr. Arthur Schwarting's pharmacy school garden at the University of Connecticut.) The *Herbarist* is published by the Herb Society of America in Boston.

I asked the vice-president in charge of research for a major pharmaceutical company—one that has a new botanical drug on the market—what publications he reads regularly. When he told me that he "covers 700 each month," I was skeptical, until I learned that he reads at the rate of 4,000 words per minute, as a result of taking a visual training course. He devours: *Lloydia, Economic Botany, J. of the Pharm. Sciences, Tetrahedron,* (and *Tetrahedron Letters*), the *J. of Med. and Pharmaceutical Chemistry, Amer. J. of Botany, AIBS Bulletin, Torrey Botanical Club Bulletin, Brittonia, Mycologia, J. of Organic Chemistry, J. of Amer. Chem. Soc., J. of the Amer. Pharmaceutical Assn., J. of Chem. Soc. (London), Science, Nature,* and such international publications as *Planta Medica, Helvetica Chemica Acta, Annalen der Chemie, Die Naturwissenschaften,* and *Experientia,* to cite some of those most oriented to botanical research findings.

To keep up with the business end of things: *Chem. and Engineering News, Chemical Week, Modern Medicine, Medical World News, Medical Tribune, Drug and Cosmetic Industry* (trade journal reports need not be dull, see "Current Sources of Botanical Drugs," E. F. Woodward, Aug. 1961), *Oil, Paint and Drug Reporter* (crude botanical prices listed on Mondays), *Drug Trade News, Drug News Weekly,* etc., plus, membership newsletters from trade association headquarters, and confidential subscription services, such as *F-D-C Reports* ("the pink sheet") and information supplied by pharmaceutical consultants like Paul de Haen (who also reports on new drugs in *Medical Science*), or Erwin Di Cyan, (who publishes a *Monthly Bulletin* of book reviews and articles such as the one on "The Herbal Seesaw," Jan., 1955).

I cite this small portion of one drug company executive's reading assignment to point up the fact that while this bibliography is lengthy, we have scarcely scratched the surface of one aspect of the search for plants that heal: the library research. There is a great deal of talk about the need to put everything on IBM cards for instant retrieval, and various research centers are working toward that goal. The University of Illinois College of Pharmacy has been given a U.S. Public Health Service grant to establish a World Reference Center for Literature on Natural Products and Plants, according to Professor Ralph F. Voight, head of the department of pharmacognosy. Wonderful news—but so far is I am concerned, it comes about four years too late. I pass it on as my last GREEN MEDICINE reference: Happy hunting!

Index

447

Index

Anticoagulants, from algae and fish toxins, 399
Antifertility drugs: for arthritis, 292; *see also* Oral contraception.
Antispasmodics, from Datura, 96
Anti-tuberculosis drugs, for leprosy, 243
Apocynaceae, 320
Apocynum, n. 219
Apocynum cannabinum, 216
Applezweig, Norman, 201, 256, 263, 270
Archbold, Richard, 40, 41
Archeology, in botanical research, 151–154
Archives of Neurology and Psychiatry (Turner and Merlis), *quoted,* 147
Arendzen-Hein, G. W., 343
Aristolochia, 302
Ark, Peter, 387
Armstrong, James G., 313
Arnold Arboretum and Gray Herbarium collection of oriental plants, 417
Arnold, Sir Edwin, *quoted,* 420
Arrow poisons: *see* Poisons.
Artemisia kurramensis Qazilbash, 422
Arthritis, 27–29, 255; antifertility drugs for, 292
Arthur, H. R., 408
Artifacts, in botanical investigation, 154
Asiaticoside, 407
Aspen tissue, research cited, n. 219
Asthma, 96, 255, 429
Atabrine, 202
Atropa belladonna, 93
Atropine, 96, n. 219, 342
Aureomycin, 201
Autumn crocus, 297
Ayahuasca, 86–87, 115, 130, 131–134, 341
Ayur-Veda, 322
Aztecs, 78–82, 272, 275, 279

Babcock and Carew, paper cited, n. 219
Baboons, as "healers," 162
Bachelor's button, 168
Bacteria, 151, 389–390
Bactericidal action, of plants, 162–163
Badianus, Juannes, 275
Badianus Manuscript, The, 275
Baldwin, John T., Jr., 34, 35, 44, 66, 67, 278
banana, 162
Banckes, Richard, 98, 168

Bancroft, E. N., 230
Banisteriopsis caapi, 130, 132–134. See also *Ayahuasca.*
Banner, Albert H., 398
Baobab, 49
Boquet, A. H., 60
Barbasco, 270
Barbiturates, 342, 353
Baxter, Ross M., 358
Baytop, Turham, 427
Beal, J. L., 220
Beaudette, Palmer T., 377
Beer, C. T., 305, 308
Bein, Hugo, 329
Bell, William B., n. 218
Belladonna, 93, 96; research cited, n. 219
Beneke, E. S., 399
Bennett, A. E., 240
Bentham, G., 423
Benzedrine, 342
Benzene rings, 342
Beriberi, 87–88
Bernard, Claude, 231
Billings, W. Dwight, 277
Biosynthesis: definition, 220; of natural products, 219–222; research papers cited, n. 219
Bissert, N., 408
Black currants, 163
Blake, William, *quoted,* 350
Blood pressure, effects of Rauwolfia on, 324–327; *see also* Hypertension.
Bloodroot, 297, 417
Bobbitt, James M., 158
Boehm, Rudolph, 239
Boeing Aircraft Company, 400
Bonellia, 394–395
Bonpland, Aimé, 189; (and Humboldt), *quoted,* 229
Book of Herbs (Shên Nung), 168
Bose, Kartick Chandra, 324
Botanic gardens, how to judge, 43
Botanical Arrangement of All the Vegetables Growing in Great Britain, A (Withering), 208
Botanical Institute of the New Kingdom of Granada, 186–188, 232
Botanical drug projects, National Institute of Mental Health conference on, 154–160
Botanical research projects, foreign, 403–431; Africa, 405–407; Australia, 408–410; Burma, 424–425; China (Main-

448

Index

Index

Hydnocarpus anthelmintica, 247; *H. castanea,* 248–249; *H. wightiana,* 252
Hydrangea, 168, 201
Hyoscyamine, 353, 371, 409; research cited, n. 219
Hypertension, 162–163, 324–327; statistics, 326–327
Hypnotics, 342
Hyoscyamus niger, 93

Iboga, 341
Ichthyosarcotoxism, 396–399
Idrobo, J. M., 90
I. G. Farbenindustrie, 202
Incas, 94, 173
Indian (East) systems of medicine, 322
Indians (N. Am.): Kiowa, 76; Navajo, 73, 259; Northwest coast, 163; Penobscot, 299
Indians (S. Am.): Amuesha, 124; Aymará, 193–194; Campa, 114–127; Guaica, 139–140; Ingano, 95; Jivaro, 94; Javas, 224; Kamsá, 95; Maquiritares, 137–138; Tanimukas, 73; Tecunas, 224; Witoto, 88; Yagua, 223–224
Indigenous Drugs of India (Chopra), *quoted,* 253
Indole rings, 342
Infections, 97, 255
Inflamation, 162
Inky caps, 372
Inocybe, 372
Insanity, *see* Mental illness.
Insomnia, 78, 323
INTERPHARM, n. 426
Intoxication, from plant substances: *ayahuasca,* 130; *culebra borrachera,* 95; mushrooms, 82, 370; ololiuqui, 78–79; peyote, 76, 77, 341; *yákee,* 99–100
Ipomoea, 81; *I. tricolor,* 364–365
Ipecac, 423
Iquitos, 130
Island (Huxley), 349
"Isolation of Sarsasapogenin from Mexican Sarsaparilla Root" (Marker), 259

Jackson, Hall, 217
Jacobs, Walter A., 30
James, William, 77
Jamestown weed, *see* Jimson weed.

Jaramillo-Arango, Jaime, 173, 189
Janiger, Oscar, 364
Jartoux, Father, 419
Jesuit's bark, 174; *see also* Cinchona, Quinine.
Jimson weed, 93
Jindra, A., 429
Jivaro, 94
Johnson & Johnson, 277
Johnson, Irving S., 310, 312
Journal of Economic Botany, 136
Joyfull Newes out of the New-Found Worlde (Monardes), 173, 260
Jungle expeditions, equipment for, 84–85, 112–113, 140–142
Jussieu, Joseph de, 180–185

Kainic acid, 386
Kapoor, L. D., 424
Karigone, Tatsuo, 420
Karrer, Paul, 143, 239
Katz, A., 66
Kawa Kawa, 403–405
Keller, F., 326, 404
Kelvin, Lord, *quoted,* 422
Kendall, Edward C., 28, 31
Kew Gardens (Royal Botanical Gardens), 32, 61
Khellin, 429
Kiang, A. K., 408
King, Albert Freeman Africanus, 170
King, Harold, 232, 239
Kiowa, 76
Kirk, Sir John, *quoted,* 32
Kline, Nathan S., 345, 346
Klohs, M. W., n. 326, 404
Klug, Guillermo G., 236–237, 239
Klug, Rosa de, 236–237
Kombé, 32
Koornhof, H. J., 387
Kostermans, A. J. G. H., 411
Krukoff, B. A., 38, 44, 66, 201, 224–225, 228, 233, 237
Kubla Khan, 163
Kupchan, S. Morris, 69, 301, n. 325
Kupzow, A. J., 277

Lääke Oy Pharmaceutical Company, 386–387
LaBarre, Weston, 76

Index

Born in Chicago and brought up in Dundee, Illinois, Margaret Kreig majored first in art at the University of Illinois and later, pre-med at the University of Chicago. After an honorable discharge from the Marine Corps Women's Reserve, she was a fashion model before deciding to enroll in Northwestern University's Medill School of Journalism.

Moving to mid-Manhattan with her husband and three young sons, she became an editor at *Parents' Magazine,* where she did much of their medical and science writing. Her articles and fiction have appeared in *This Week, Reader's Digest, Good Housekeeping, Mademoiselle,* and many other national magazines. She served as head of the Midwest Chapter of Mystery Writers of America, and belongs to the American Association for the Advancement of Science, the National Association of Science Writers, the American Medical Writers' Association, and the Society of Magazine Writers.

Her four-year research on GREEN MEDICINE included personal interviews with hundreds of scientists here and abroad and correspondence with countless others. She accompanied a scientific expedition to the Amazon and observed field botanists at work in remote parts of Mexico. Despite her stint as a lady marine and participation in jungle treks, her hobbies do not include active sports; she enjoys collecting very old children's books and experimenting with exotic recipes.